play guitar with...

20 metal bands

Wise Publications
London/New York/Paris/Sydney/Copenhagen/Berlin/Madrid/Tokyo

Exclusive distributors:
Music Sales Limited
8/9 Frith Street,
London W1D 3JB, England
Music Sales Pty Limited
120 Rothschild Avenue,
Rosebery, NSW 2018, Australia

Order No. AM976745
ISBN 0-7119-9860-4

Music compiled and arranged by Arthur Dick
Music processed by Andrew Shiels
Cover photographs courtesy of London Features International
Printed in Malta by Interprint Limited.

CD recorded, mixed and mastered by Jonas Persson
All guitars by Arthur Dick
Bass by Paul Townsend
Drums by Ian Thomas
Piano & keyboards by Allan Rogers

www.musicsales.com

guitar tablature explained

Guitar music can be notated three different ways: on a musical stave, in tablature, and in rhythm slashes.

RHYTHM SLASHES are written above the stave. Strum chords in the rhythm indicated. Round noteheads indicate single notes.

THE MUSICAL STAVE shows pitches and rhythms and is divided by lines into bars. Pitches are named after the first seven letters of the alphabet.

TABLATURE graphically represents the guitar fingerboard. Each horizontal line represents a string, and each number represents a fret.

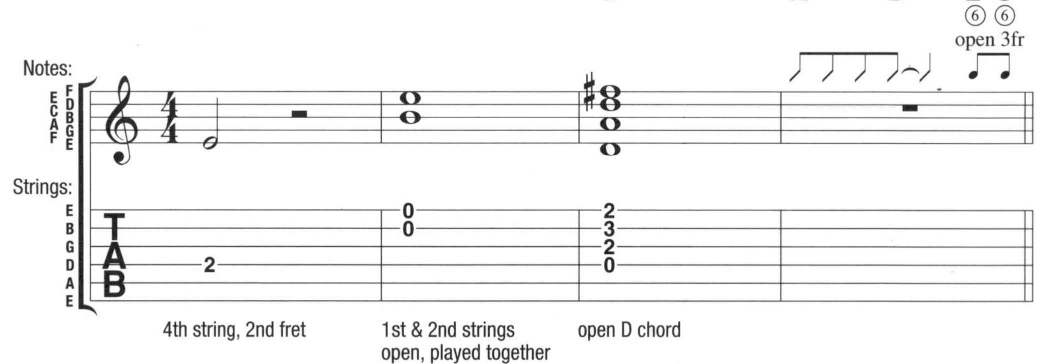

definitions for special guitar notation

SEMI-TONE BEND: Strike the note and bend up a semi-tone (1/2 step).

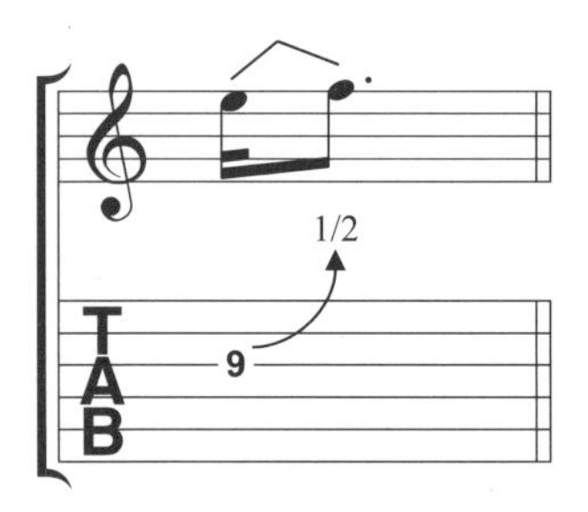

WHOLE-TONE BEND: Strike the note and bend up a whole-tone (whole step).

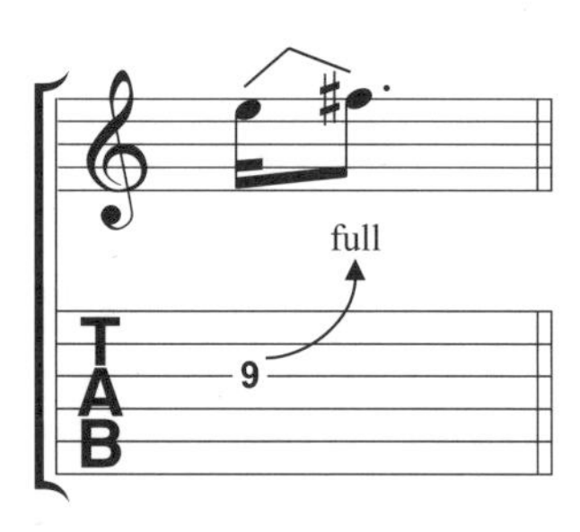

GRACE NOTE BEND: Strike the note and bend as indicated. Play the first note as quickly as possible.

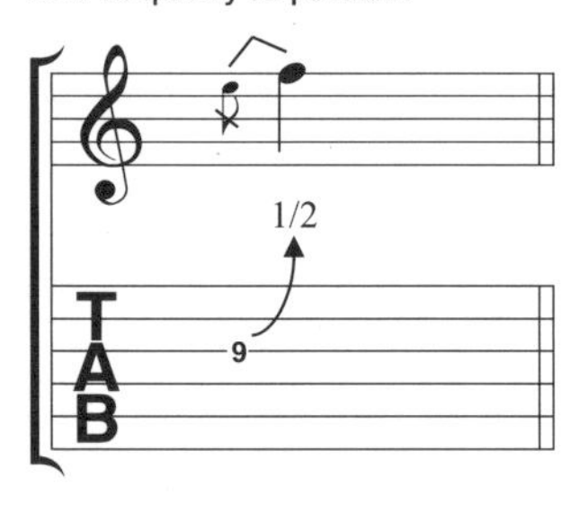

QUARTER-TONE BEND: Strike the note and bend up a 1/4 step.

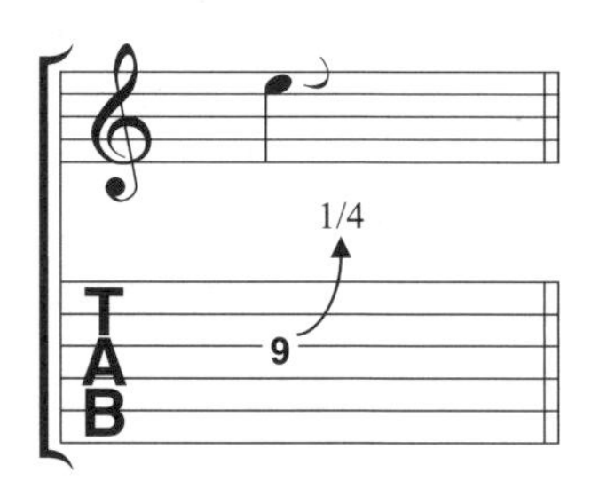

BEND & RELEASE: Strike the note and bend up as indicated, then release back to the original note.

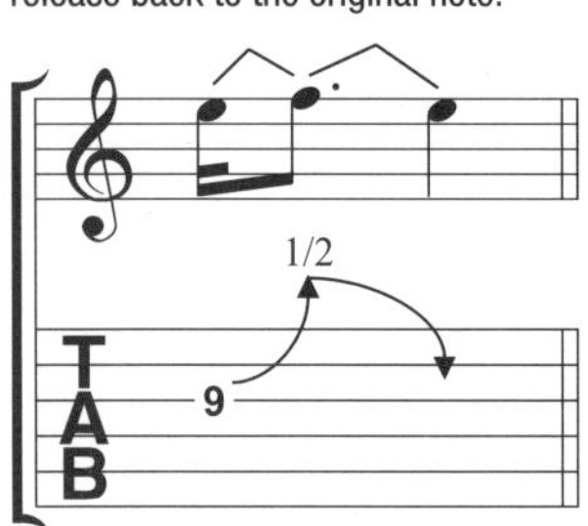

COMPOUND BEND & RELEASE: Strike the note and bend up and down in the rhythm indicated.

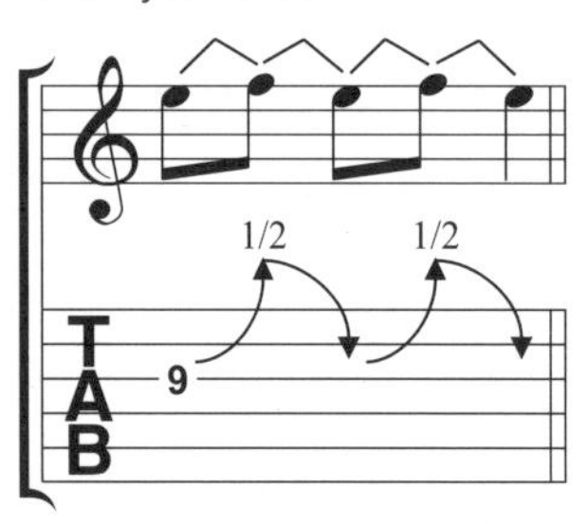

PRE-BEND: Bend the note as indicated, then strike it.

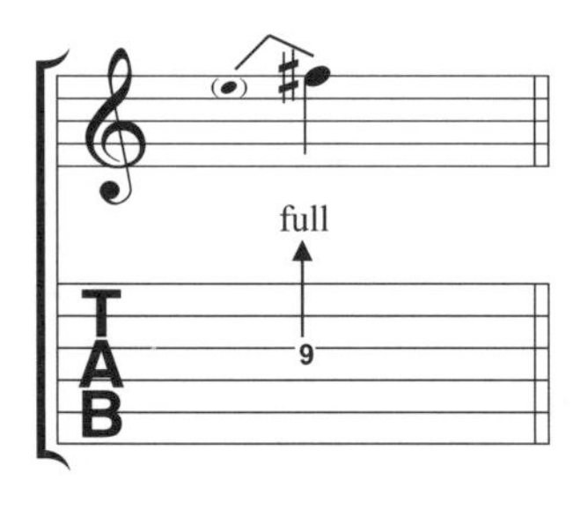

PRE-BEND & RELEASE: Bend the note as indicated. Strike it and release the note back to the original pitch.

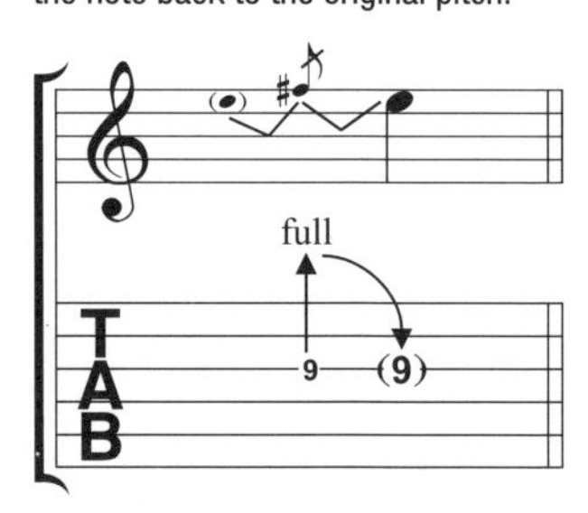

UNISON BEND: Strike the two notes simultaneously and bend the lower note up to the pitch of the higher.

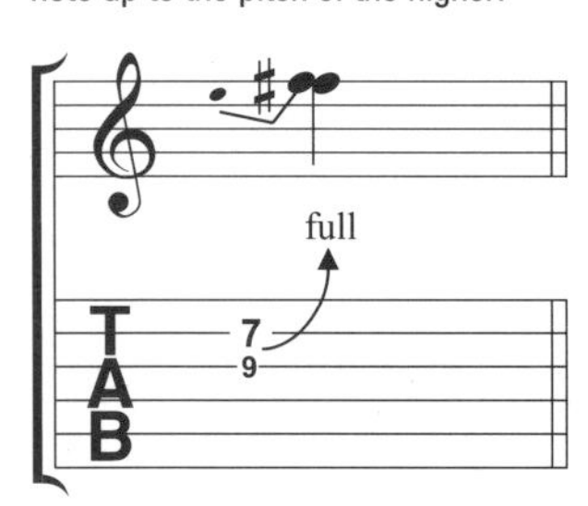

BEND & RESTRIKE: Strike the note and bend as indicated then restrike the string where the symbol occurs.

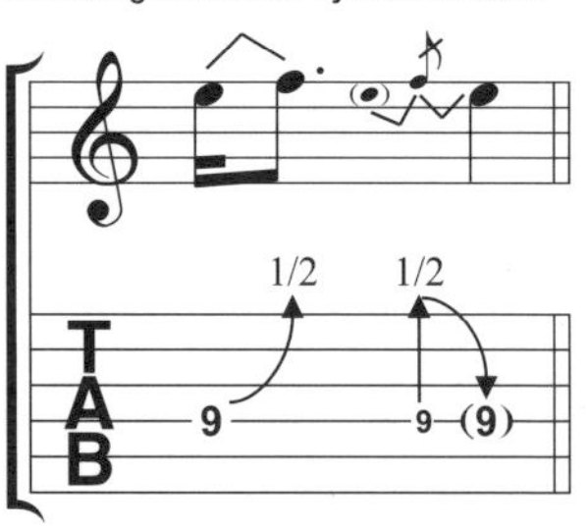

BEND, HOLD AND RELEASE: Same as bend and release but hold the bend for the duration of the tie.

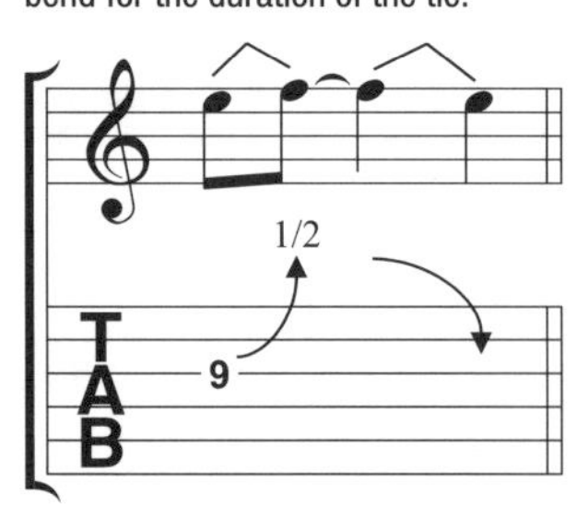

BEND AND TAP: Bend the note as indicated and tap the higher fret while still holding the bend.

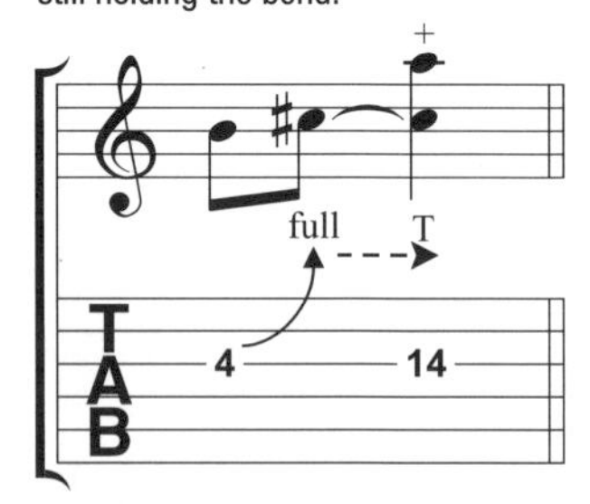

VIBRATO: The string is vibrated by rapidly bending and releasing the note with the fretting hand.

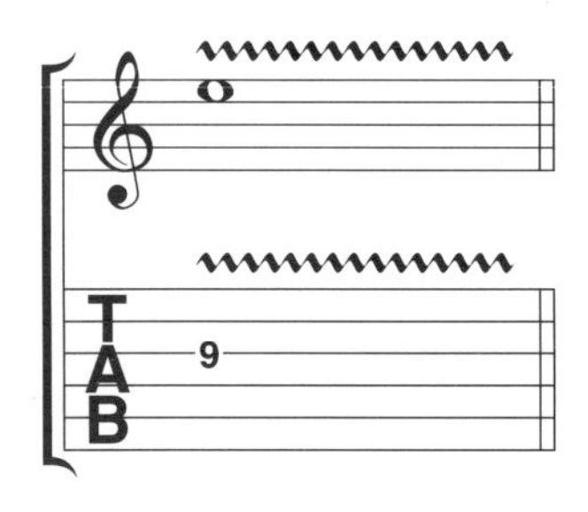

HAMMER-ON: Strike the first note with one finger, then sound the second note (on the same string) with another finger by fretting it without picking.

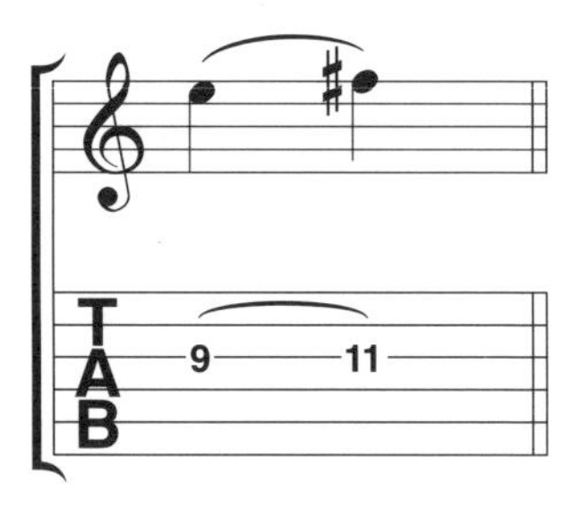

PULL-OFF: Place both fingers on the notes to be sounded, strike the first note and without picking, pull the finger off to sound the second note.

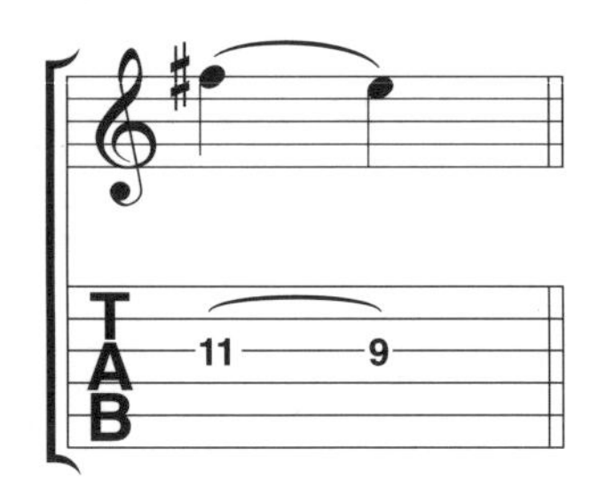

LEGATO SLIDE (GLISS): Strike the first note and then slide the same fret-hand finger up or down to the second note. The second note is not struck.

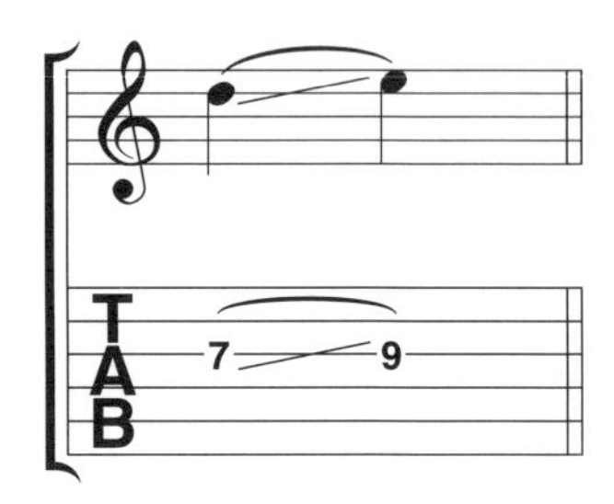

NOTE: The speed of any bend is indicated by the music notation and tempo.

SHIFT SLIDE (GLISS & RESTRIKE): Same as legato slide, except the second note is struck.

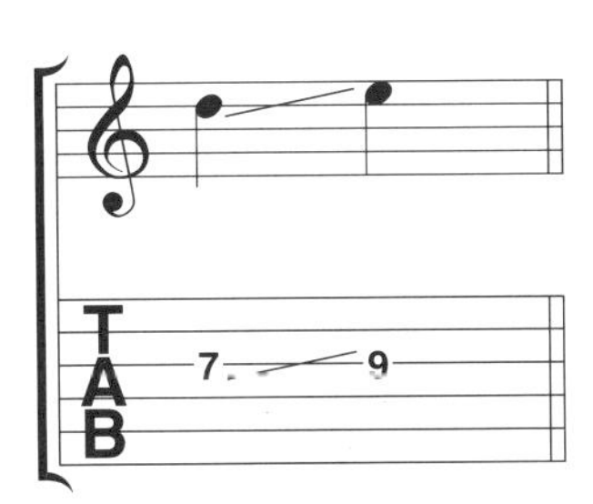

TRILL: Very rapidly alternate between the notes indicated by continuously hammering on and pulling off.

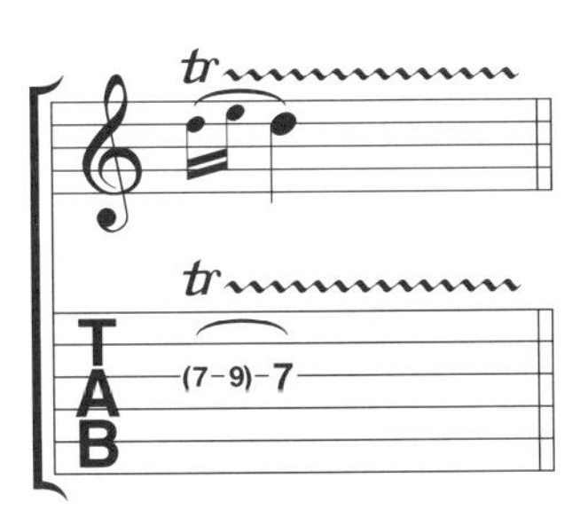

TAPPING: Hammer ("tap") the fret indicated with the pick-hand index or middle finger and pull off to the note fretted by the fret hand.

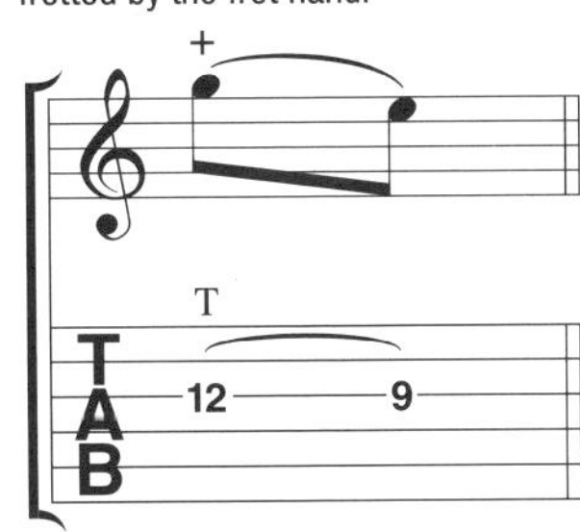

PICK SCRAPE: The edge of the pick is rubbed down (or up) the string, producing a scratchy sound.

MUFFLED STRINGS: A percussive sound is produced by laying the fret hand across the string(s) without depressing, and striking them with the pick hand.

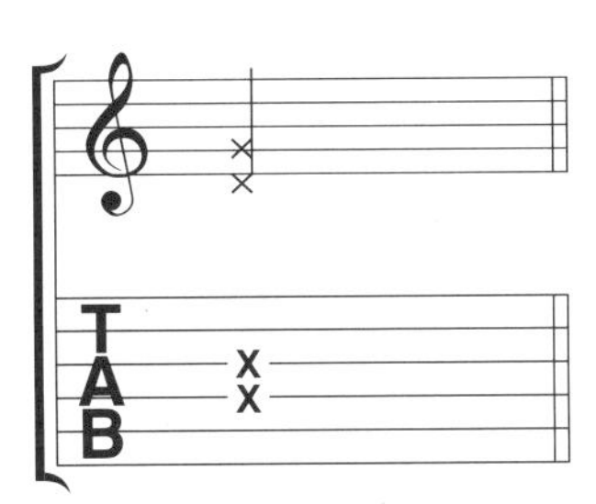

NATURAL HARMONIC: Strike the note while the fret-hand lightly touches the string directly over the fret indicated.

PINCH HARMONIC: The note is fretted normally and a harmonic is produced by adding the edge of the thumb or the tip of the index finger of the pick hand to the normal pick attack.

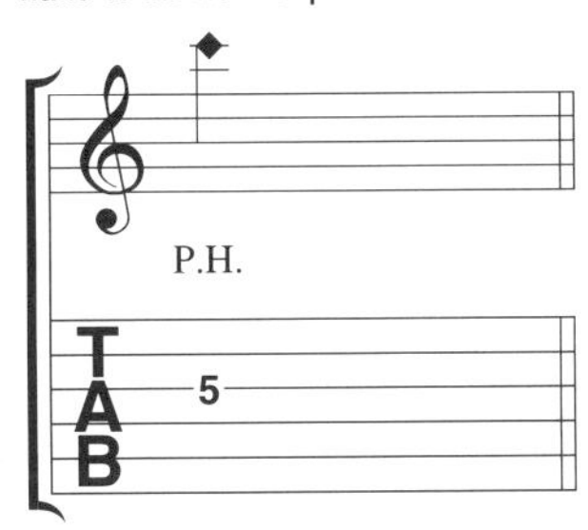

HARP HARMONIC: The note is fretted normally and a harmonic is produced by gently resting the pick hand's index finger directly above the indicated fret (in brackets) while plucking the appropriate string.

PALM MUTING: The note is partially muted by the pick hand lightly touching the string(s) just before the bridge.

RAKE: Drag the pick across the strings indicated with a single motion.

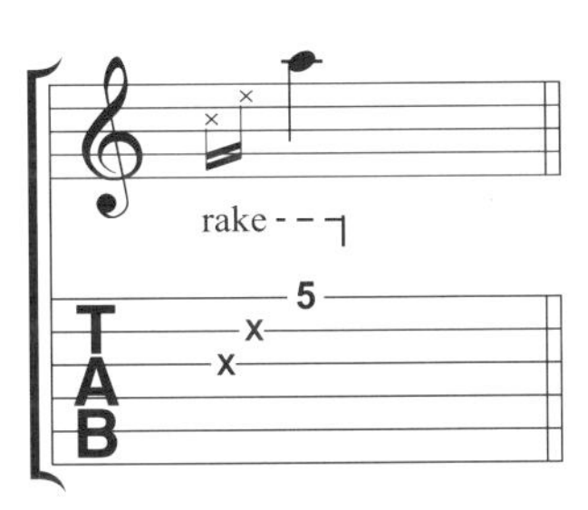

TREMOLO PICKING: The note is picked as rapidly and continuously as possible.

ARPEGGIATE: Play the notes of the chord indicated by quickly rolling them from bottom to top.

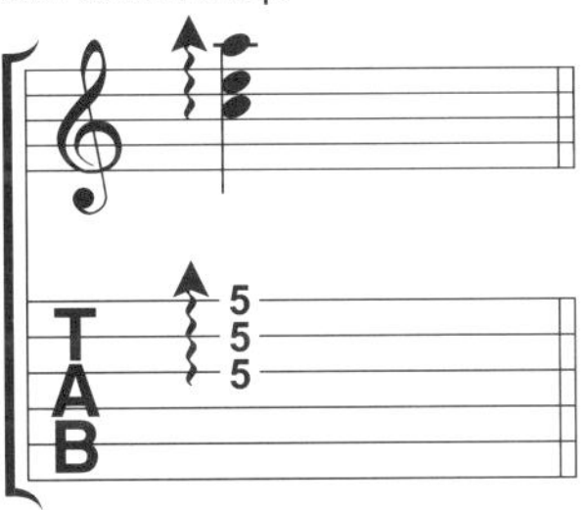

SWEEP PICKING: Rhythmic downstroke and/or upstroke motion across the strings.

VIBRATO DIVE BAR AND RETURN: Thepitch of the note or chord is dropped a specific number of steps (in rhythm) then returned to the original pitch.

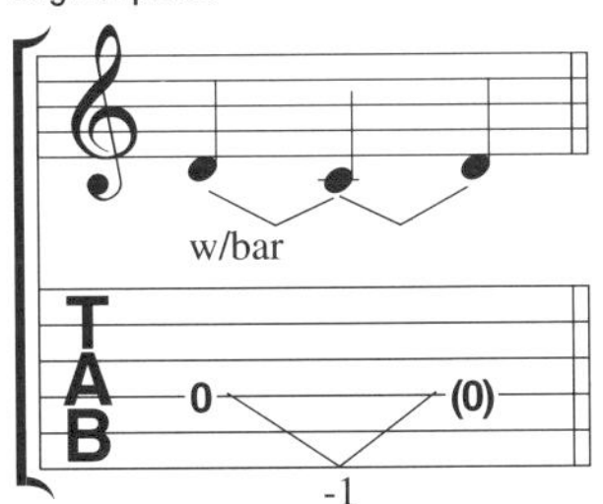

VIBRATO BAR SCOOP: Depress the bar just before striking the note, then quickly release the bar.

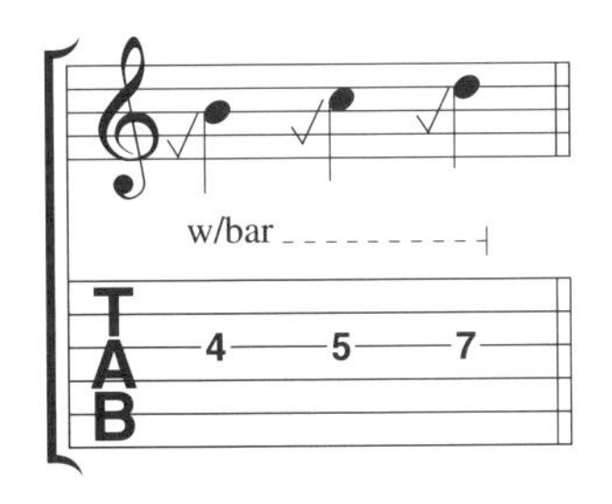

VIBRATO BAR DIP: Strike the note and then immediately drop a specific number of steps, then release back to the original pitch.

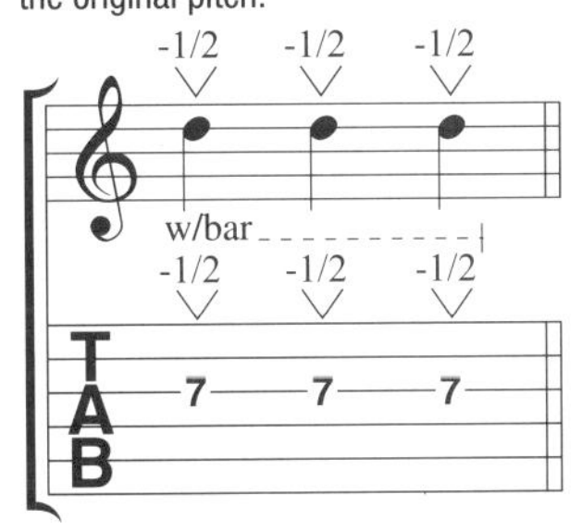

additional musical definitions

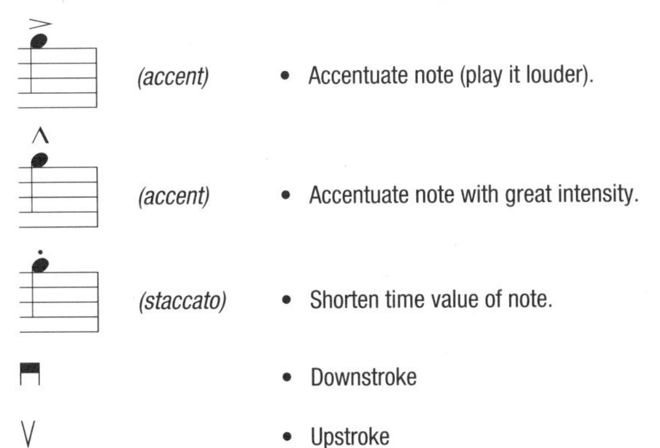

- (accent) • Accentuate note (play it louder).
- (accent) • Accentuate note with great intensity.
- (staccato) • Shorten time value of note.
- • Downstroke
- V • Upstroke

NOTE: Tablature numbers in brackets mean:
1. The note is sustained, but a new articulation (such as hammer on or slide) begins.
2. A note may be fretted but not necessarily played.

- ***D.%. al Coda*** • Go back to the sign (%), then play until the bar marked ***To Coda*** ⊕ then skip to the section marked ⊕ ***Coda.***
- ***D.C. al Fine*** • Go back to the beginning of the song and play until the bar marked ***Fine.***
- tacet • Instrument is silent (drops out).
- • Repeat bars between signs.

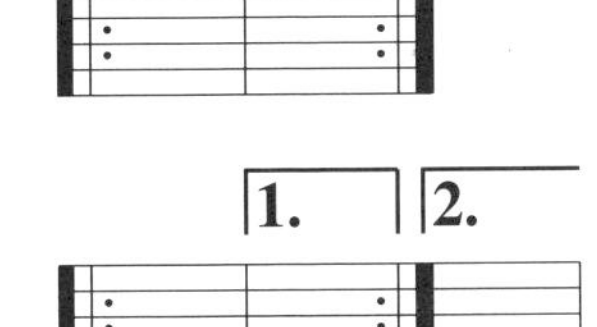

- • When a repeated section has different endings, play the first ending only the first time and the second ending only the second time.

Words & Music by Marcos Curiel, Mark Daniels, Paul Sandoval & Noah Bernardo

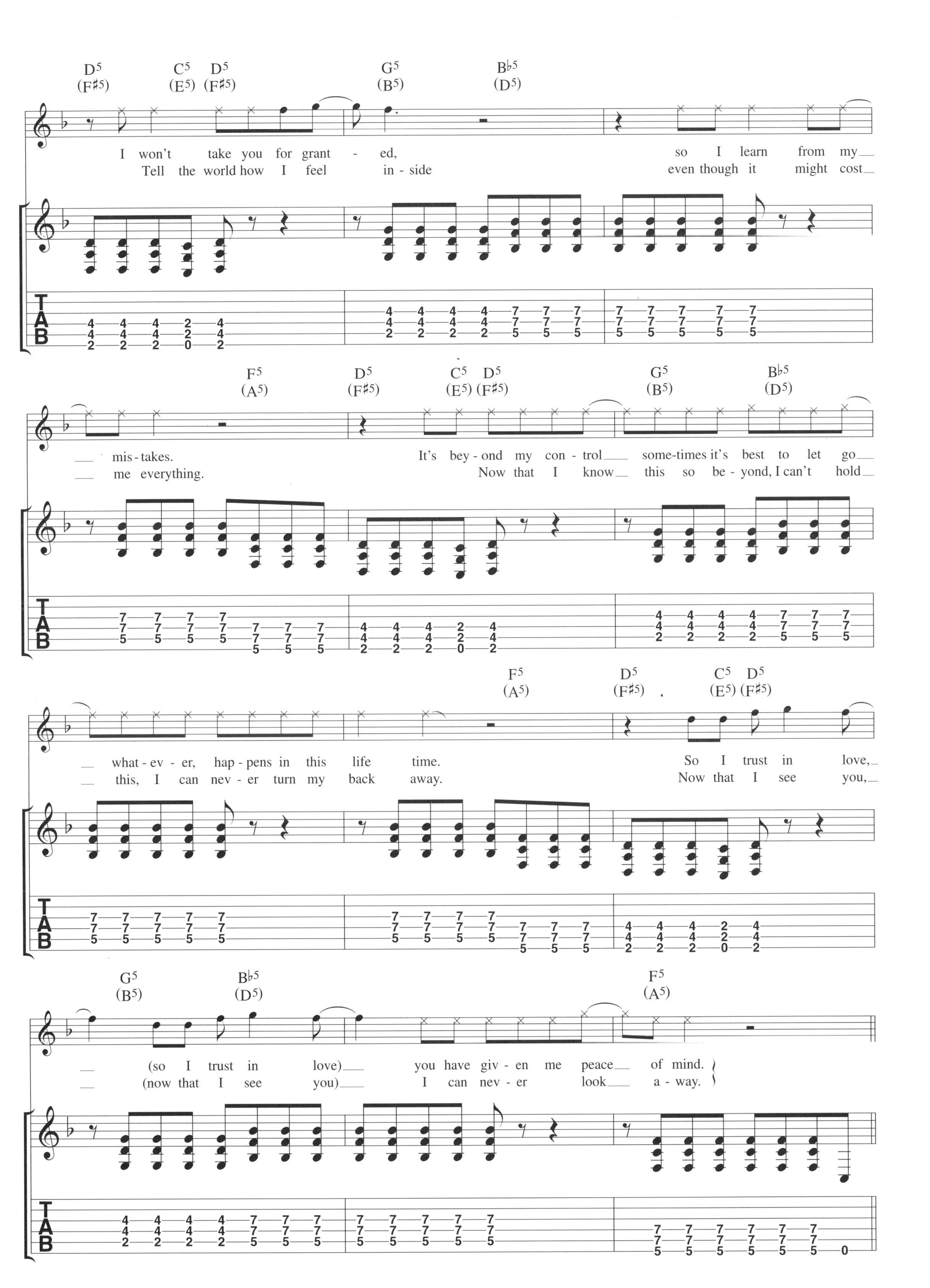
D5 (F♯5) C5 (E5) D5 (F♯5) G5 (B5) B♭5 (D5)
I won't take you for grant - ed, so I learn from my
Tell the world how I feel in - side even though it might cost
F5 (A5) D5 (F♯5) C5 (E5) D5 (F♯5) G5 (B5) B♭5 (D5)
mis - takes. It's bey - ond my con - trol some-times it's best to let go
me everything. Now that I know this so be - yond, I can't hold
F5 (A5) D5 (F♯5) C5 (E5) D5 (F♯5)
what - ev - er, hap - pens in this life time. So I trust in love,
this, I can nev - er turn my back away. Now that I see you,
G5 (B5) B♭5 (D5) F5 (A5)
(so I trust in love) you have giv - en me peace of mind.
(now that I see you) I can nev - er look a - way.

Chorus
F/B♭
(A/D)
D5
(F♯5)
Dsus2
(F♯sus2)
I,
I feel so a - live
let ring . . .
let ring . . .
let ring . . .
F5
(A5)
for the ve - ry first time
I can't de - ny
you.
N.C.
I feel so a - live.
F/B♭
(A/D)
I,
let ring . . .
let ring . . .
D5
(F♯5)
Dsus2
(Fsus2)
I feel so a - live (I feel so a - live) for the ve - ry first time
let ring . . .

F5
(A5)
1.
N.C.
(for the ve - ry first time)
and I think I can fly.
(fly, fly . . . .)
2.
N.C.
Bridge
w/ad lib vocal fx
w/delay
8va
(8va)
loco
And now that I know you,

I could nev - er turn my back a - way.
And now that I see you,
+ad lib vib
I could nev - er look a - way.
And now that I know you,
I could nev - er turn my back a - way.
And now that I see
you,
I be - lieve no mat - ter what they say.
8va
(8va)
T
A
B

Chorus
F/B♭
(A/D)
D5
(F♯5)
Dsus2
(F♯sus2)
I,
I feel so a - live
let ring . . .
let ring . . .
let ring . . .
F5
(A5)
for the ve - ry first time
1° only I can't de - ny
N.C.
F/B♭
(A/D)
you.
I feel so a - live.
2° only and I think I can fly
I,
tacet 2°
let ring . . .
D5
(F♯5)
Dsus2
(F♯sus2)
I feel so a - live (I feel so a - live) for the ve - ry first time
let ring

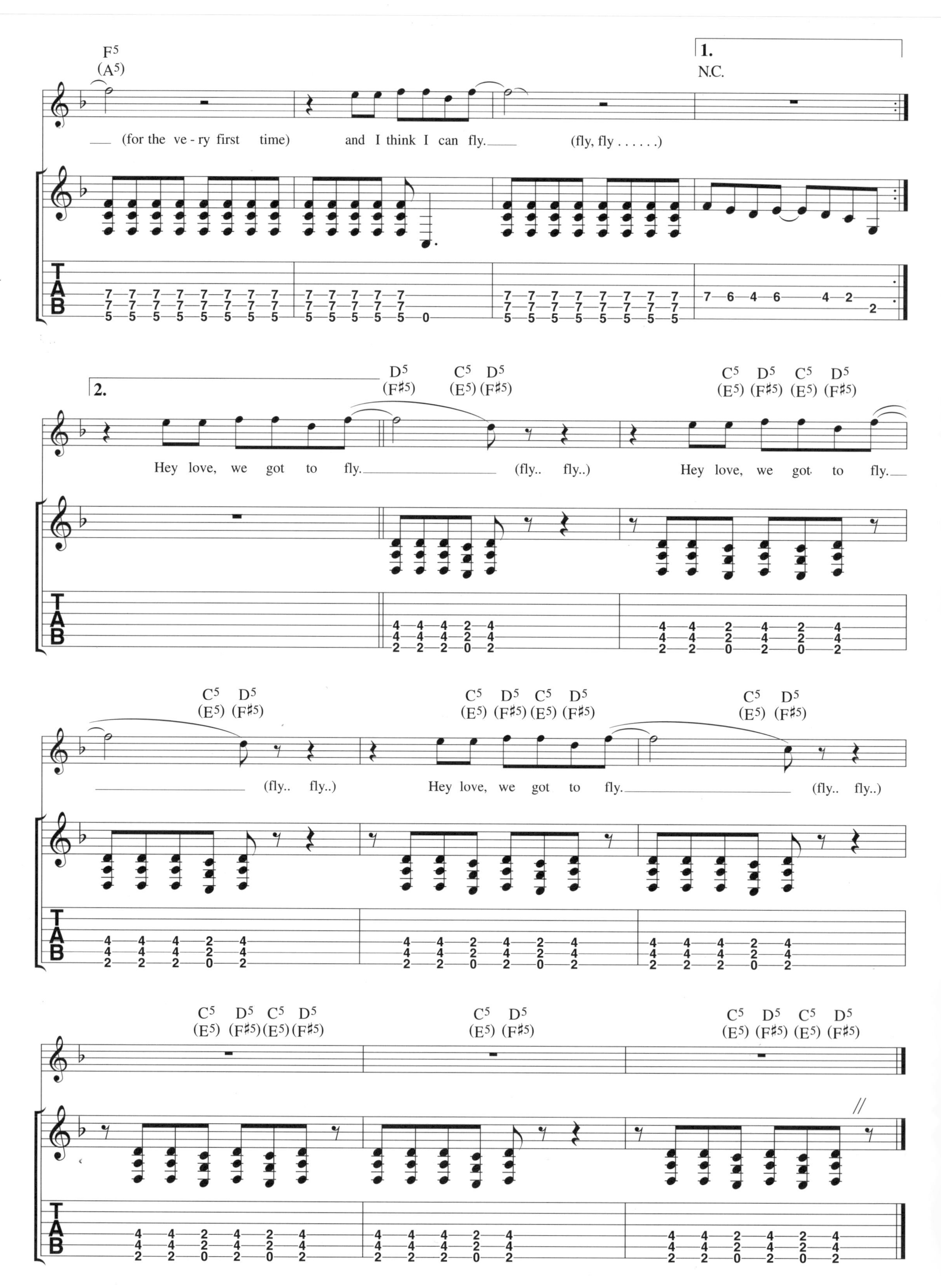
F5
(A5)
1.
N.C.
(for the ve - ry first time)
and I think I can fly.
(fly, fly . . . . . .)
TAB
2.
D5
(F♯5)
C5
(E5)
Hey love, we got to fly.
(fly.. fly..)
Hey love, we got to fly.

chop suey!

Words by Serj Tankian & Daron Malakian
Music by Daron Malakian

Tune gtr. Drop D tuning, down a tone:

⑥ = C ③ = F
⑤ = G ② = A
④ = C ① = D

* chords in brackets refer to standard tuning chord shapes/positions

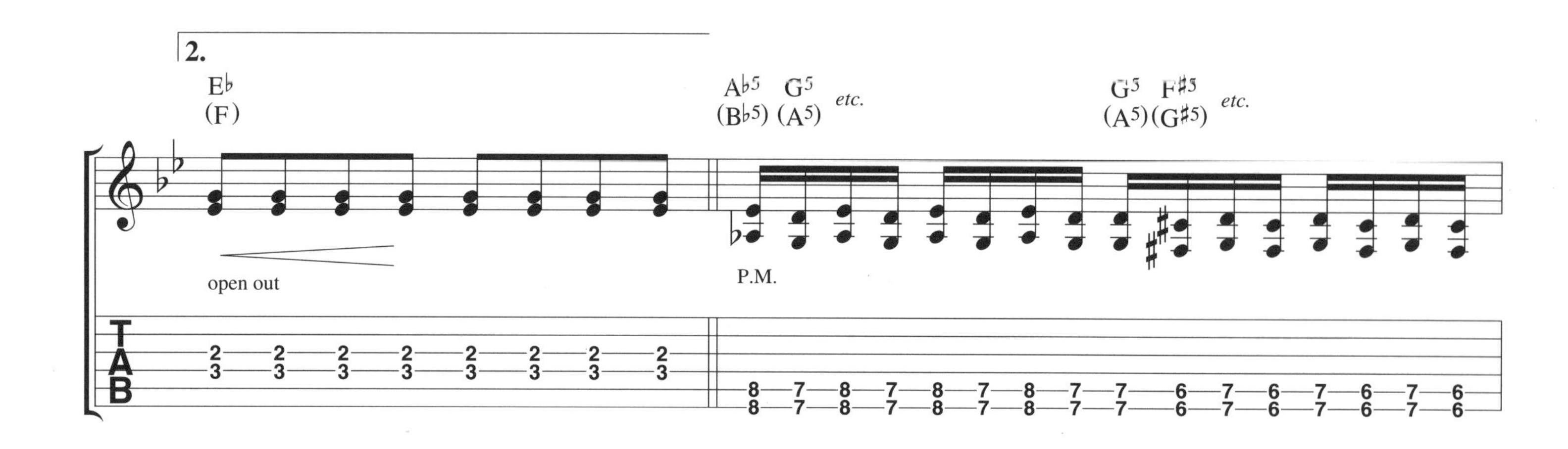
2.
E♭
(F)
A♭5 G5
(B♭5) (A5)
etc.
G5 F♯5
(A5)(G♯5)
etc.
open out
P.M.
TAB

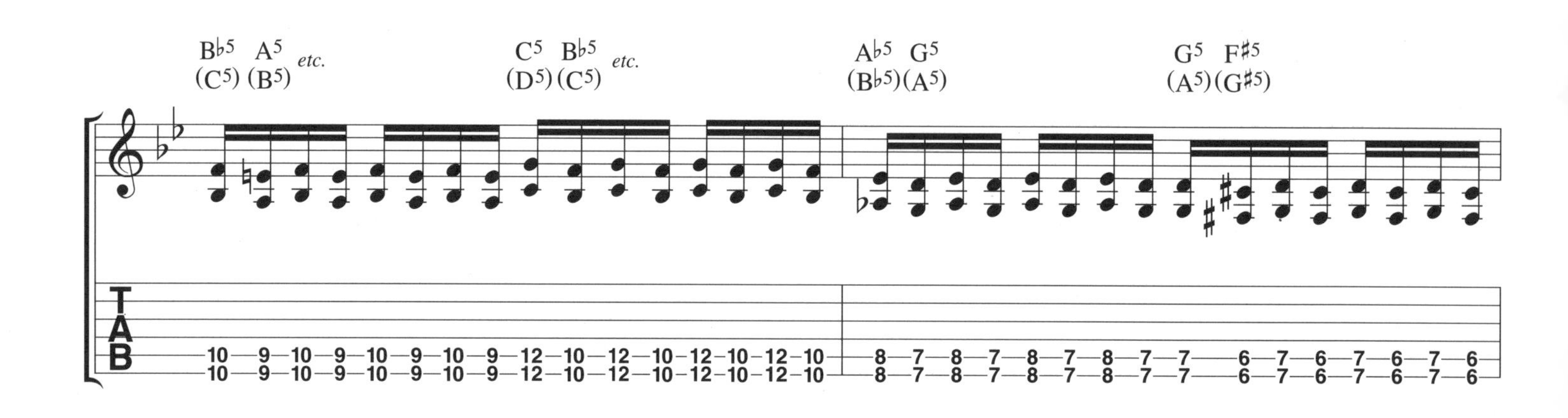
B♭5 A5
(C5) (B5)
etc.
C5 B♭5
(D5) (C5)
etc.
A♭5 G5
(B♭5)(A5)
G5 F♯5
(A5)(G♯5)
TAB

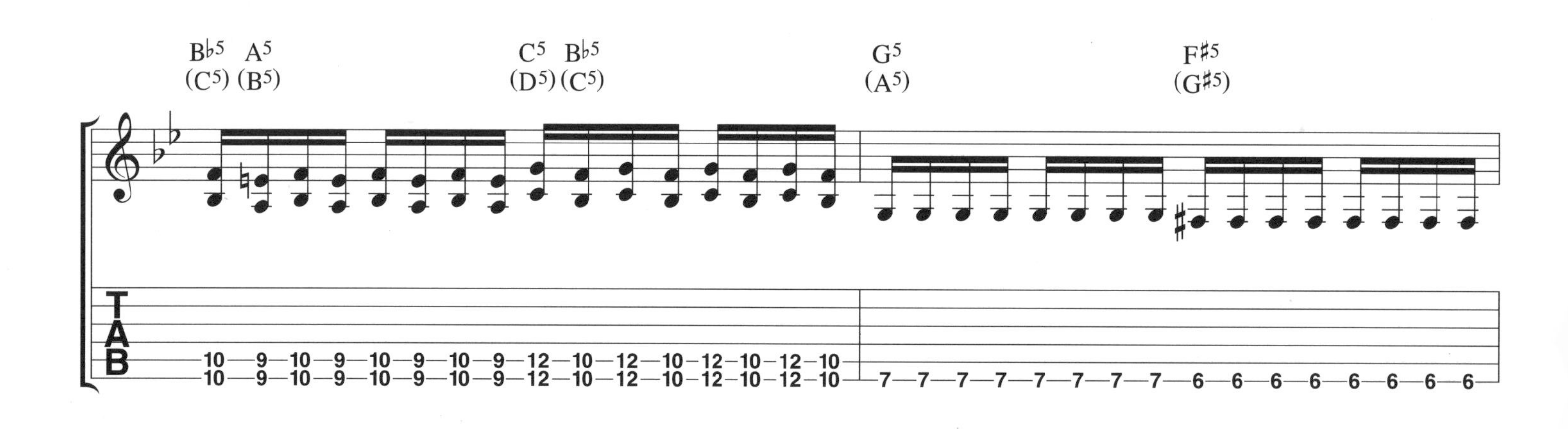
B♭5 A5
(C5) (B5)
C5 B♭5
(D5) (C5)
G5
(A5)
F♯5
(G♯5)
TAB

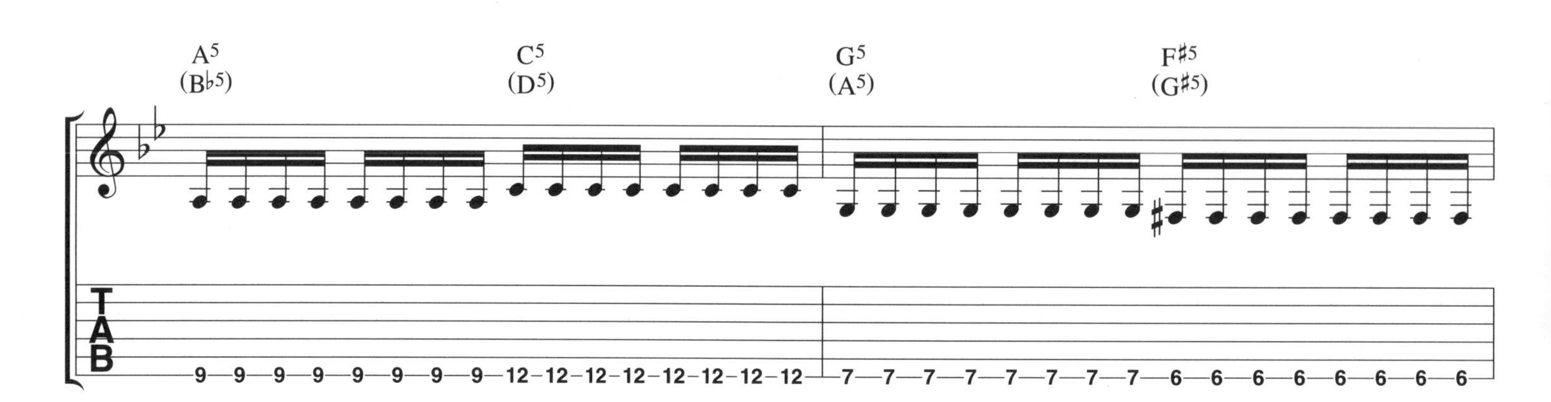
A5
(B♭5)
C5
(D5)
G5
(A5)
F♯5
(G♯5)
TAB

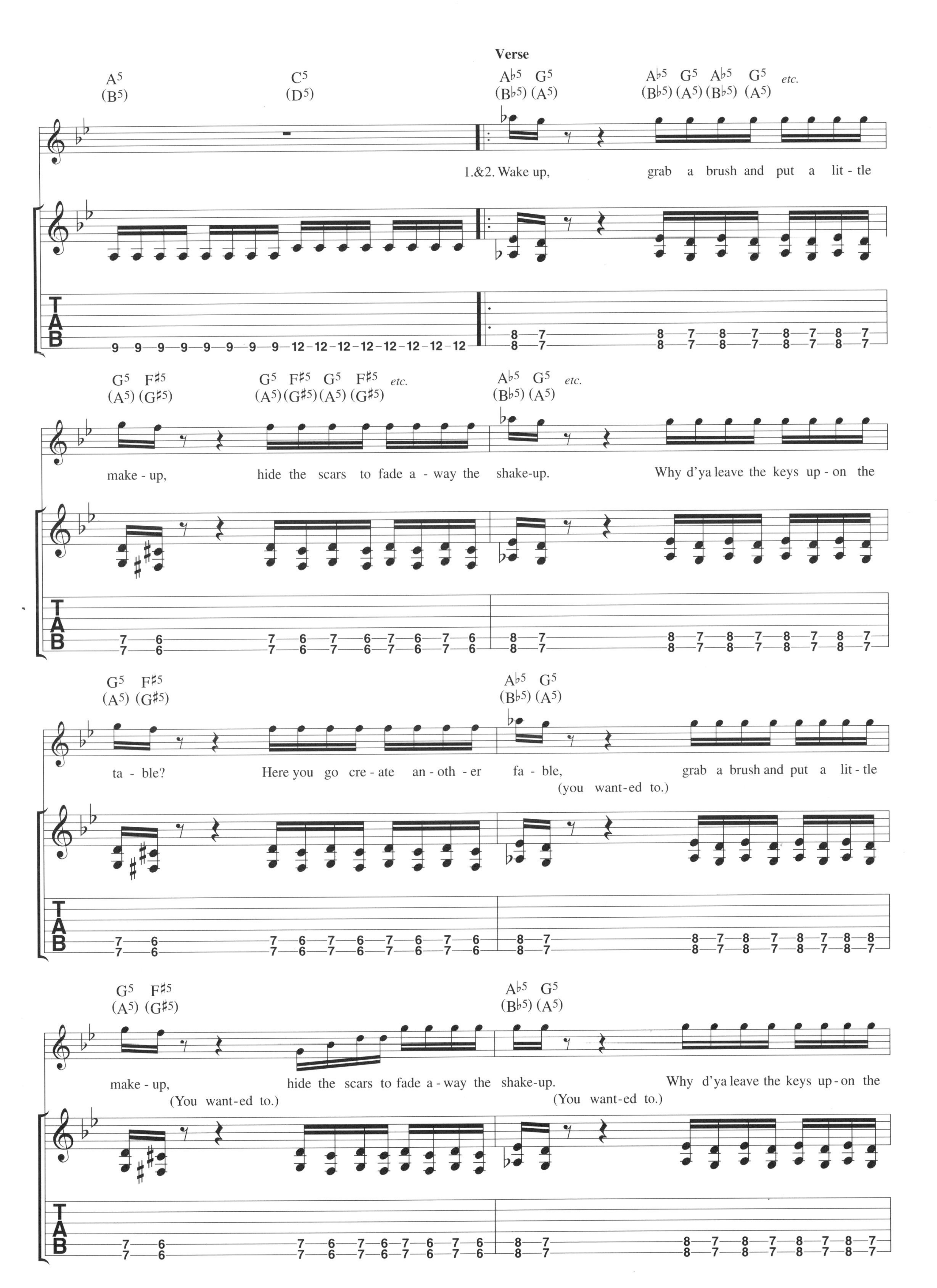
Verse
A5 (B5)
C5 (D5)
A♭5 G5 (B♭5) (A5)
A♭5 G5 A♭5 G5 (B♭5) (A5) (B♭5) (A5) etc.
1.&2. Wake up, grab a brush and put a lit - tle
G5 F♯5 (A5) (G♯5)
G5 F♯5 G5 F♯5 (A5) (G♯5) (A5) (G♯5) etc.
A♭5 G5 (B♭5) (A5) etc.
make - up, hide the scars to fade a - way the shake-up. Why d'ya leave the keys up - on the
G5 F♯5 (A5) (G♯5)
A♭5 G5 (B♭5) (A5)
ta - ble? Here you go cre - ate an - oth - er fa - ble, grab a brush and put a lit - tle
(you want-ed to.)
G5 F♯5 (A5) (G♯5)
A♭5 G5 (B♭5) (A5)
make - up, hide the scars to fade a - way the shake-up. Why d'ya leave the keys up - on the
(You want-ed to.)
(You want-ed to.)
TAB

Chorus
G5 F♯5 (A5) (G♯5)
Gm (Am)
Am/G (Bm/A)
tab - le? I don't think you trust in
(You want-ed to.)
mf w/slight P.M.
* adapted from Gtr. w/capo at 3rd fret
F/G (G/A)
E♭/G (F/A)
Gm (Am)
my self right - eous su - i - cide.
Am/G (Bm/A)
F/G (G/A)
E♭/G (F/A)
I cry when an - gels de - serve to
1.
A♭5 G5 (B♭5) (A5) etc.
G5 F♯5 (A5) (G♯5)
B♭5 A5 (C5) (B5)
C5 B♭5 (D5) (C5)
die.
ff P.M.

1. cont.
A♭5 (B♭5) G5 (A5) G5 (A5) F♯5 (G♯5) B♭5 (C5) A5 (B5) C5 (D5) B♭5 (C5)
1. cont.
A♭5 (B♭5) G5 (A5)
Aagh!
2.
Gm (Am)
die
Am/G (Bm/A)
in
F/G (G/A)
my
E♭/G (F/A)
self right - eous su - i - cide.
Gm (Am)
Am/G (Bm/A)
I
F/G (G/A)
cry
E♭/G (F/A)
when an - gels de-serve to die.

Bridge
A♭5 G5
(B♭5) (A5)
G5 F♯5
(A5) (G♯5)
B♭5 A5
(C5) (B5)
(C5) B♭5
(D5) (C5)
ff
Vocal: (shouted) Father!
Father!
P.M.
Fa - ther in - to your hands, I com - mend my spi - rit.

G5
(A5)
F♯5
(G♯5)
A5
(B5)
C5
(D5)
Fa - ther in - to your hands, why have you for -
G5
(A5)
E♭5
(F5)
B♭5
(C5)
- sa - ken me in your eyes? For - sa - ken me
E♭5
(F5)
G5
(A5)
E♭5
(F5)
in your thoughts? For - sa - ken me in your heart? For -
B♭5
(C5)
E♭5
(F5)
G5
(A5)
sa - ken me. I'll trust

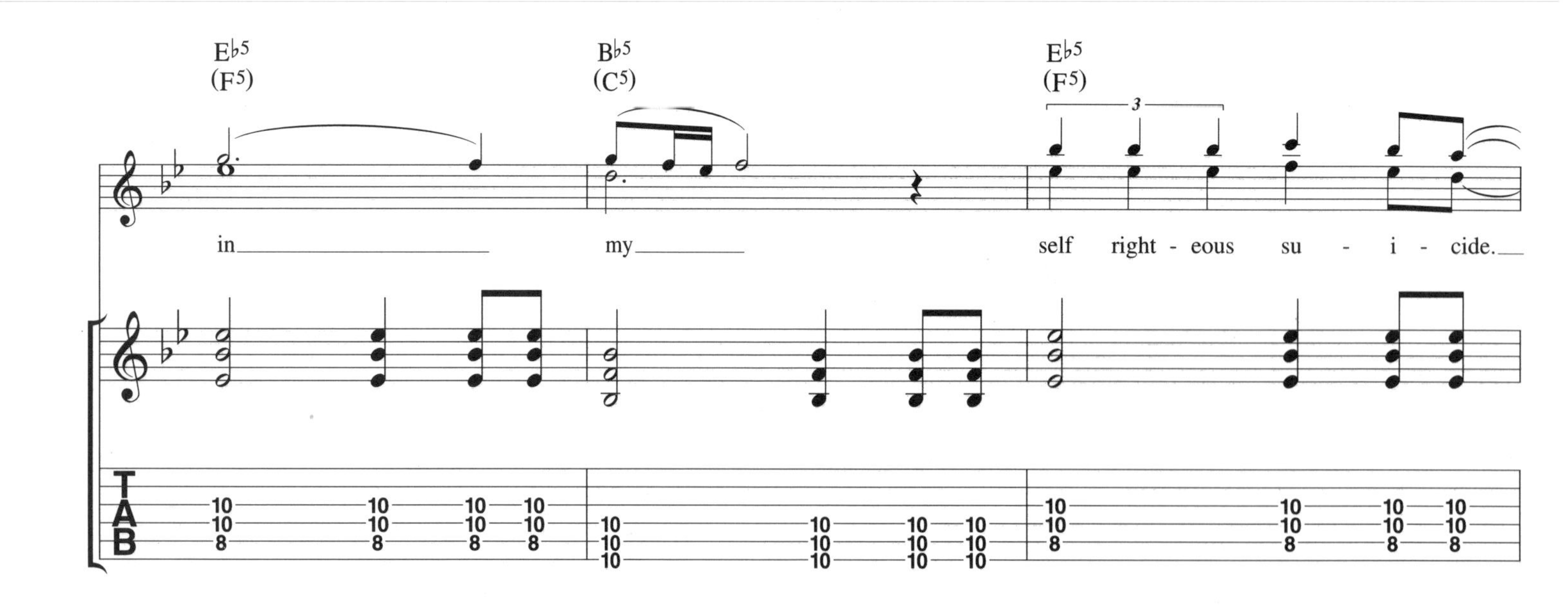
E♭5 (F5)
B♭5 (C5)
E♭5 (F5)
in my self right - eous su - i - cide.
TAB
10 10 8 10 10 8 10 10 8 10 10 8
10 10 10 10 10 10 10 10 10 10 10 10
10 10 8 10 10 8 10 10 8 10 10 8

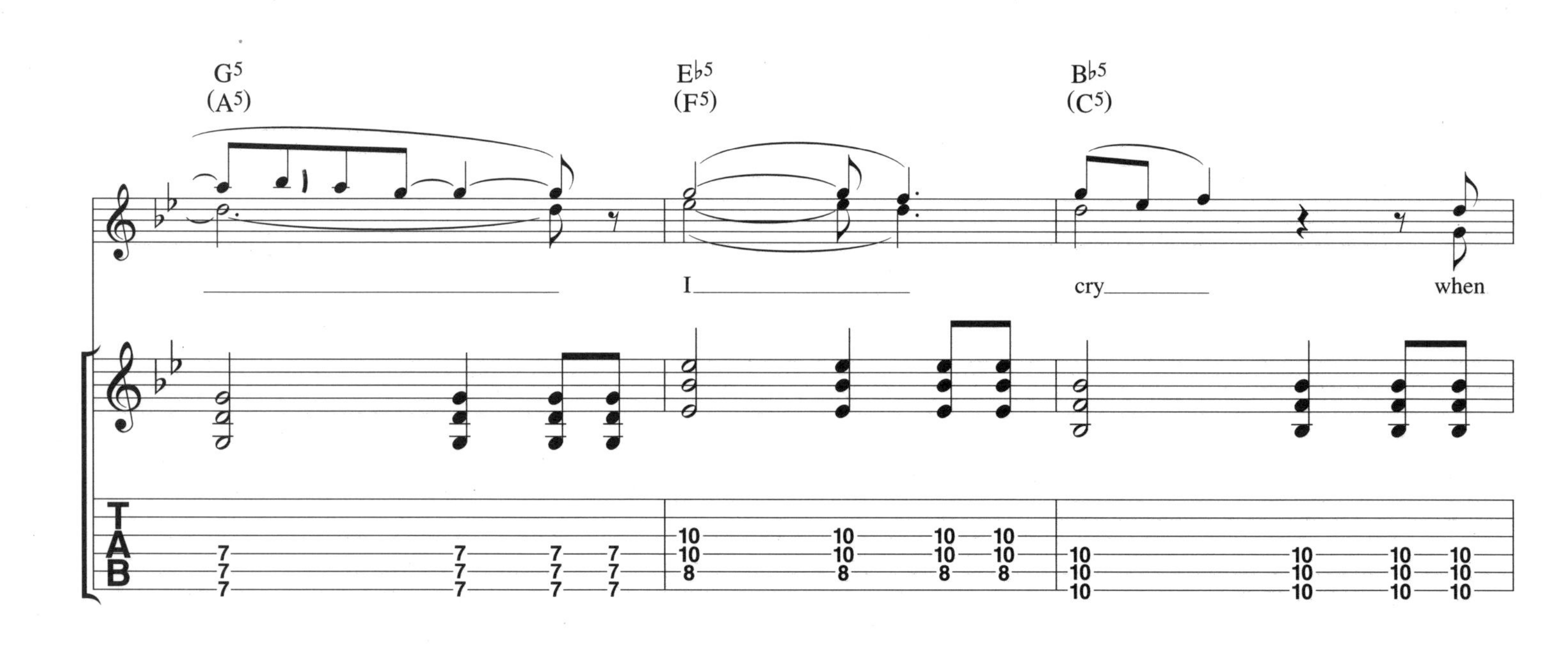
G5 (A5)
E♭5 (F5)
B♭5 (C5)
I cry when
TAB
7 7 7 7 7 7 7 7 7 7 7 7
10 10 8 10 10 8 10 10 8 10 10 8
10 10 10 10 10 10 10 10 10 10 10 10

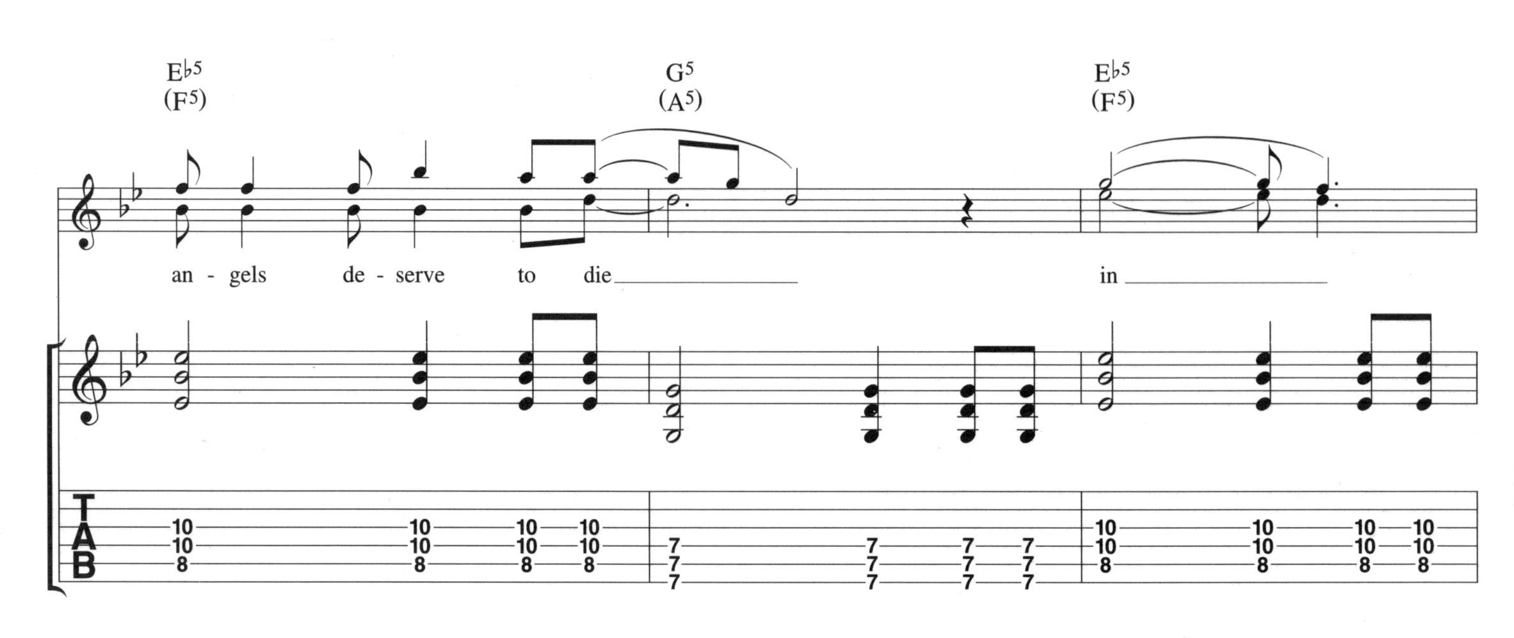
E♭5 (F5)
G5 (A5)
E♭5 (F5)
an - gels de - serve to die in
TAB
10 10 8 10 10 8 10 10 8 10 10 8
7 7 7 7 7 7 7 7 7 7 7 7
10 10 8 10 10 8 10 10 8 10 10 8

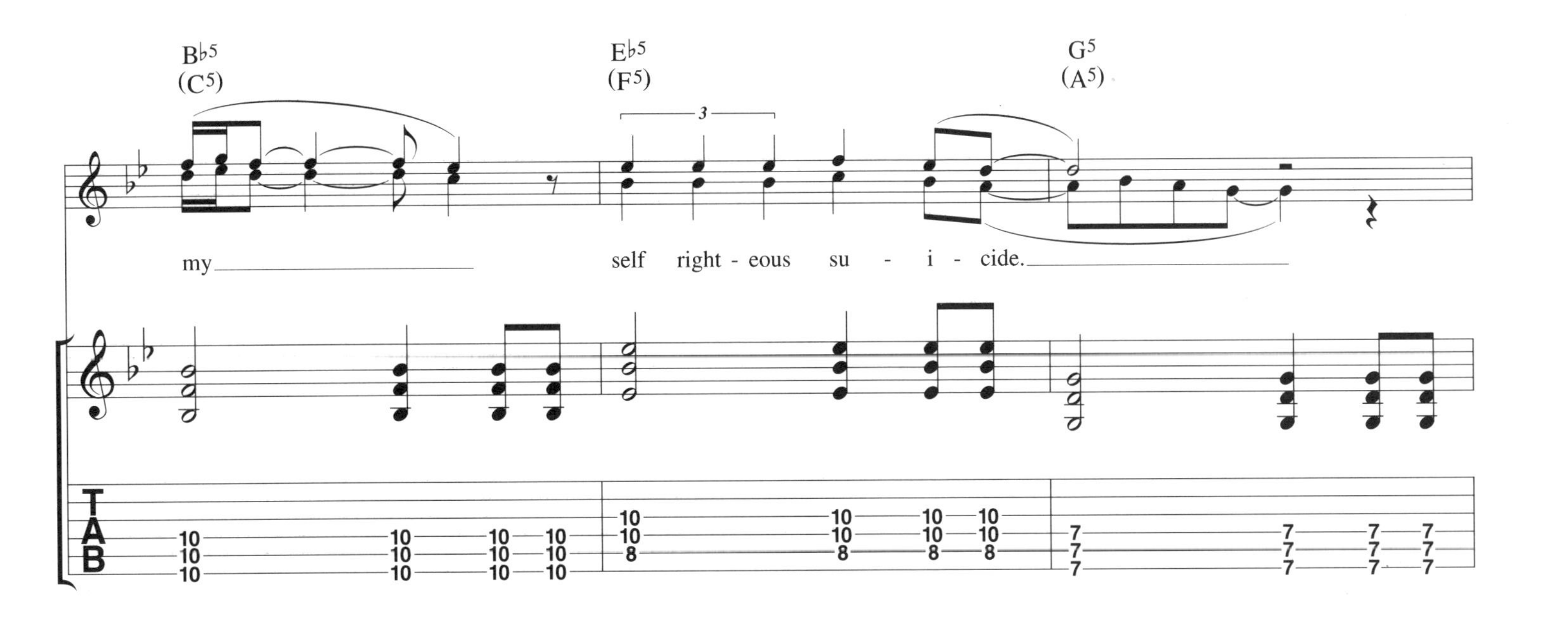
B♭5
(C5)
E♭5
(F5)
G5
(A5)
my
self right - eous su - i - cide.

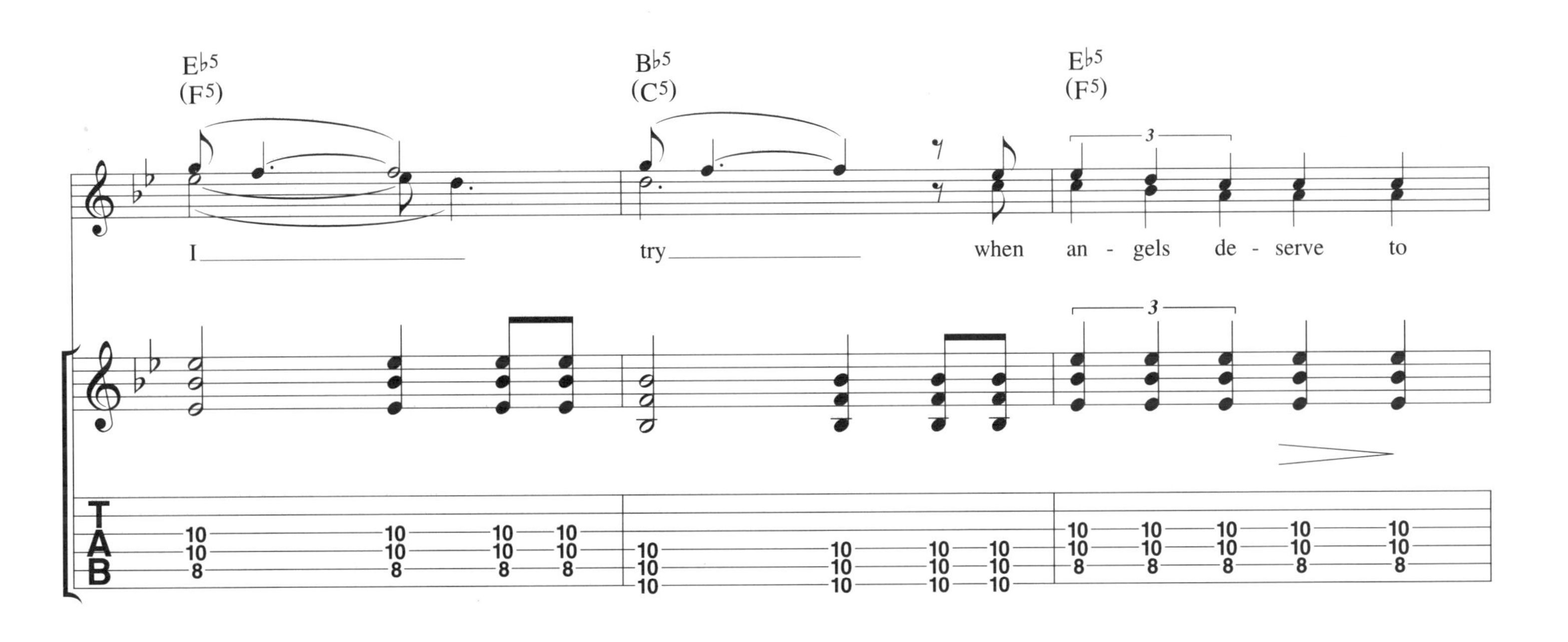
E♭5
(F5)
B♭5
(C5)
E♭5
(F5)
I
try
when an - gels de - serve to

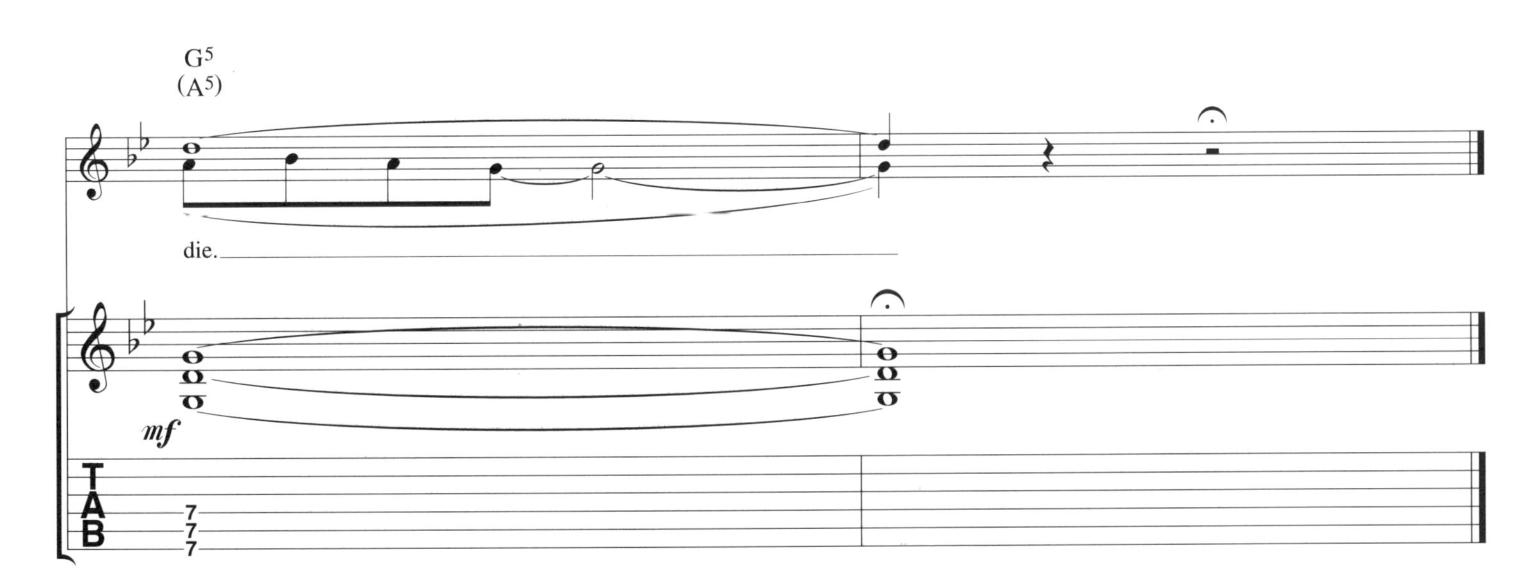
G5
(A5)
die.
mf

back in black

Words & Music by Angus Young, Malcolm Young & Brian Johnson

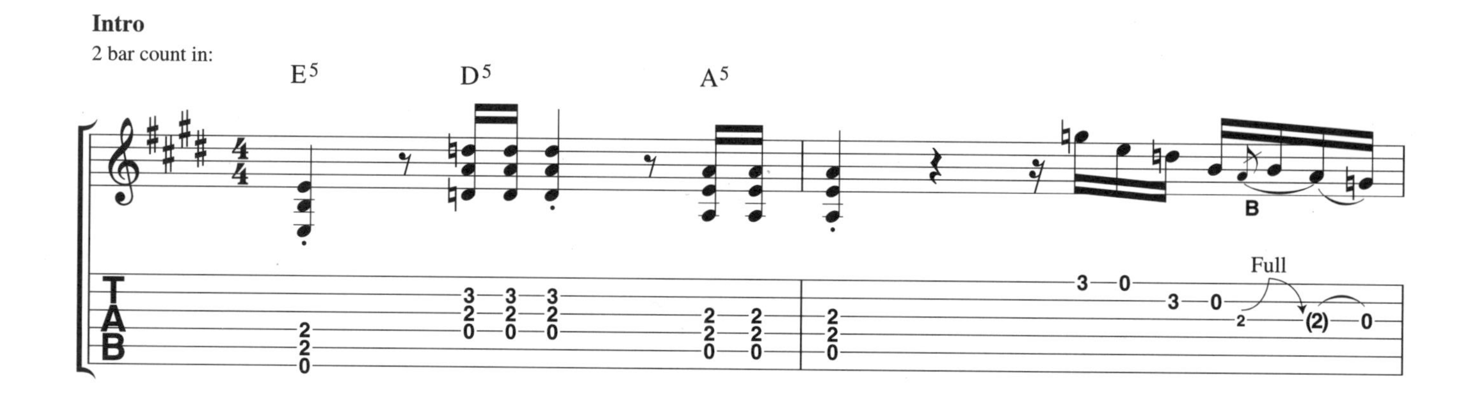

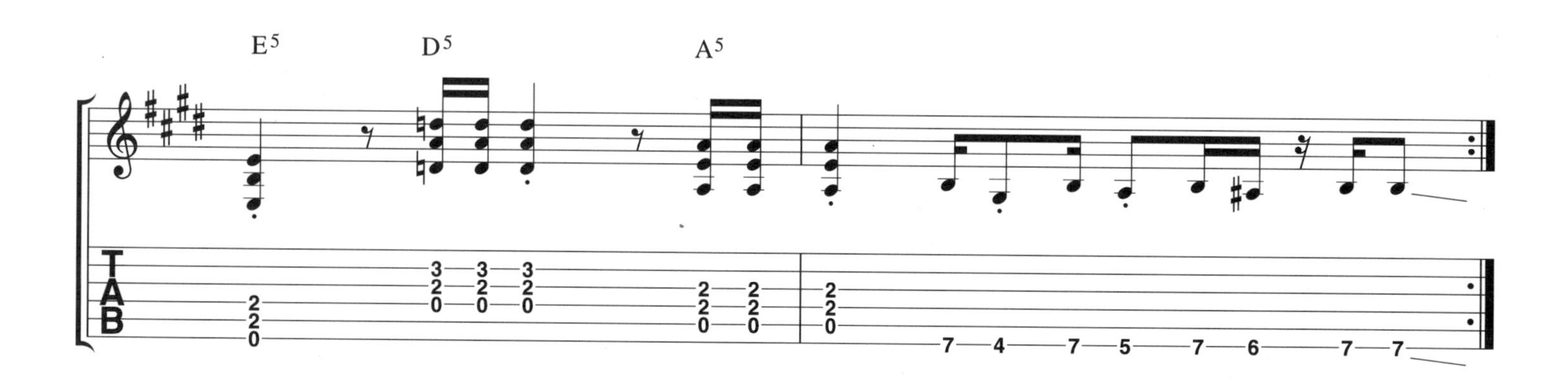

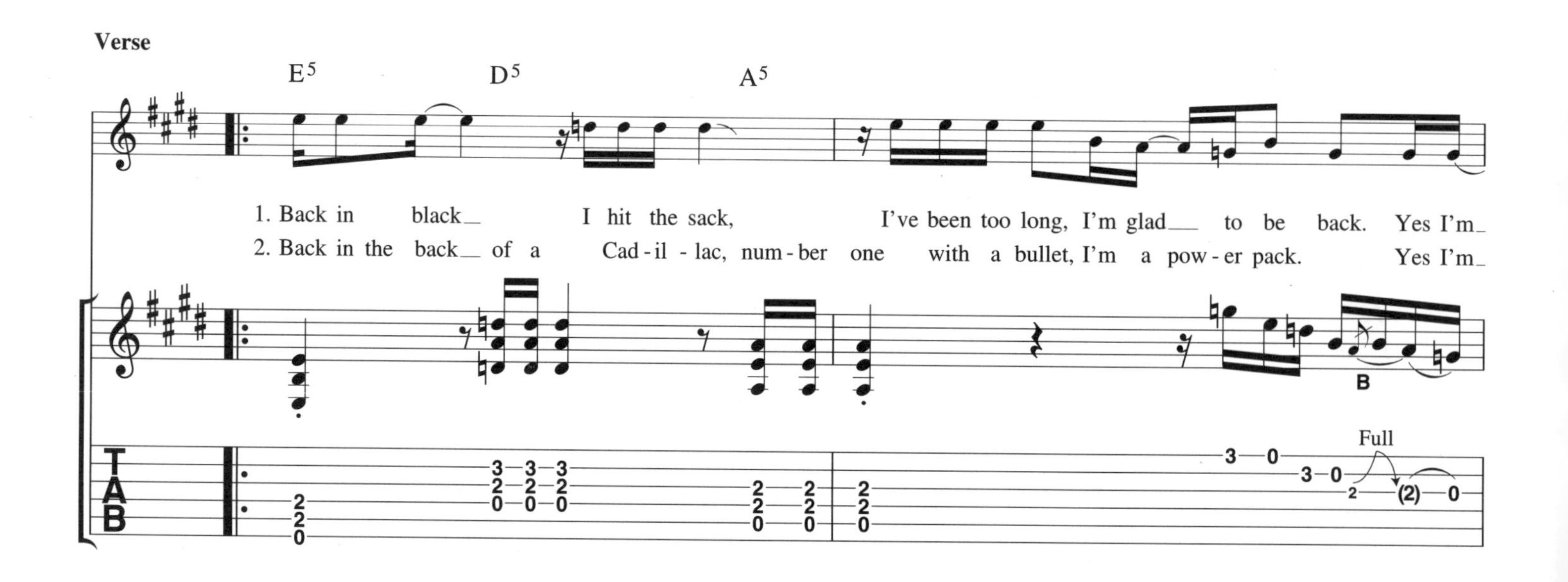

E5 D5 A5
let loose from the noose that's kept me hang - in' a - bout. I keep
in a bang with a gang, they got - ta catch me if they want me to hang. 'Cause I'm
E5 D5 A5
look - in' at the sky 'cause it's get - tin' me high. For - get the hearse 'cause I'll nev - er die. I got
back on the track and I'm beatin' the flack, no - bo - dy's gon - na get on an - oth - er rap. So
B
Full
E5 D5 A5
nine lives, cat's eyes a - bus - in' ev - 'ry one of them and run - nin' wild.
look at me now, I'm just - a mak - in' my play, don't try to push your luck, just get out - ta my way.
'Cause I'm
Chorus
A5 E5 B5 A5 B5 A5 E5 B5 A5 B5
back, yes I'm back. Well I'm

G5
D5
A5
back,
yes I'm
back.
Well I'm
E5
B5
back,
back.
Well I'm
To Coda
1.
2.
back in black,
yes I'm
back in black.
Solo
E5
D5
A5
E5
B
¼
T
A
B

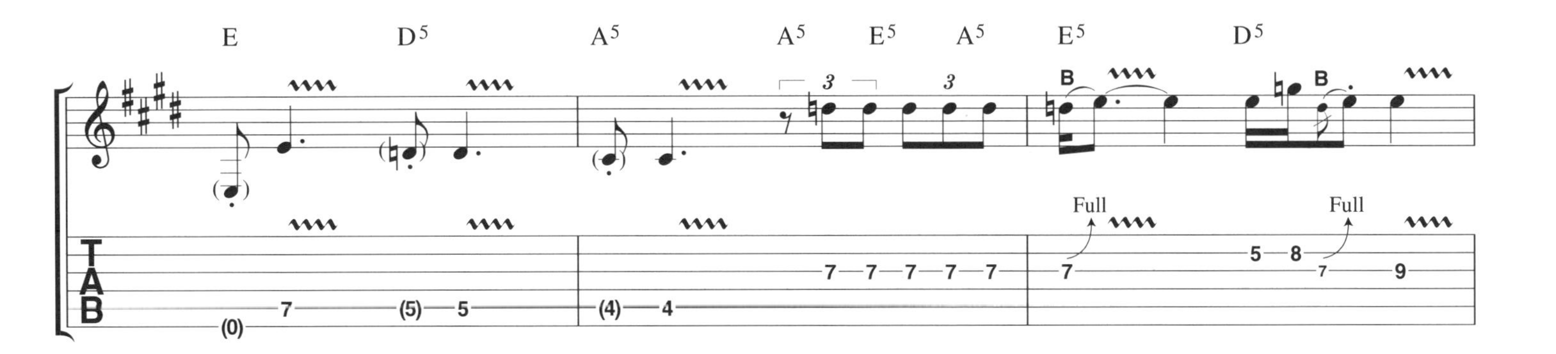
E
D5
A5
A5
E5
A5
E5
D5
Full
Full

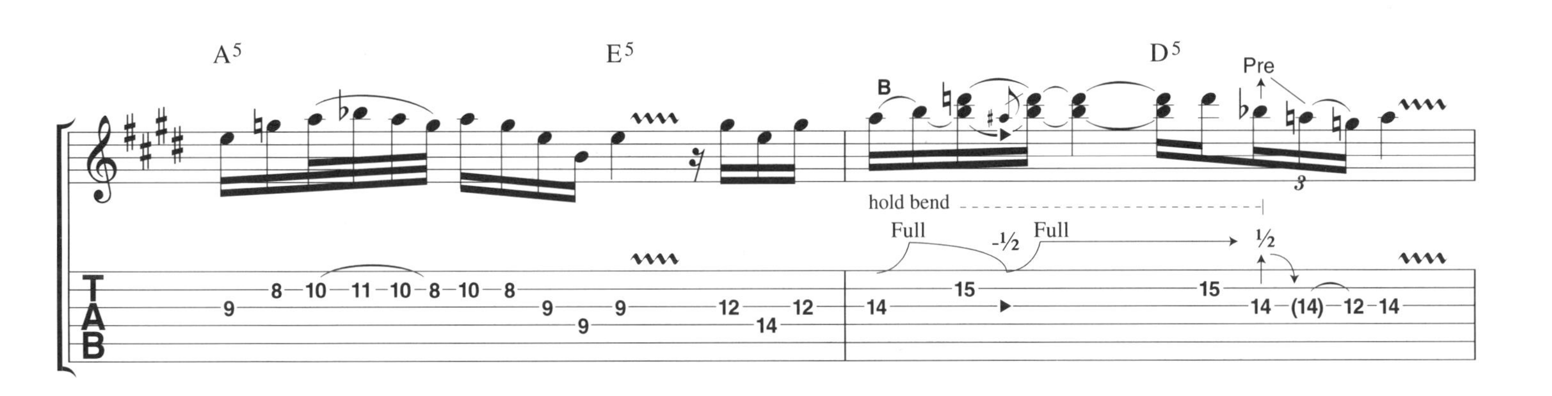
A5
E5
D5
Pre
hold bend
Full
-½
Full
½

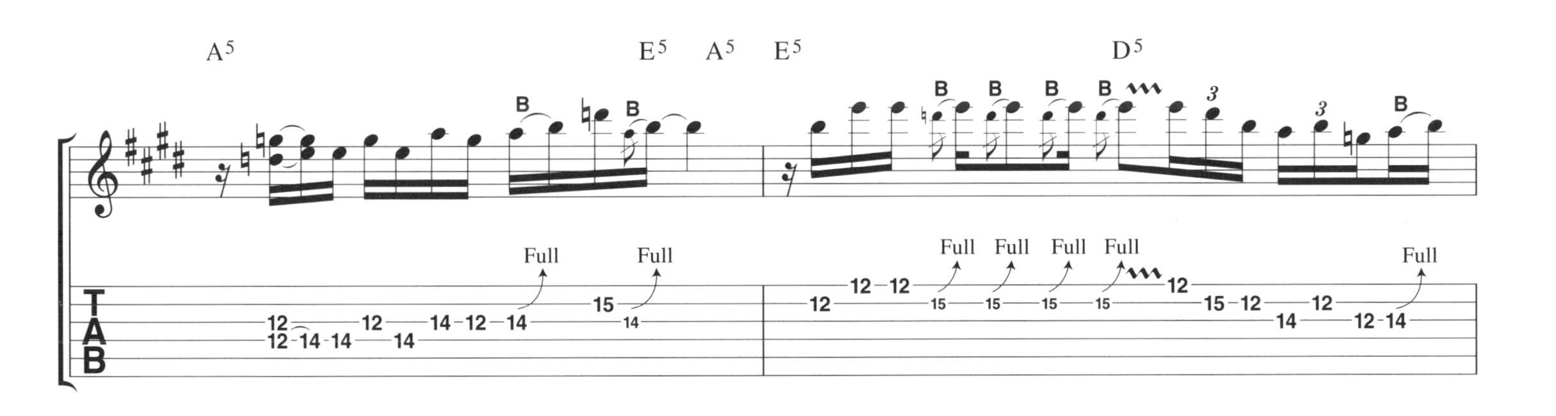
A5
E5
A5
E5
D5
Full
Full
Full
Full
Full
Full
Full

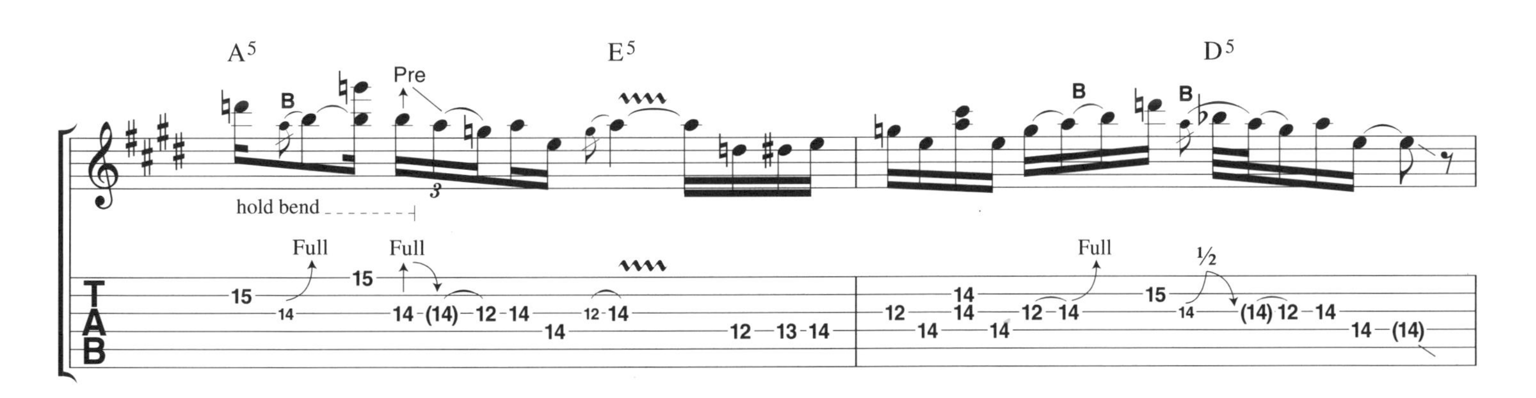
A5
E5
D5
Pre
hold bend
Full
Full
Full
½

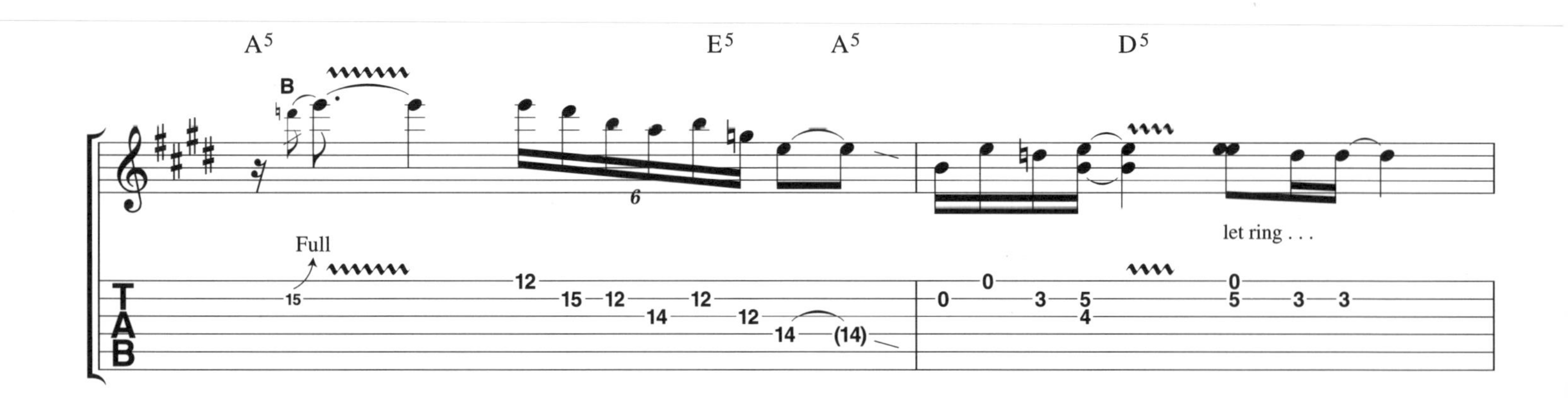
A5
E5
A5
D5
B
Full
let ring . . .

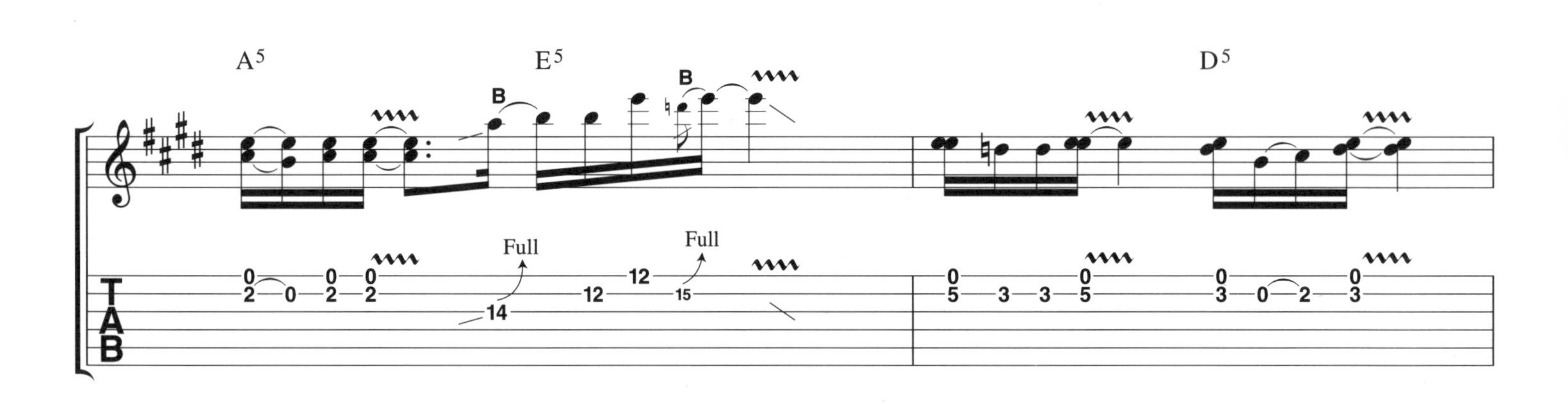
A5
E5
D5
B
B
Full
Full

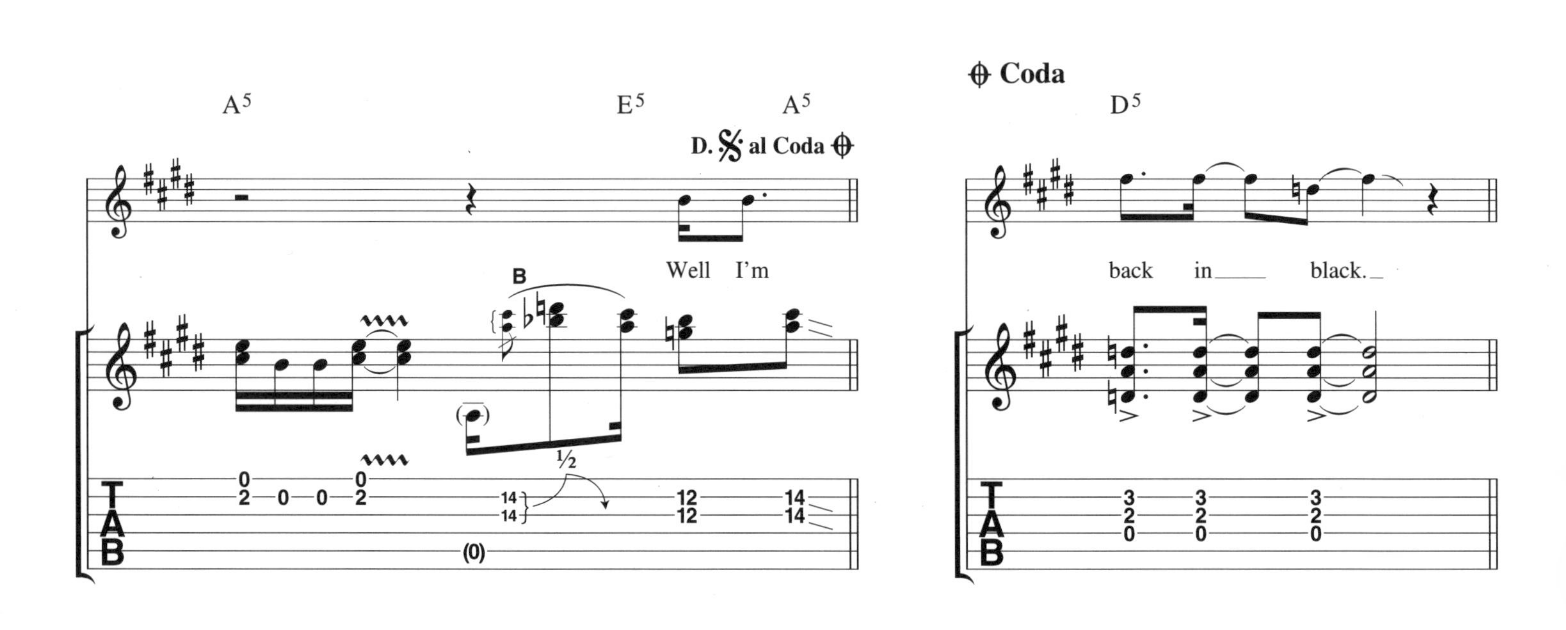
Coda
A5
E5
A5
D5
D.S. al Coda
Well I'm
back in black.
B
½

(E5)
B
B
¼
¼

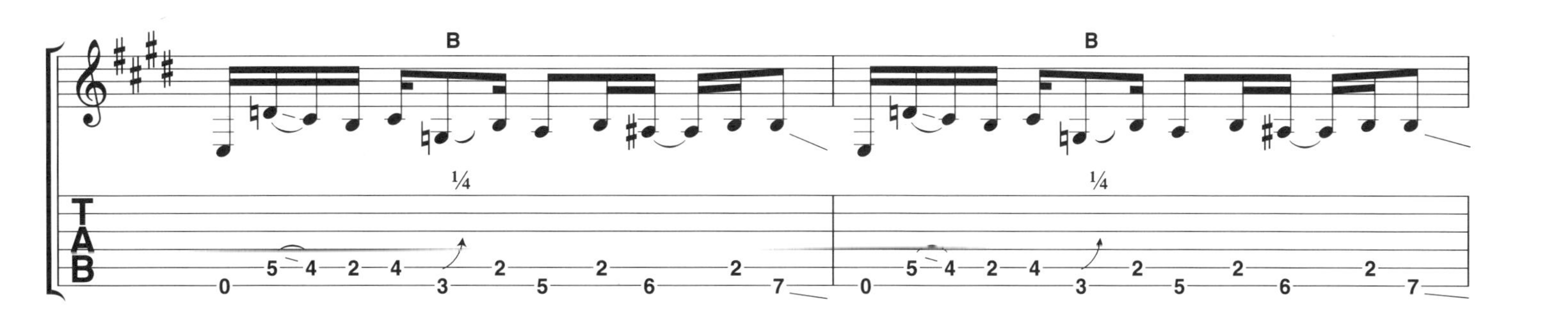
B
¼
B
¼

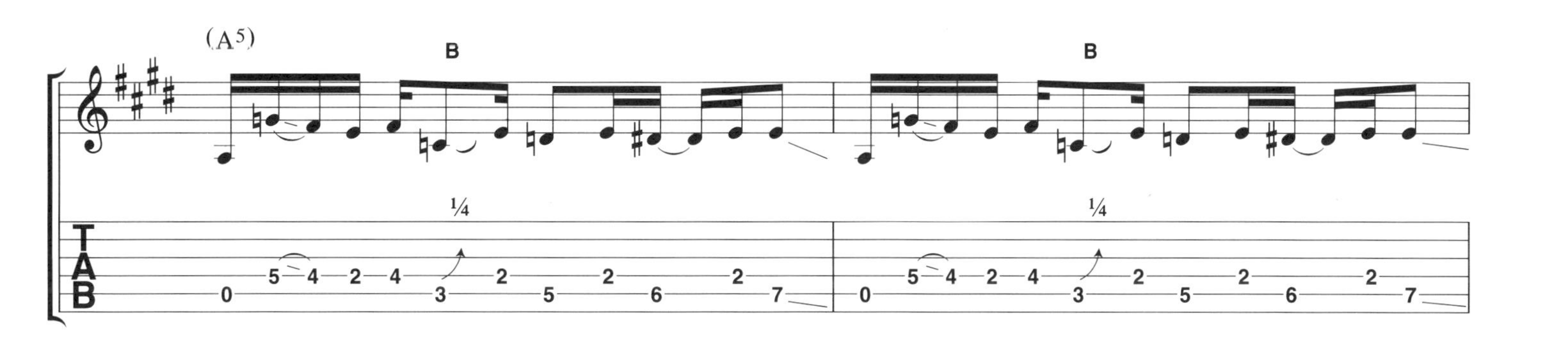
(A5)
B
¼
B
¼

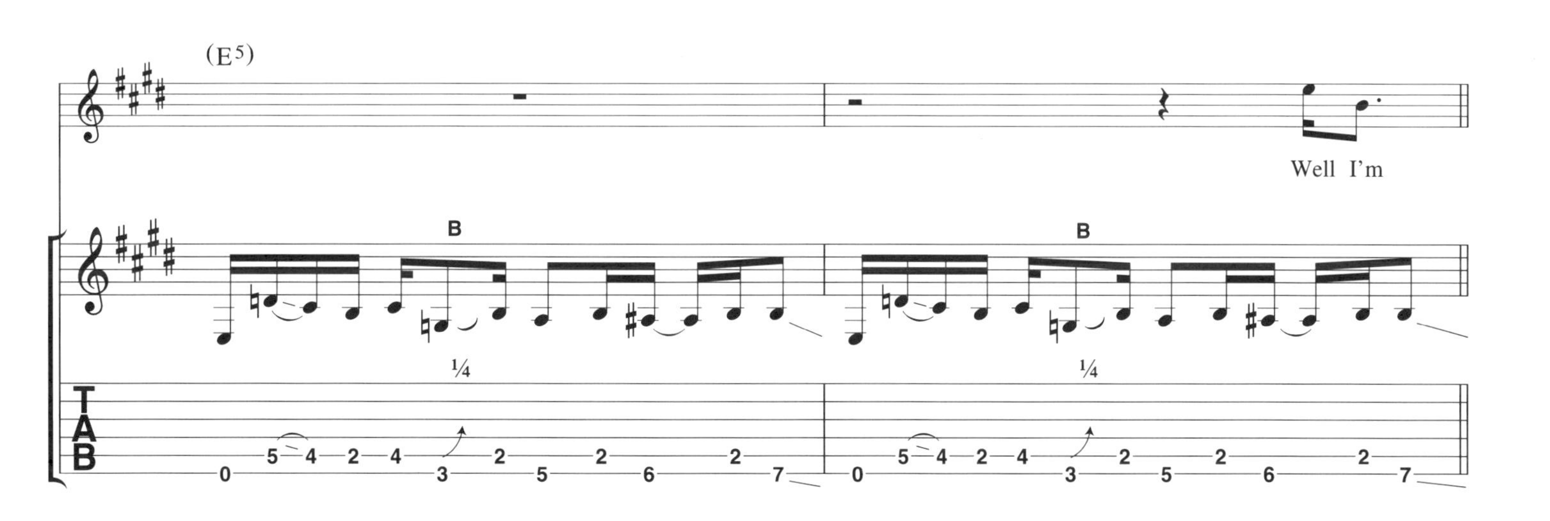
(E5)
Well I'm
B
¼
B
¼

Chorus

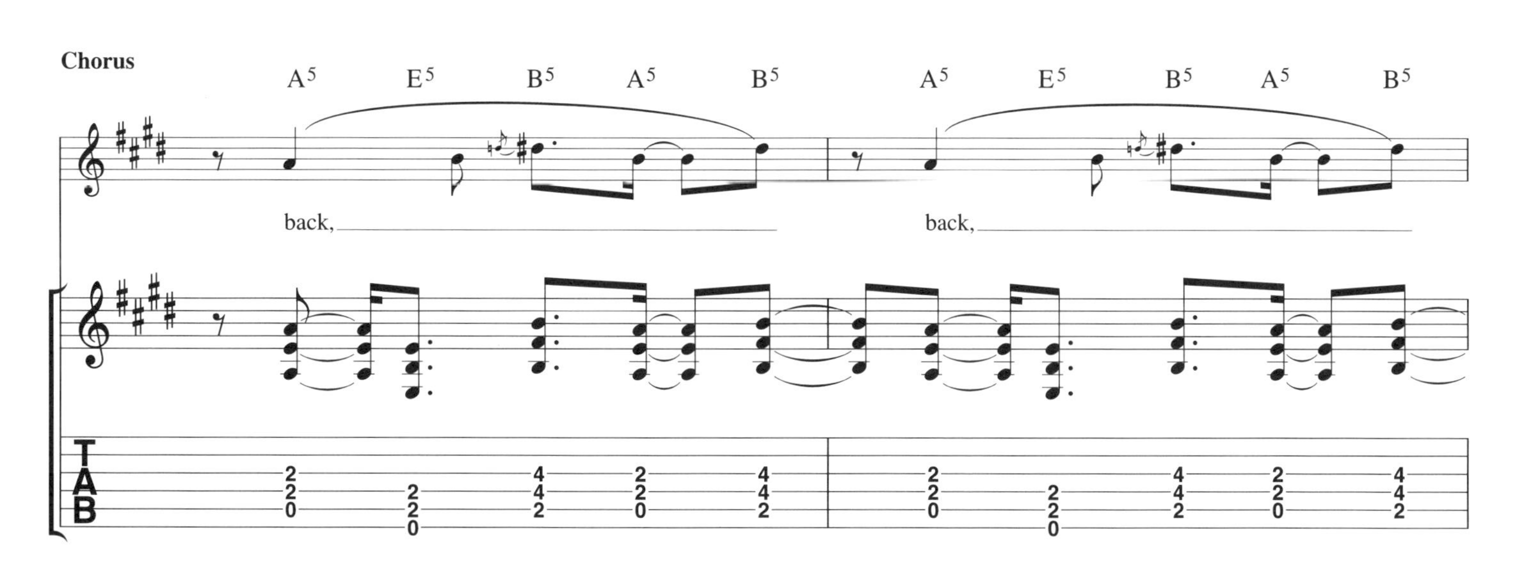
A5 E5 B5 A5 B5
A5 E5 B5 A5 B5
back,
back,

G5
D5
A5
back,
B
¼
E5
B5
I'm
back in black,
yes I'm back in black.
I wan - na say it!
½

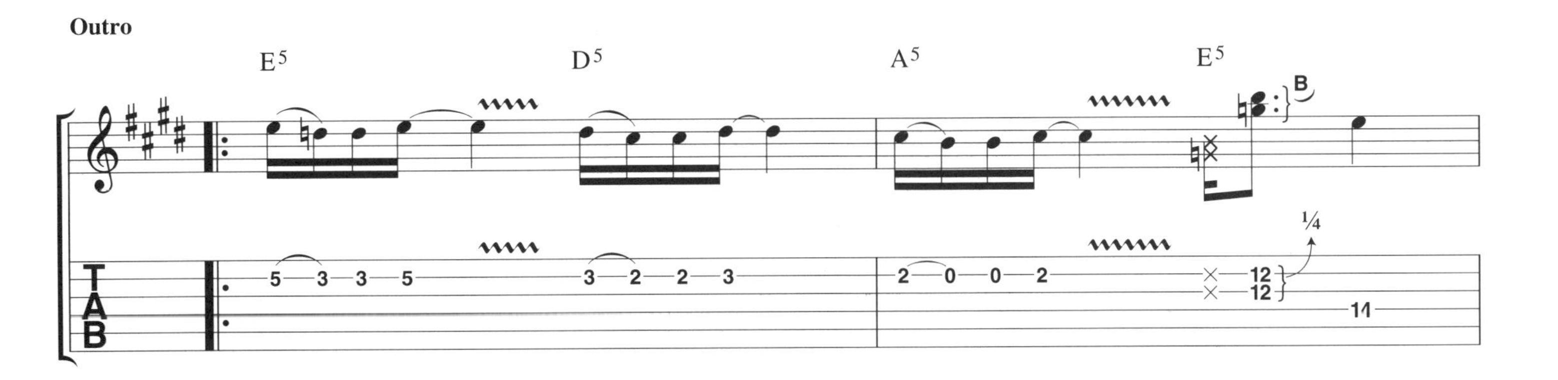
Outro
E5
D5
A5
E5
B
¼

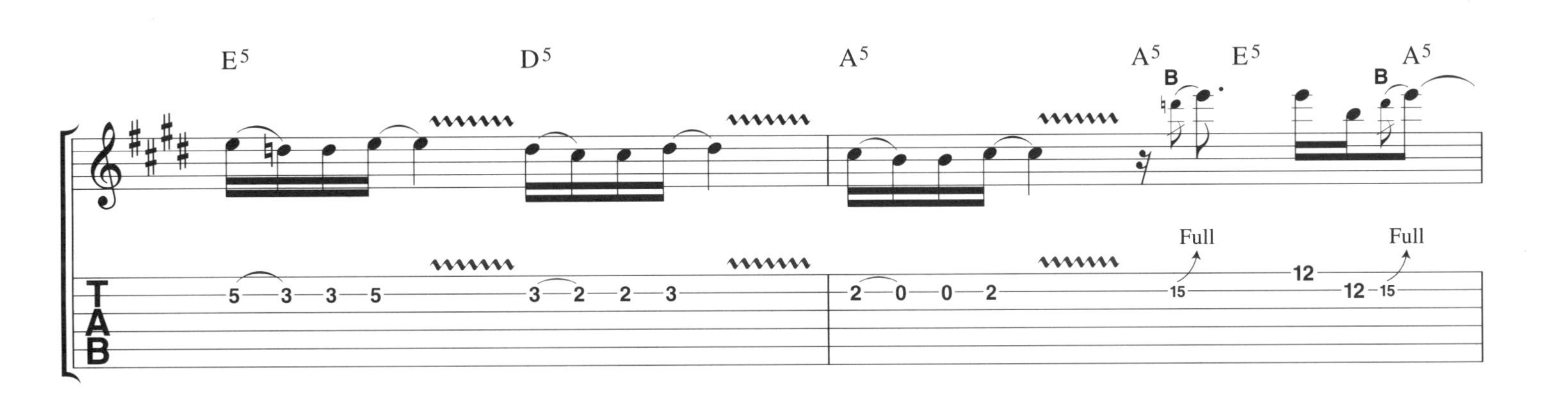
E5
D5
A5
A5
E5
A5
B
B
Full
Full

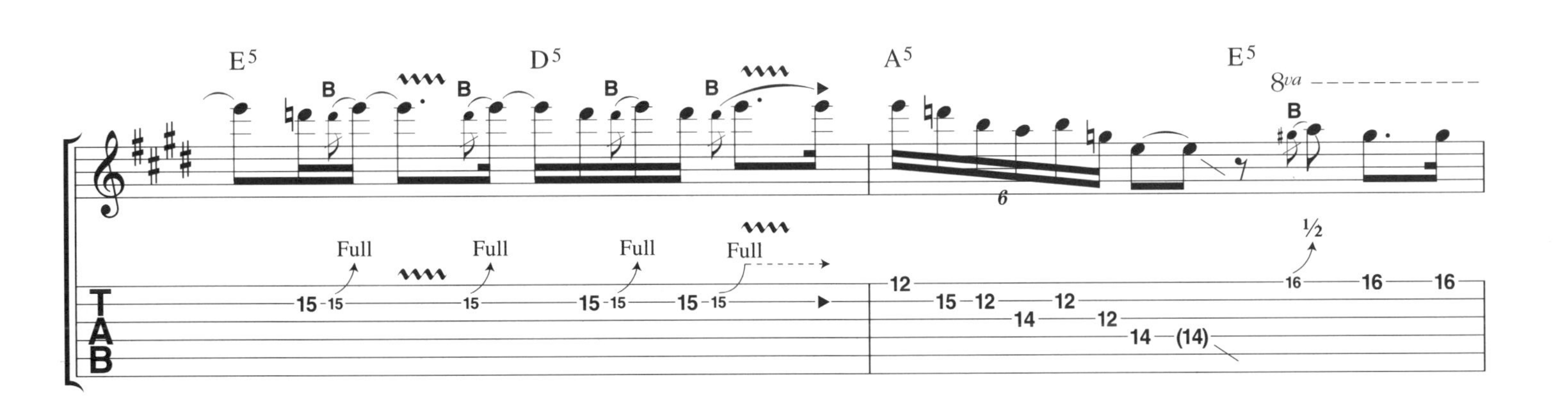
E5
D5
A5
E5
8va
B
B
B
B
B
Full
Full
Full
Full
½

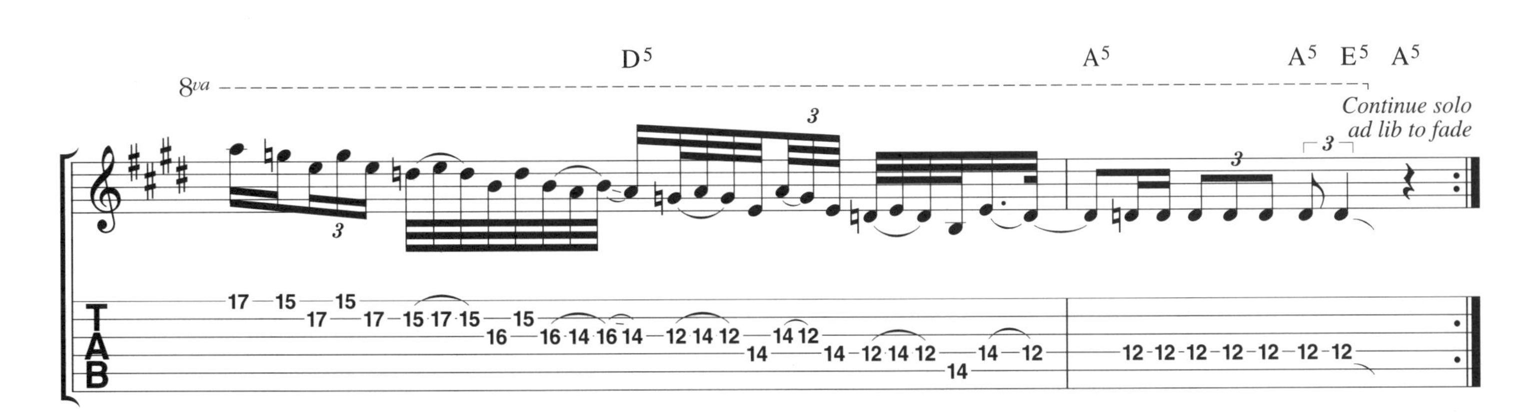
8va
D5
A5
A5
E5
A5
Continue solo
ad lib to fade

bring your daughter... to the slaughter

Words & Music by Bruce Dickinson

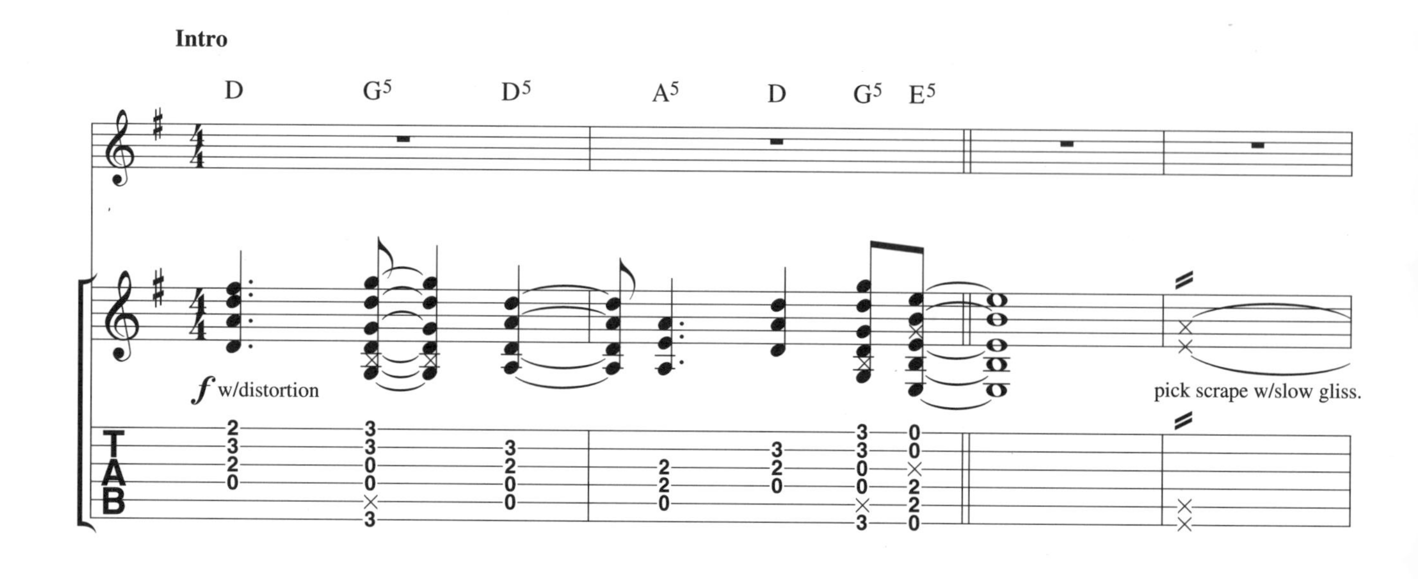

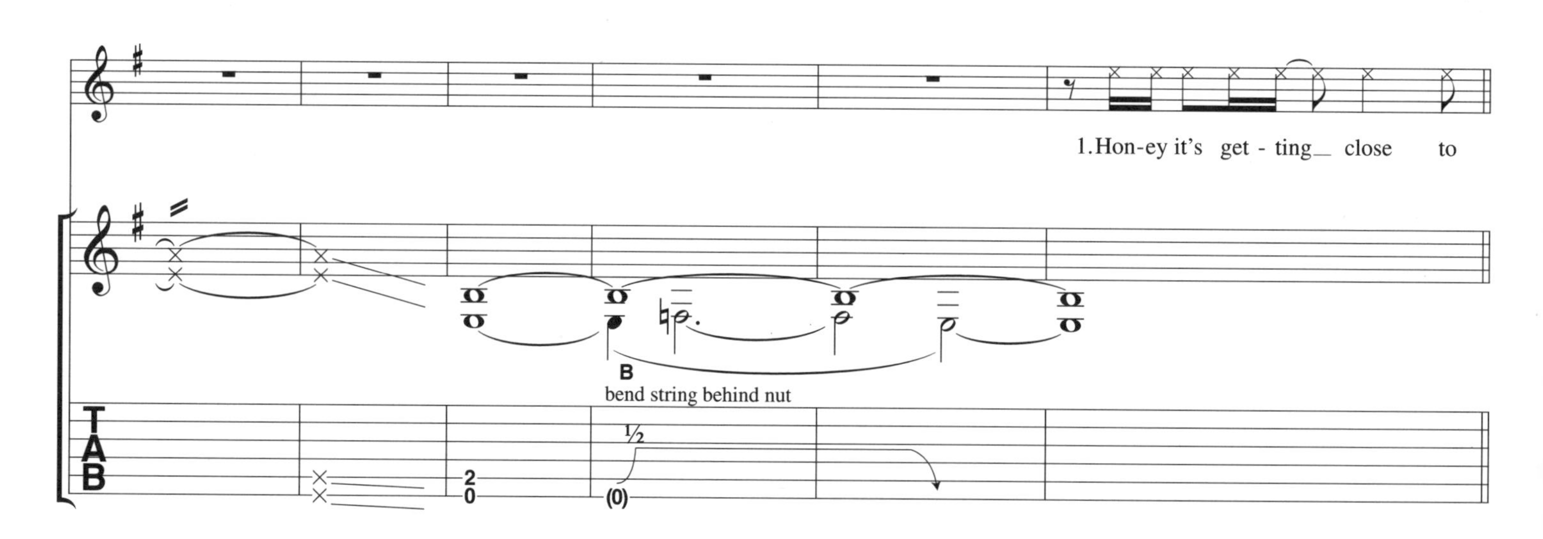

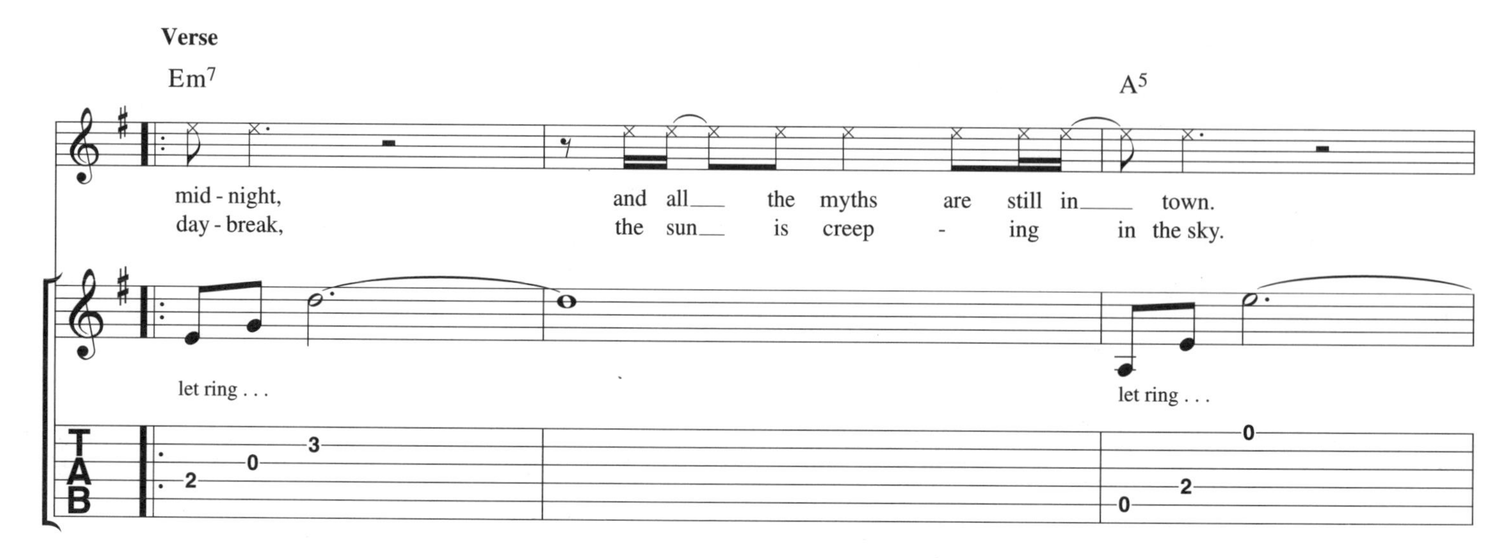

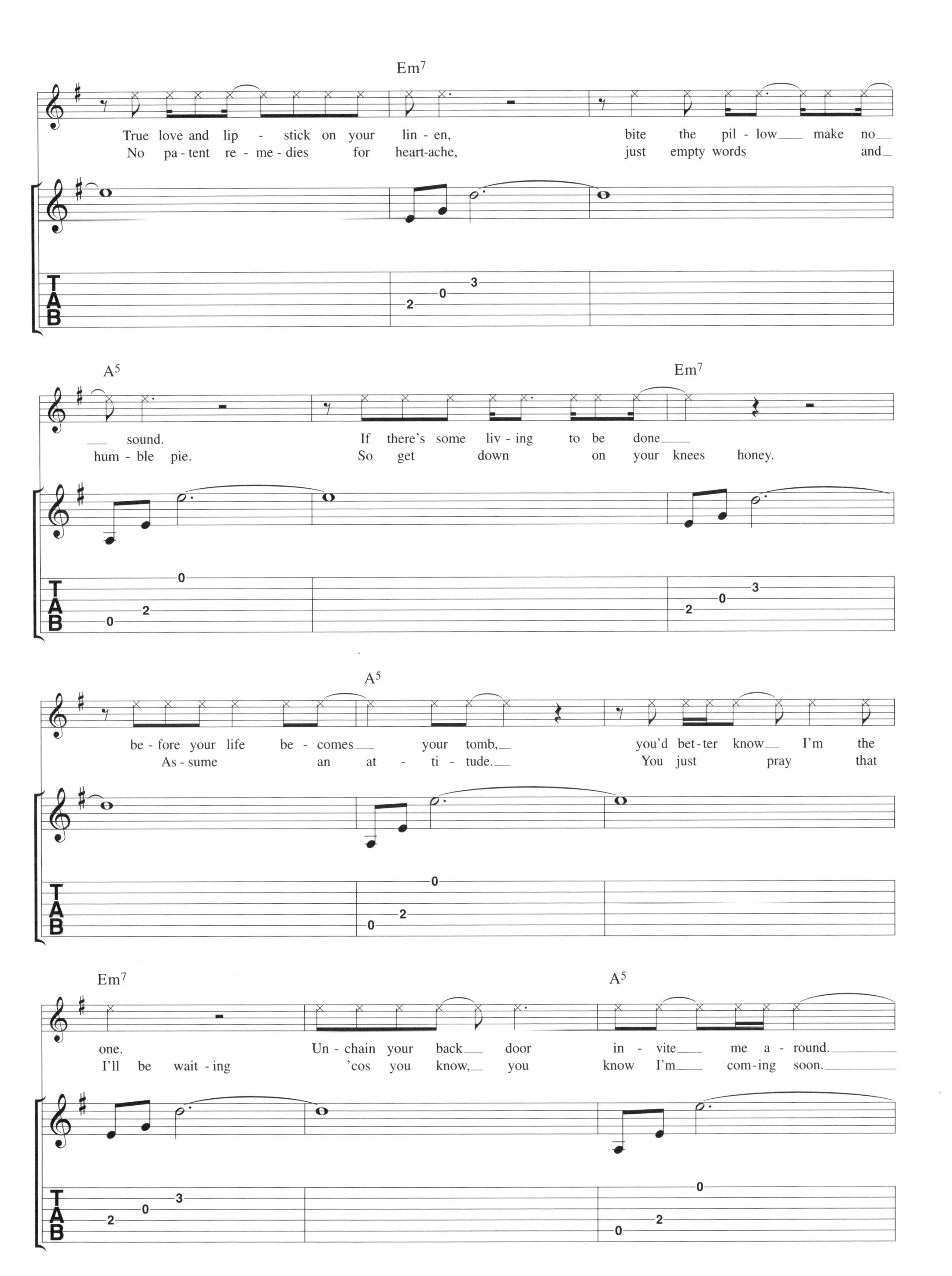
Em7
True love and lip - stick on your lin - en,
No pa - tent re - me - dies for heart-ache,
bite the pil - low make no
just empty words and
A5
sound.
hum - ble pie.
Em7
If there's some liv - ing to be done
So get down on your knees honey.
A5
be - fore your life be - comes your tomb,
As - sume an at - ti - tude.
you'd bet - ter know I'm the
You just pray that
Em7
one.
I'll be wait - ing
A5
Un - chain your back door in - vite me a - round.
'cos you know, you know I'm com - ing soon.
T
A
B

Chorus
D5 E5 D5 E5 C5
Bring your daugh - ter, bring your daugh - ter, to the slaugh -
A5 D5 A5
- ter, let her go, let her go,
P.M.
E5 D5
let her go. Bring your daugh -
B
1/4
E5 D5 E5 C5 A5
- ter, bring your daugh - ter to the slaugh - ter,
P.M.

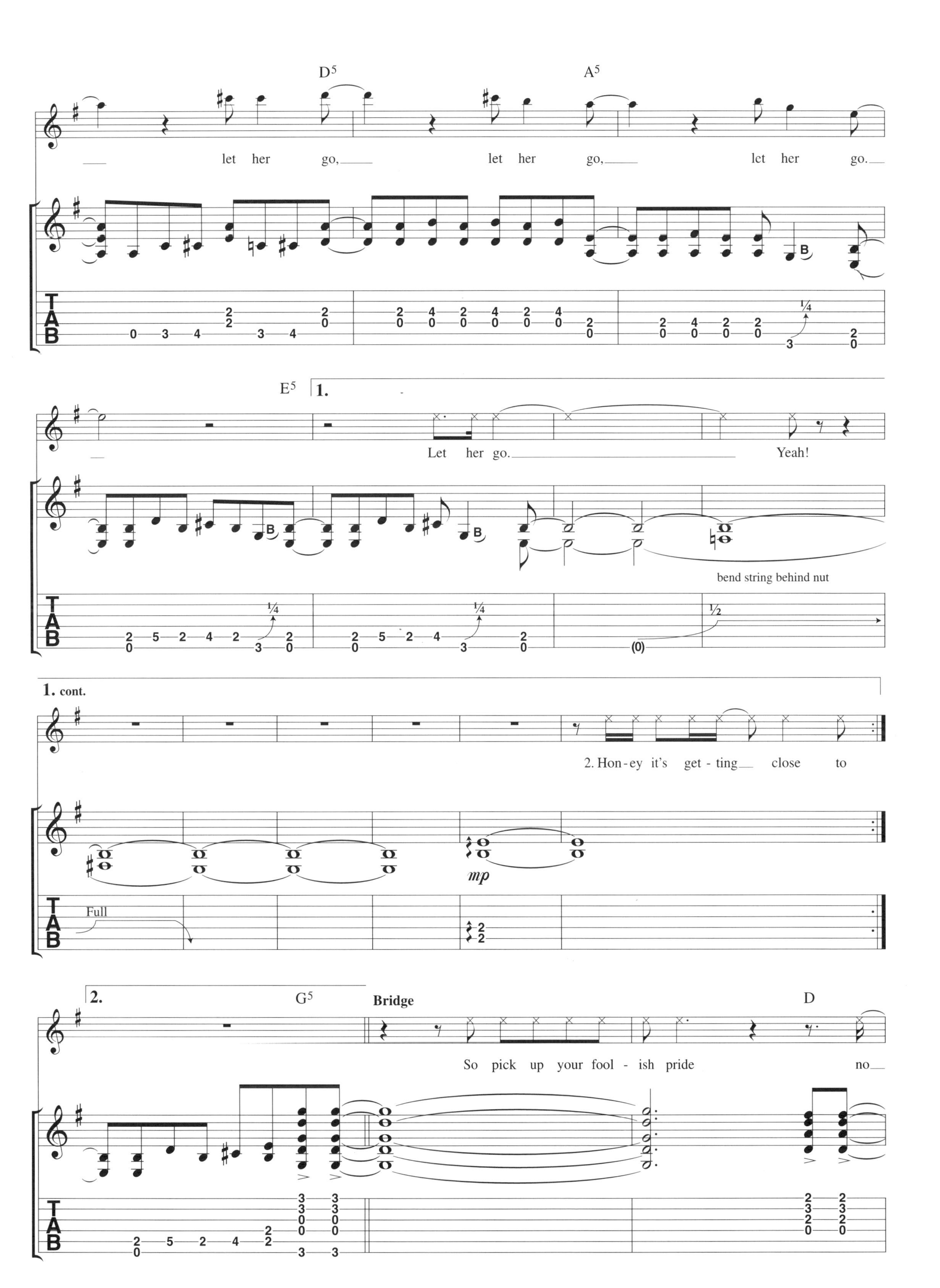
D5
A5
let her go,
let her go,
let her go.
E5
1.
Let her go.
Yeah!
bend string behind nut
1. cont.
2. Hon-ey it's get-ting close to
mp
Full
2.
G5
Bridge
D
So pick up your fool-ish pride no

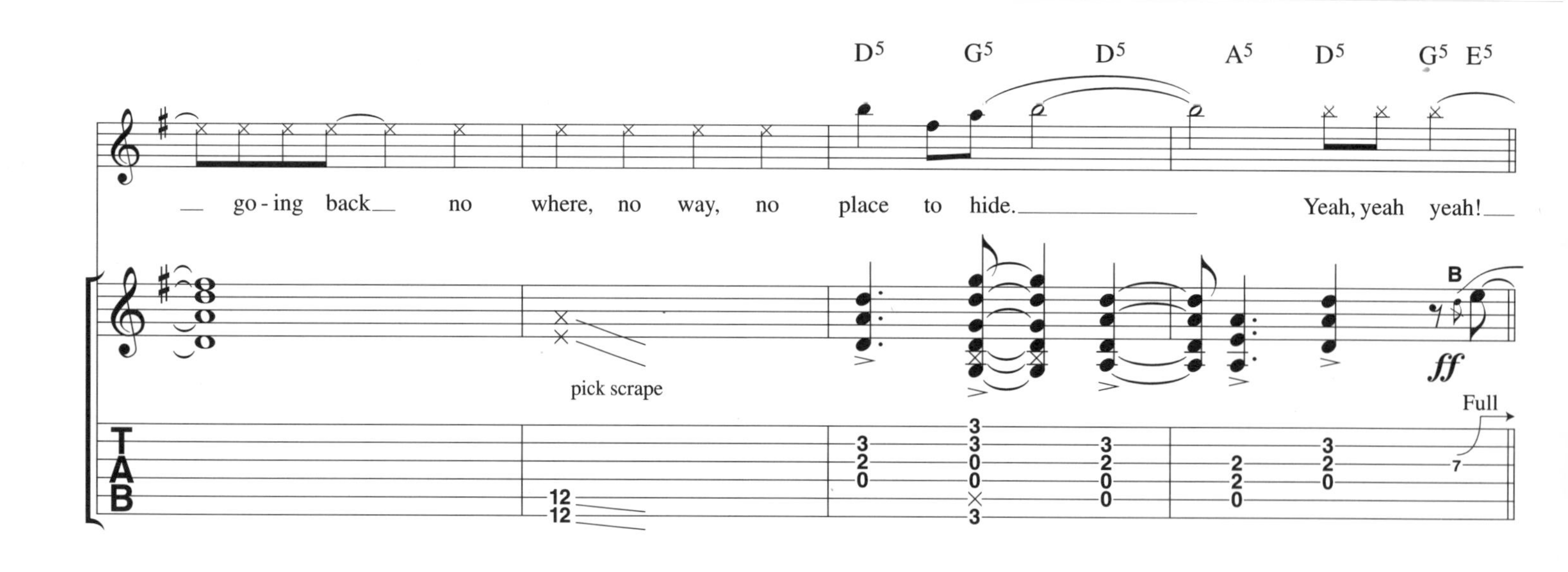
D5 G5 D5 A5 D5 G5 E5
go-ing back no where, no way, no place to hide. Yeah, yeah yeah!
pick scrape
B
ff
Full
TAB

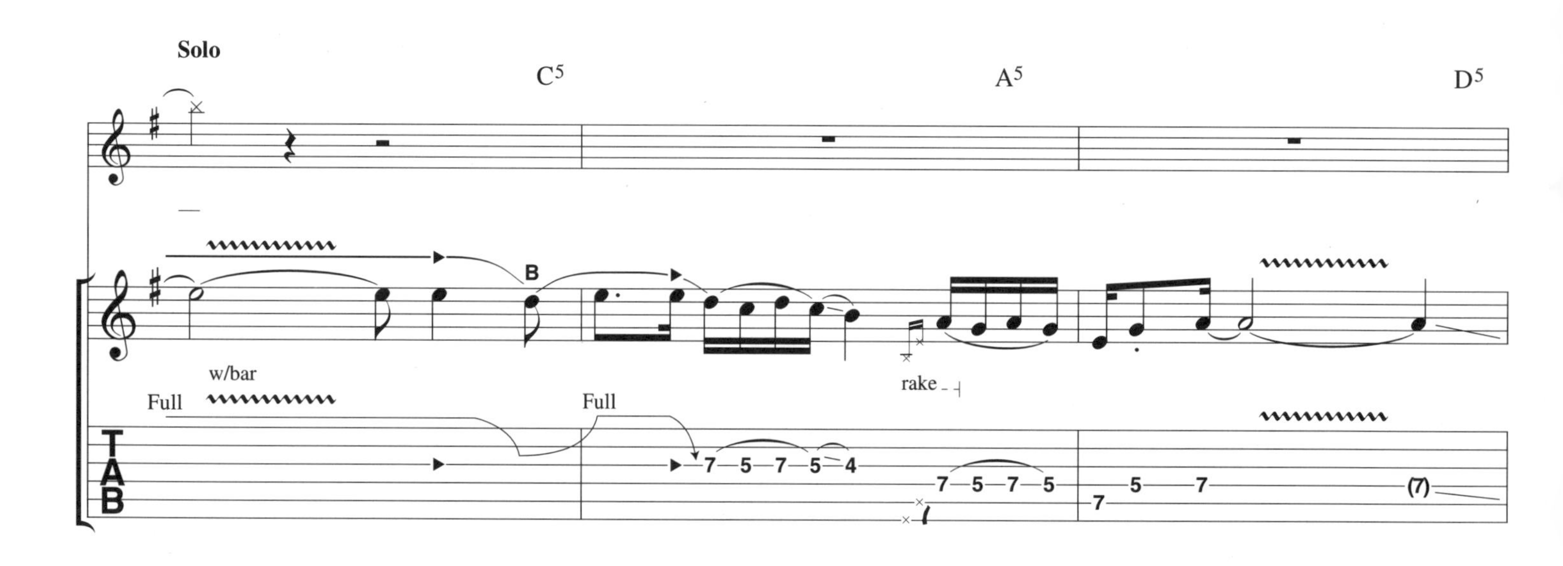
Solo
C5 A5 D5
B
w/bar
Full
Full
rake
TAB

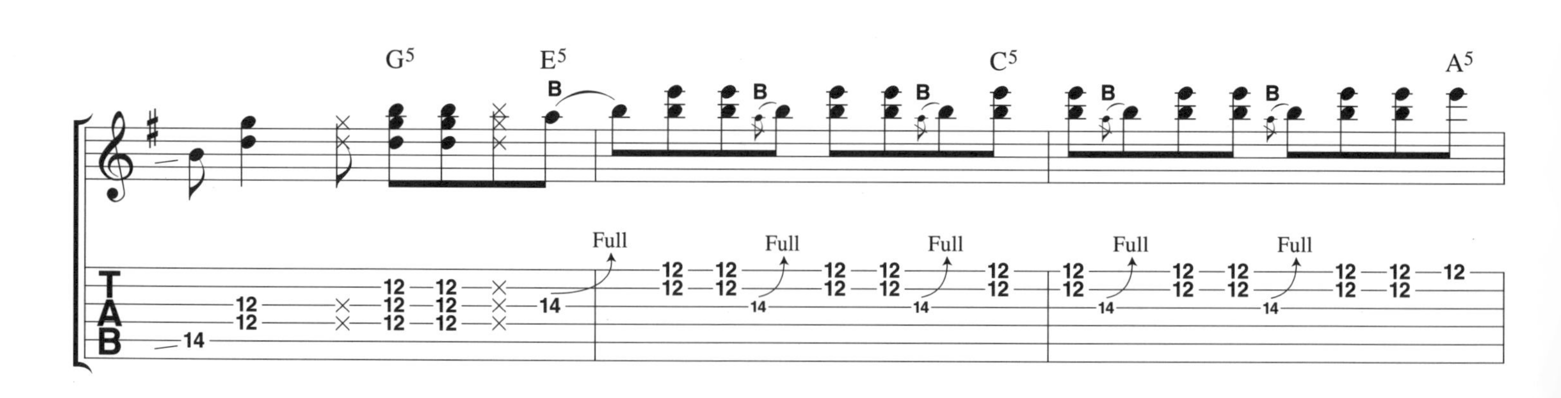
G5 E5 C5 A5
B
Full
TAB

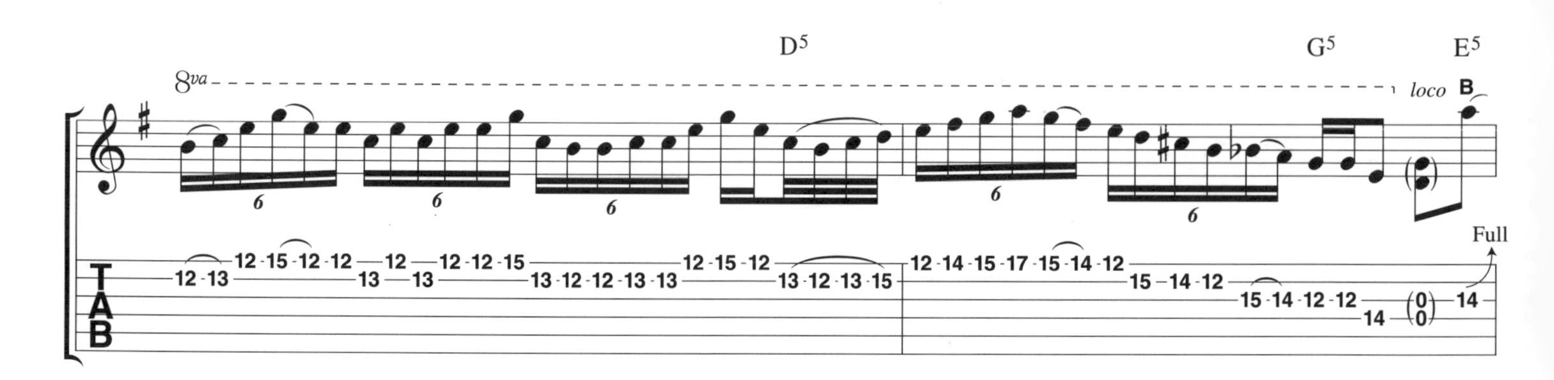
D5 G5 E5
8va
loco
B
Full
TAB

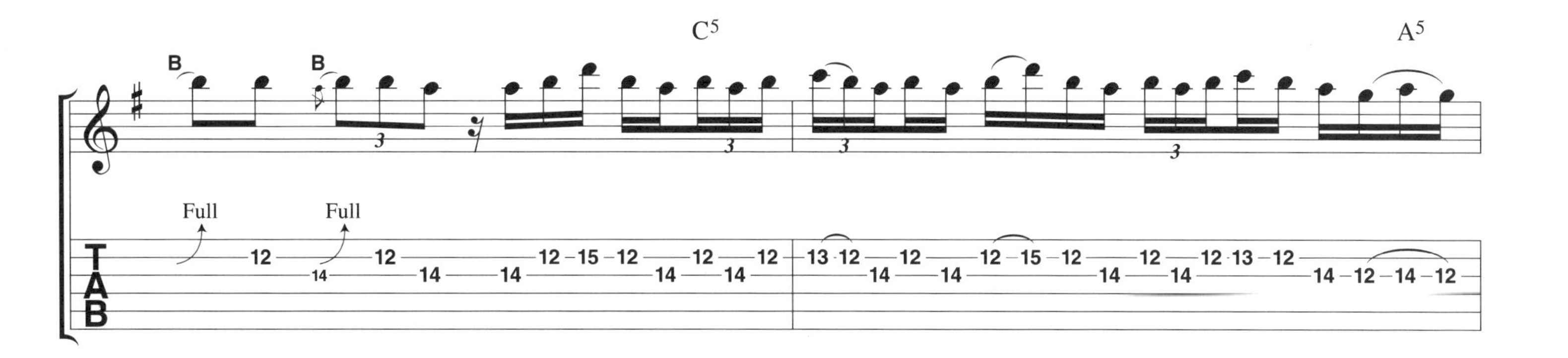
C5
A5
B
B
Full
Full

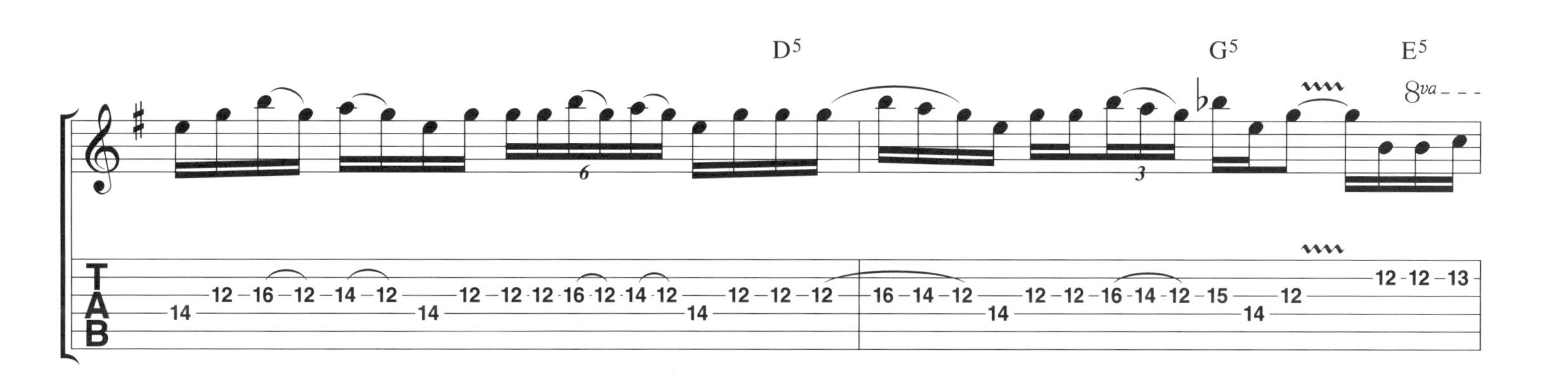
D5
G5
E5
8va

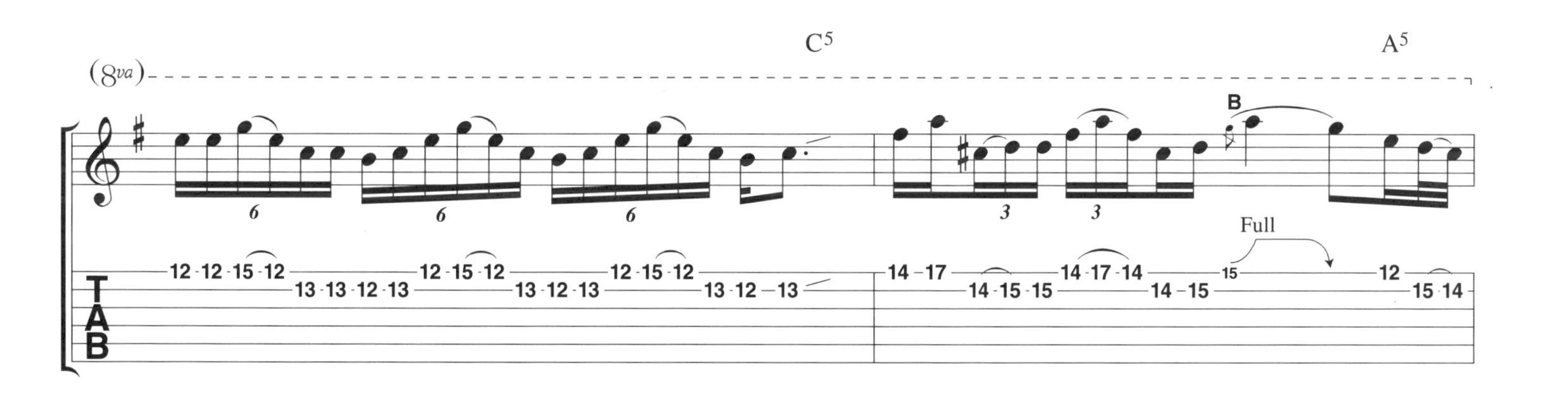
(8va)
C5
A5
B
Full

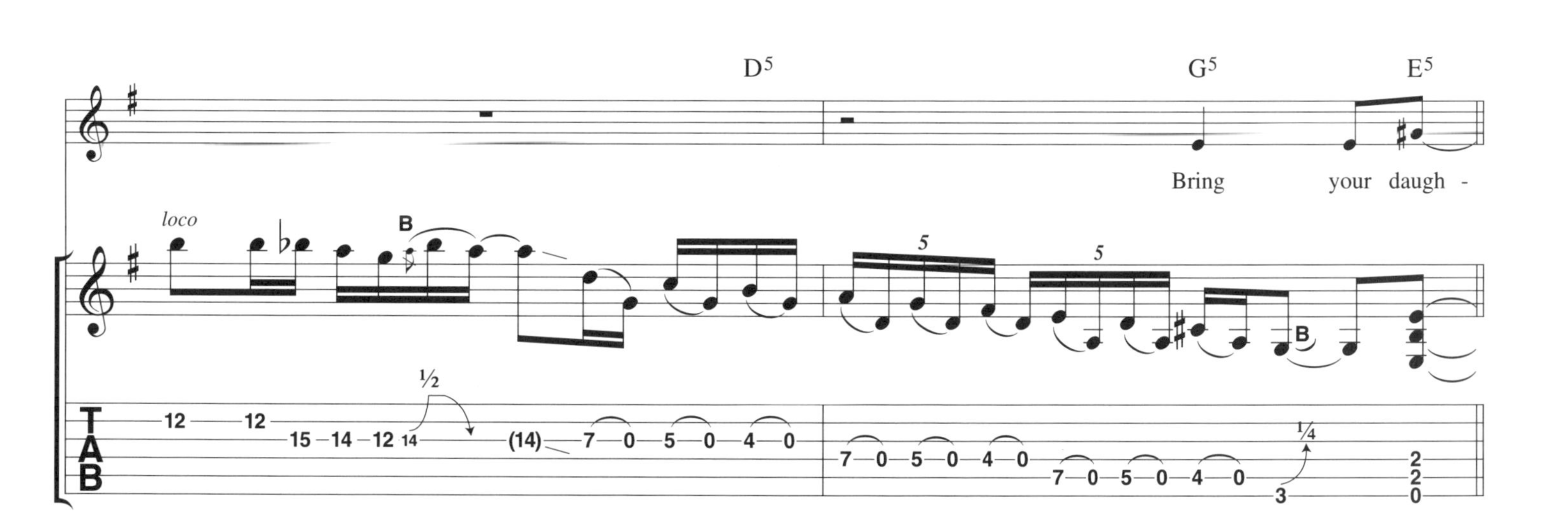
D5
G5
E5
Bring your daugh -
loco
B
½
¼

Bridge
(G5)
(A5)
- ter, bring your daugh - ter, bring your daugh - ter, bring your daugh -
C5
D5
- ter, bring your daugh - ter, bring your daugh - ter, to the slaugh -
mp P.M.
E5
- ter.
Bring your daugh - ter, fetch your daugh -
G5
A5
- ter, bring your daugh - ter fetch your daugh - ter, bring your daugh -

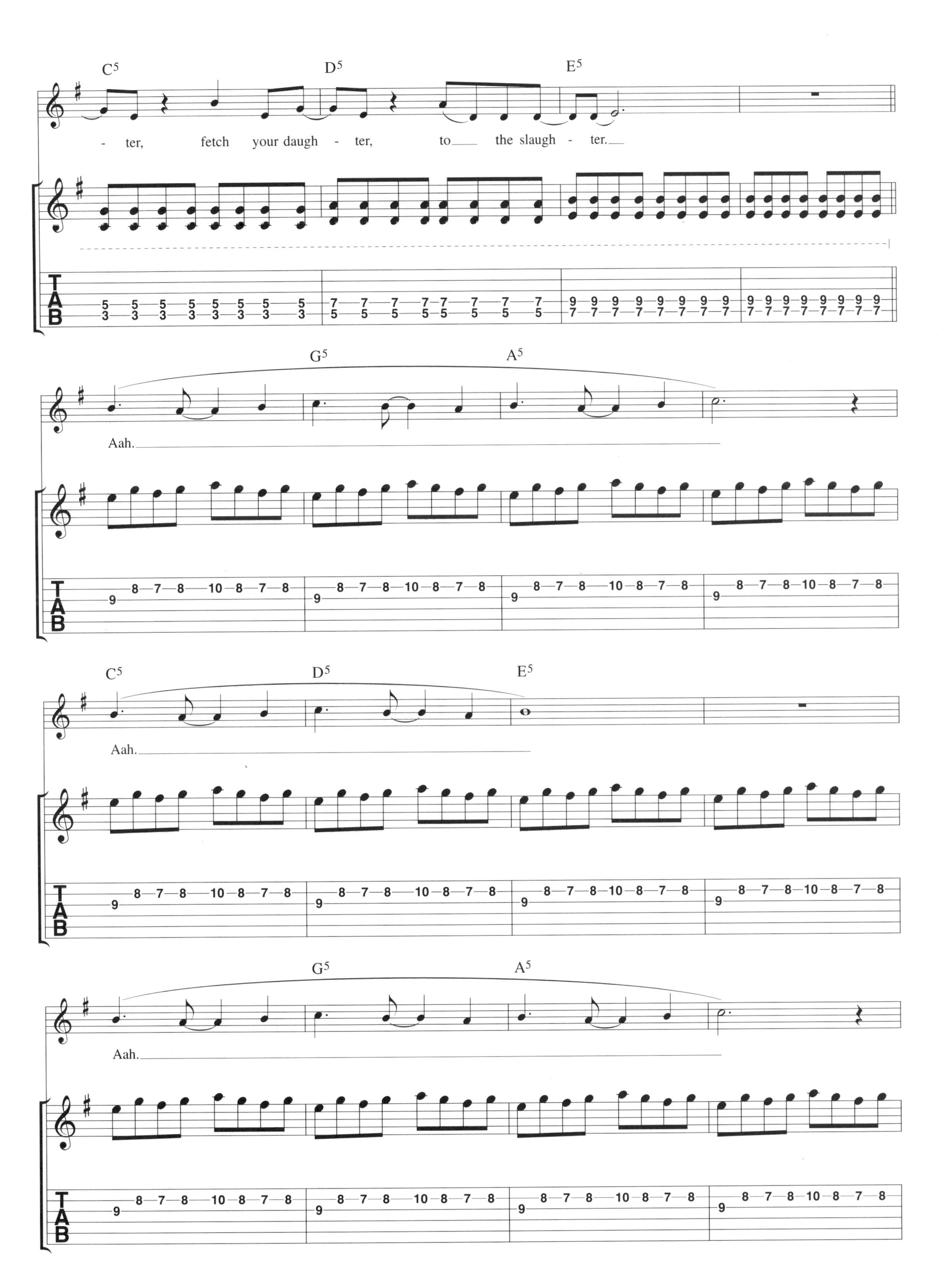
C5
D5
E5
- ter, fetch your daugh - ter, to the slaugh - ter.
G5
A5
Aah.
C5
D5
E5
Aah.
G5
A5
Aah.

C5
D5
E5
Aah.
Oh.
8va
ff
Full
Chorus
D5
E5
D5
E5
C5
Bring your daugh - ter, bring your daugh - ter, to the slaugh -
loco
A5
D5
A5
- ter, let her go, let her go,
E5
1.2.
D5
let her go.
Bring your daugh -
8va

3.
A5 G5 E5
-ter
Let her go,
let her go,
let her go.
Free time
Yeah I'm com-ing to get ya!
Now!
ad lib
Full
B

crawling

Words & Music by Chester Bennington, Rob Bourdon, Brad Delson, Joseph Hahn & Mike Shinoda

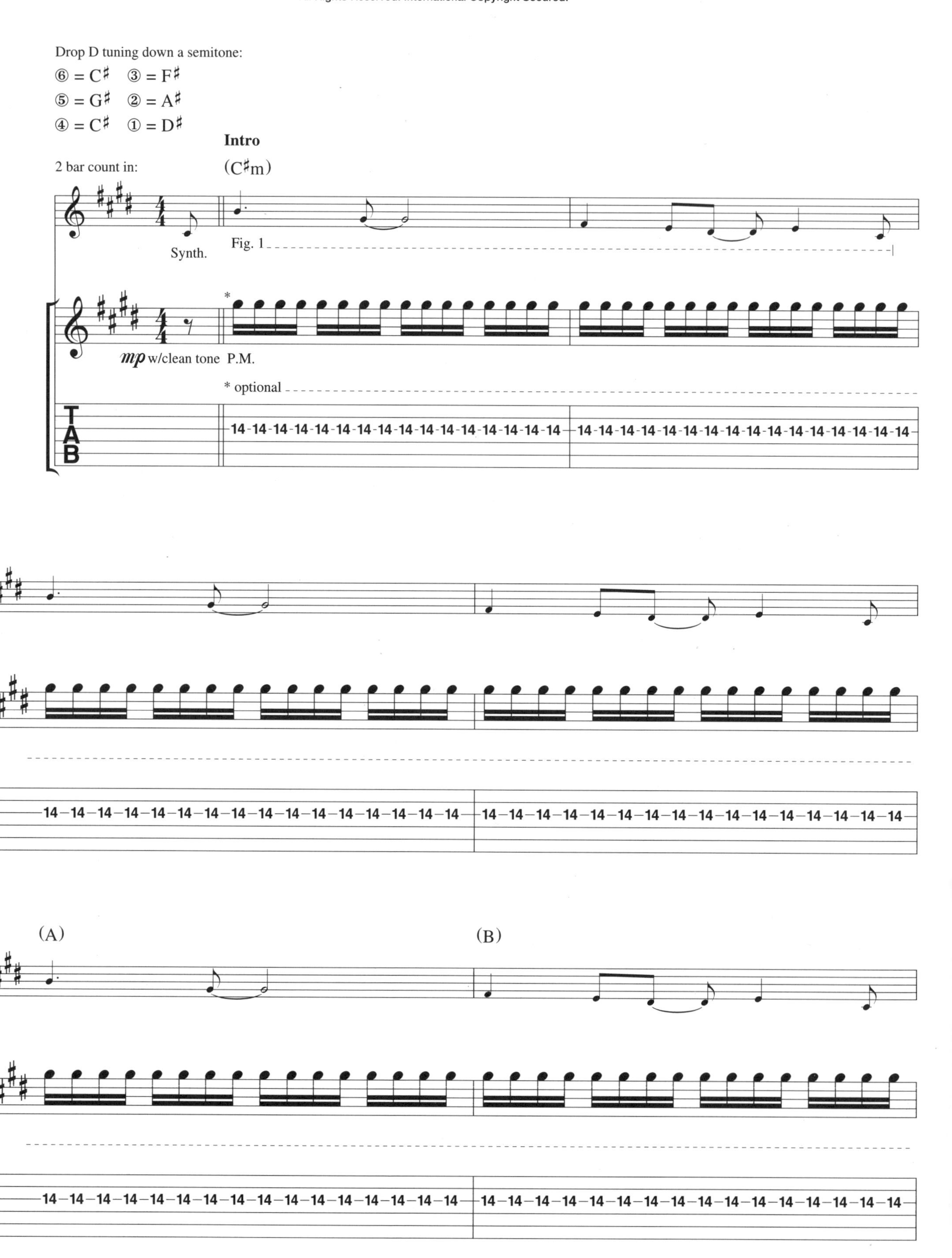

(C♯m)
ff w/distortion
T
A
B
14 14 14 14 14 14 14 14 14 14 14 14 14 14 14 14
14 14 14 14 14 5 5 5 5 5 7
Chorus
C♯5
A5
E5
B5
G♯5
C♯5
Crawl - ing in my skin, these wounds, they will not he - al.
Fear is how I
A5
E5
B5
G♯5
N.C.(C♯m)
(A)
(E)
(B)
fall con - fus - ing what is re - al.
Oh.
w/Fig. 1 Synth cue (x2)
Verse
N.C.(C♯m)
(A)
1.There's some - thing in - side me that pulls be - neath the sur - face,
P.M.
mp w/clean tone
optional

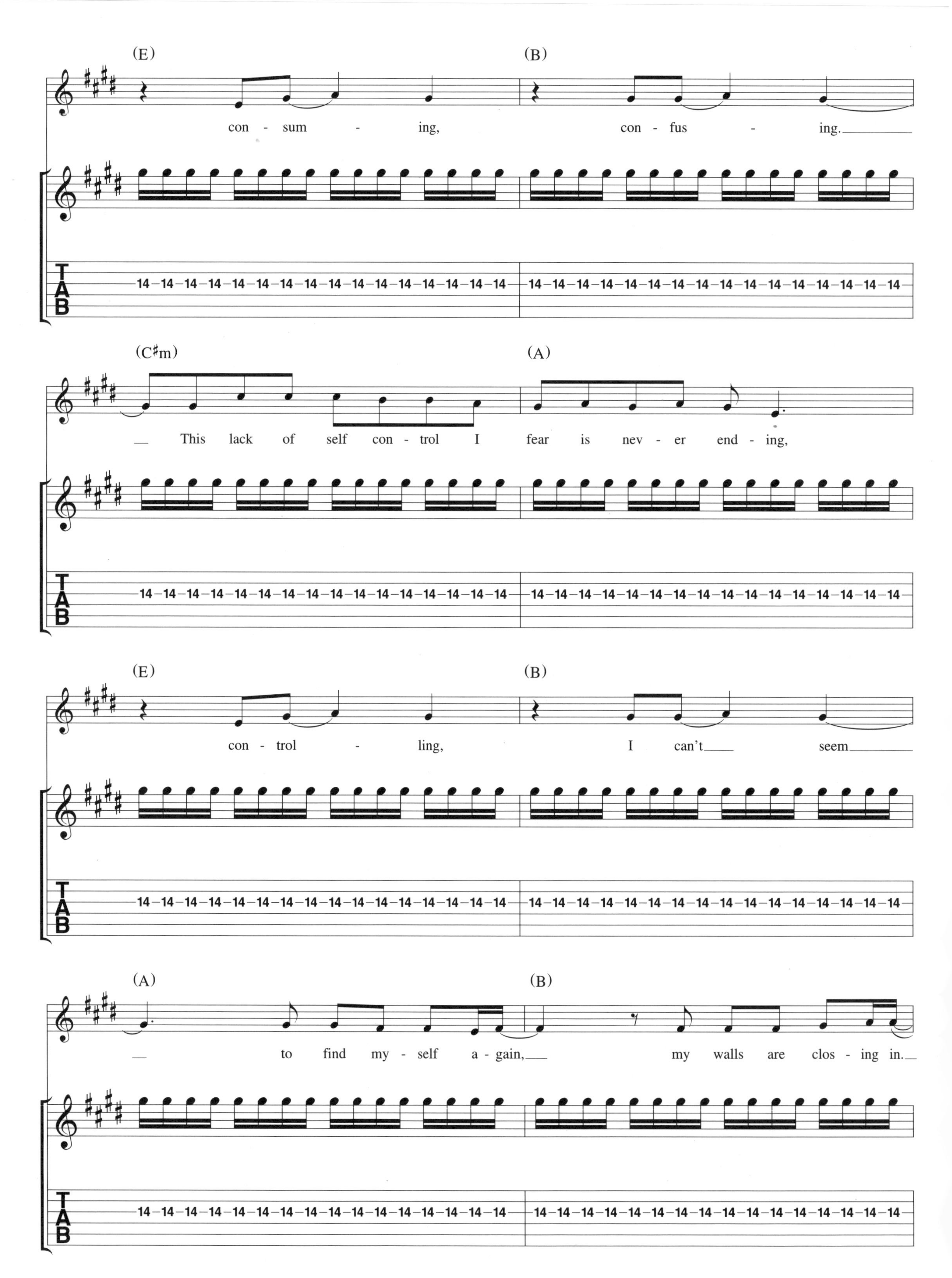
(E)
(B)
con - sum - ing,
con - fus - ing.
14–14–14–14–14–14–14–14–14–14–14–14–14–14–14–14
14–14–14–14–14–14–14–14–14–14–14–14–14–14–14–14
(C♯m)
(A)
This lack of self con - trol I fear is nev - er end - ing,
14–14–14–14–14–14–14–14–14–14–14–14–14–14–14–14
14–14–14–14–14–14–14–14–14–14–14–14–14–14–14–14
(E)
(B)
con - trol - ling,
I can't seem
14–14–14–14–14–14–14–14–14–14–14–14–14–14–14–14
14–14–14–14–14–14–14–14–14–14–14–14–14–14–14–14
(A)
(B)
to find my - self a - gain,
my walls are clos - ing in.
14–14–14–14–14–14–14–14–14–14–14–14–14–14–14–14
14–14–14–14–14–14–14–14–14–14–14–14–14–14–14–14

(C♯m)
(Without a sense of confidence, I'm convinced that there's just too much pressure to take.)
(A)
(B)
I've felt this way be - fore, so in - se -
(C♯m)
- cure.
ff w/distortion
Chorus
C♯5
A5
C♯5
B5
G♯5
Crawl - ing in my skin, these wounds they will not he - al,

C♯5
A5
E5
B5
G♯5
Fear is how I fall, con - fus - ing what is re - al.
Verse
N.C.(C♯m)
(A)
2. Dis - com - fort end - less - ly has pulled it - self up - on me,
w/P.M.
mp optional . . .
(E)
(B)
dis - tract - ing, re - act - ing.
(C♯m)
(A)
A - gainst my will I stand be - side my own re - flec - tion,

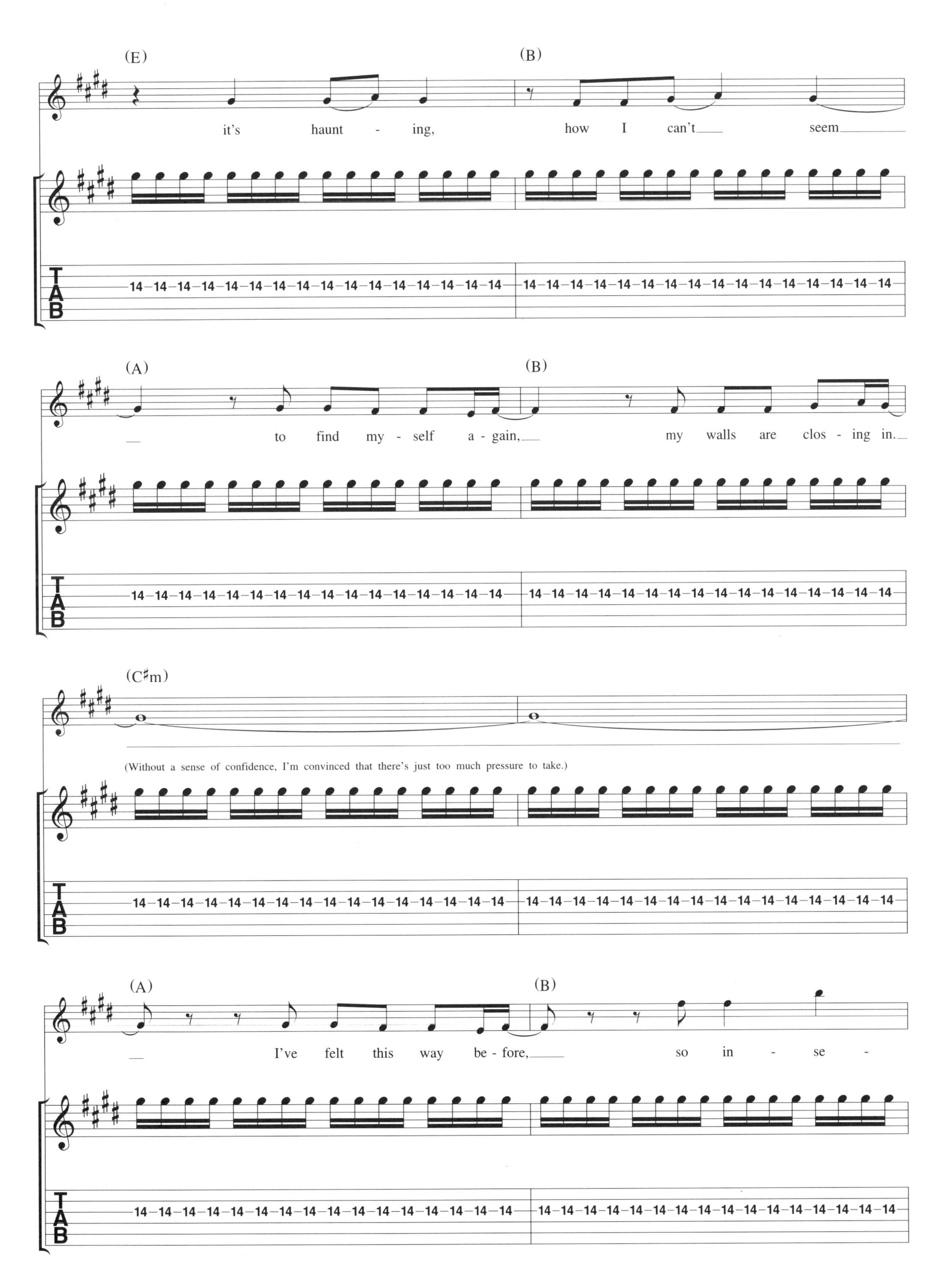
(E)
(B)
it's haunt - ing, how I can't seem
(A)
(B)
to find my - self a - gain, my walls are clos - ing in.
(C♯m)
(Without a sense of confidence, I'm convinced that there's just too much pressure to take.)
(A)
(B)
I've felt this way be - fore, so in - se -
14–14–14–14–14–14–14–14–14–14–14–14–14–14–14–14

(C♯m)
cure.
Chorus
C♯5
A5
E5
Crawl - ing in my skin, these wounds, they will not
ff w/distortion
B5
G♯5
C♯5
A5
E5
B5
G♯5
he - al.
Fear is how I fall, con - fus - ing what is re - al.
C♯5
A5
E5
B5
G♯5
Crawl - ing in my skin, these wounds, they will not he - al.

C♯5 A5 E5 B5 G♯5
Fear is how I fall, con - fus - ing, con - fus - ing what is
C♯5 A5 E5
real. Con -
(There's some-thing in - side me that pulls be - neath the sur - face, con - sum - ing.) -
B5 G♯5 C♯5 A5
- fus - ing what is real.
(This lack of self con - trol I fear is nev - er end - ing,
E5 B5 G♯5
Con - fus - ing what is real.
con - trol - ling.)

enter sandman

Words & Music by James Hetfield, Lars Ulrich & Kirk Hammett

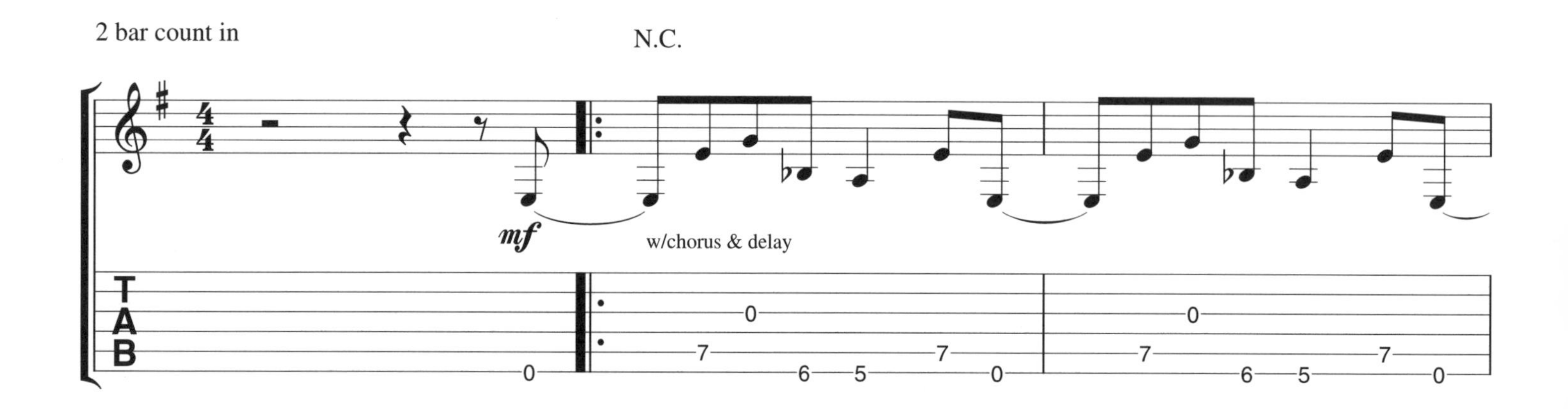

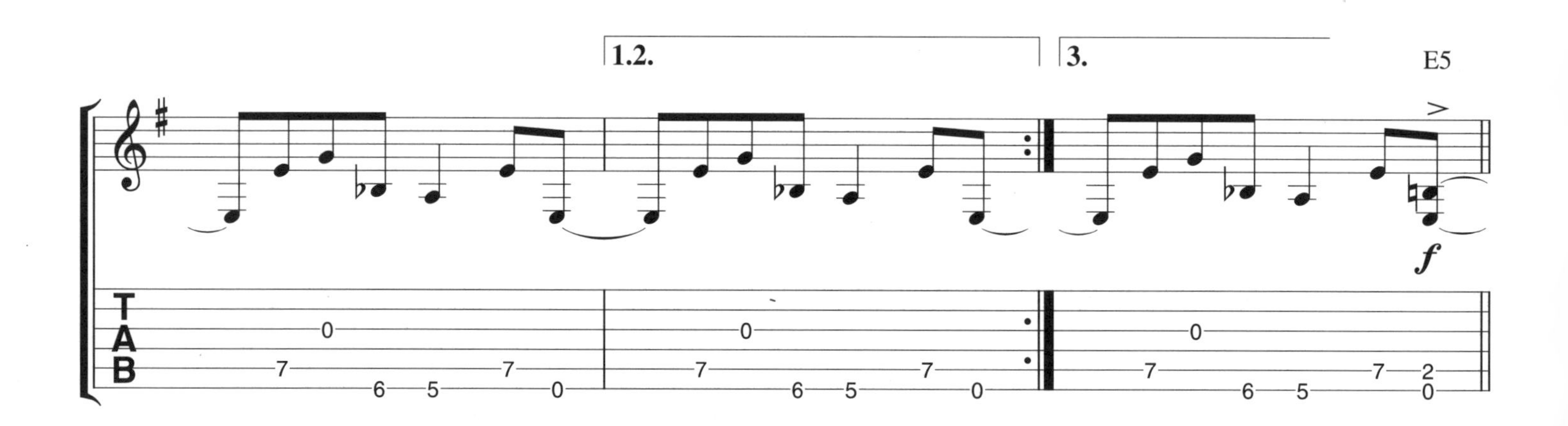

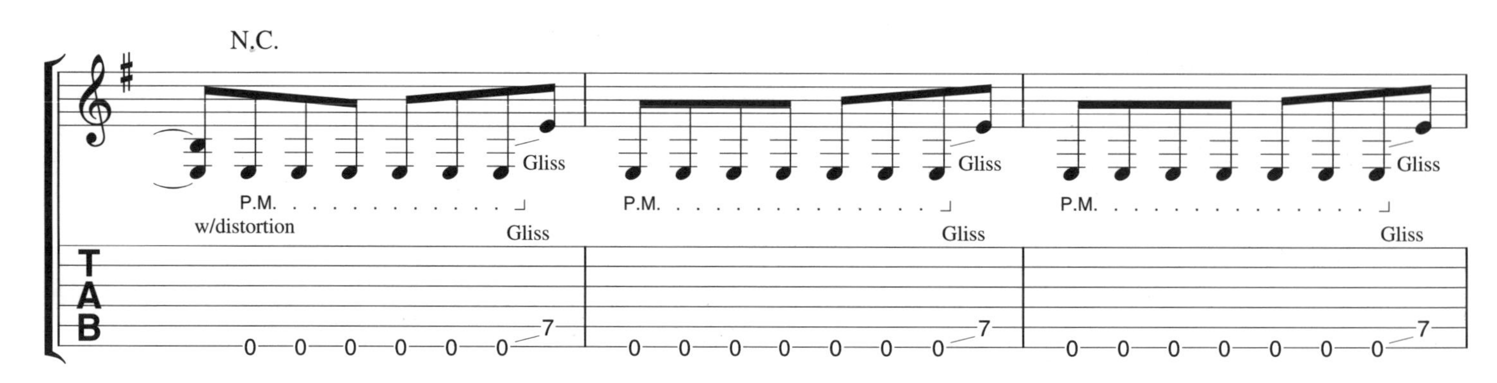

F5

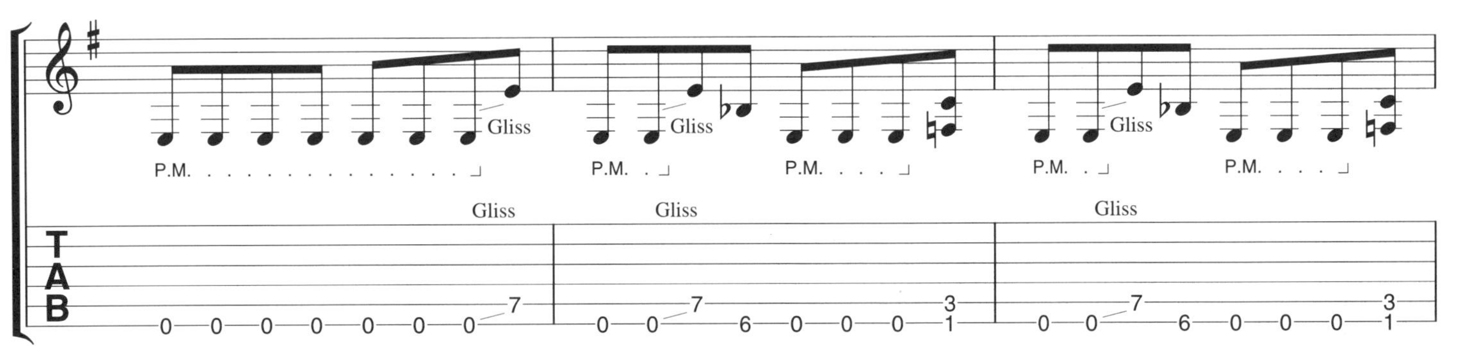
Gliss
Gliss
Gliss
P.M.
P.M.
P.M.
P.M.
P.M.
Gliss
Gliss
Gliss
TAB

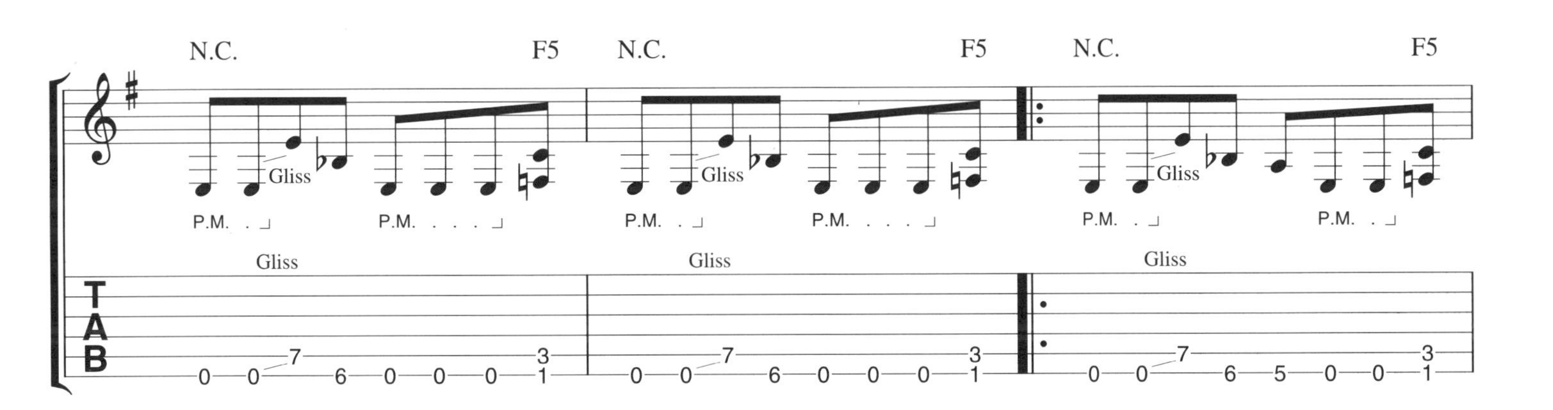
N.C.
F5
N.C.
F5
N.C.
F5
Gliss
Gliss
Gliss
P.M.
P.M.
P.M.
P.M.
P.M.
P.M.
Gliss
Gliss
Gliss
TAB

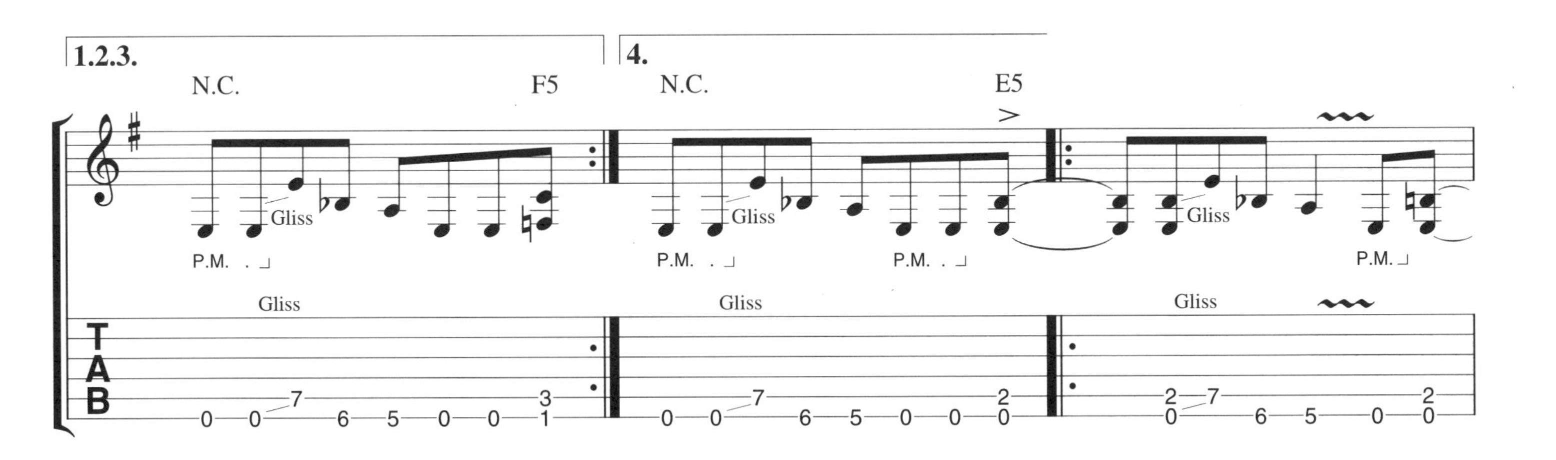
1.2.3.
4.
N.C.
F5
N.C.
E5
Gliss
Gliss
Gliss
P.M.
P.M.
P.M.
P.M.
Gliss
Gliss
Gliss
TAB

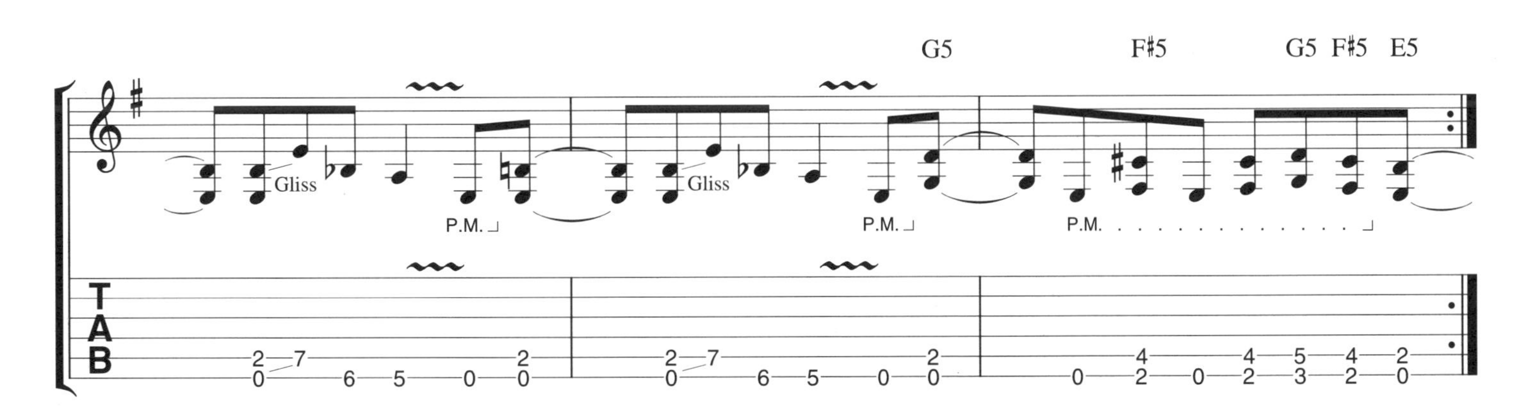
G5
F♯5
G5
F♯5
E5
Gliss
Gliss
P.M.
P.M.
P.M.
TAB

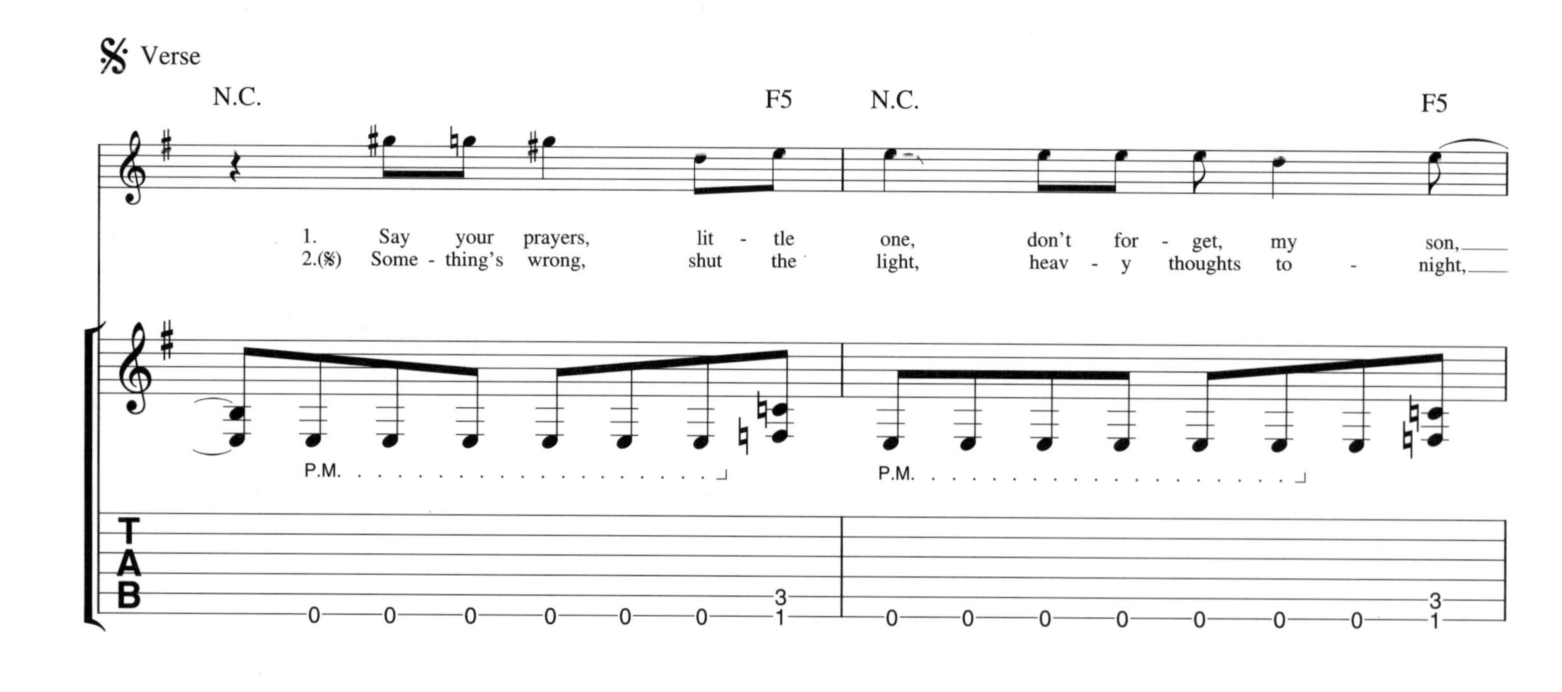
Verse
N.C.
F5
N.C.
F5
1. Say your prayers, lit - tle one, don't for - get, my son,
2.(𝄋) Some - thing's wrong, shut the light, heav - y thoughts to - night,
P.M.
P.M.

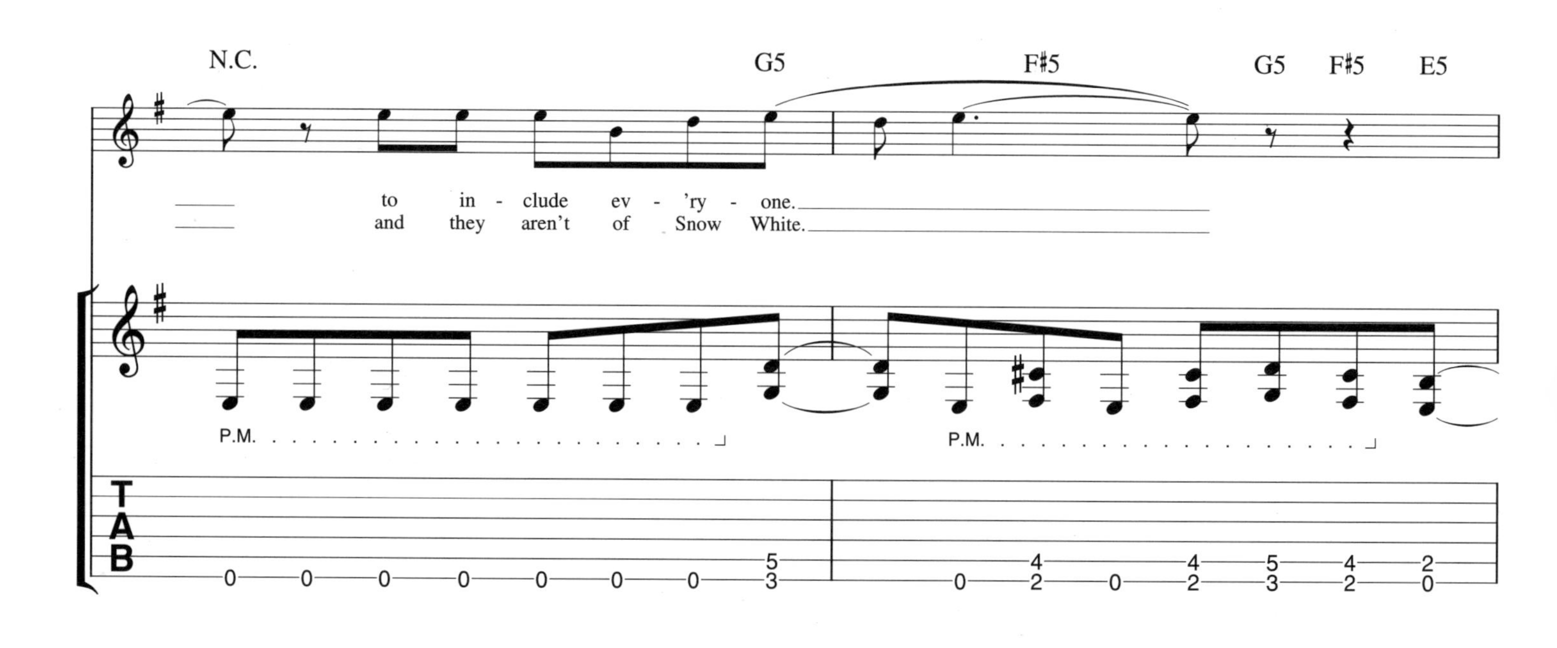
N.C.
G5
F♯5
G5
F♯5
E5
to in - clude ev - 'ry - one.
and they aren't of Snow White.
P.M.
P.M.

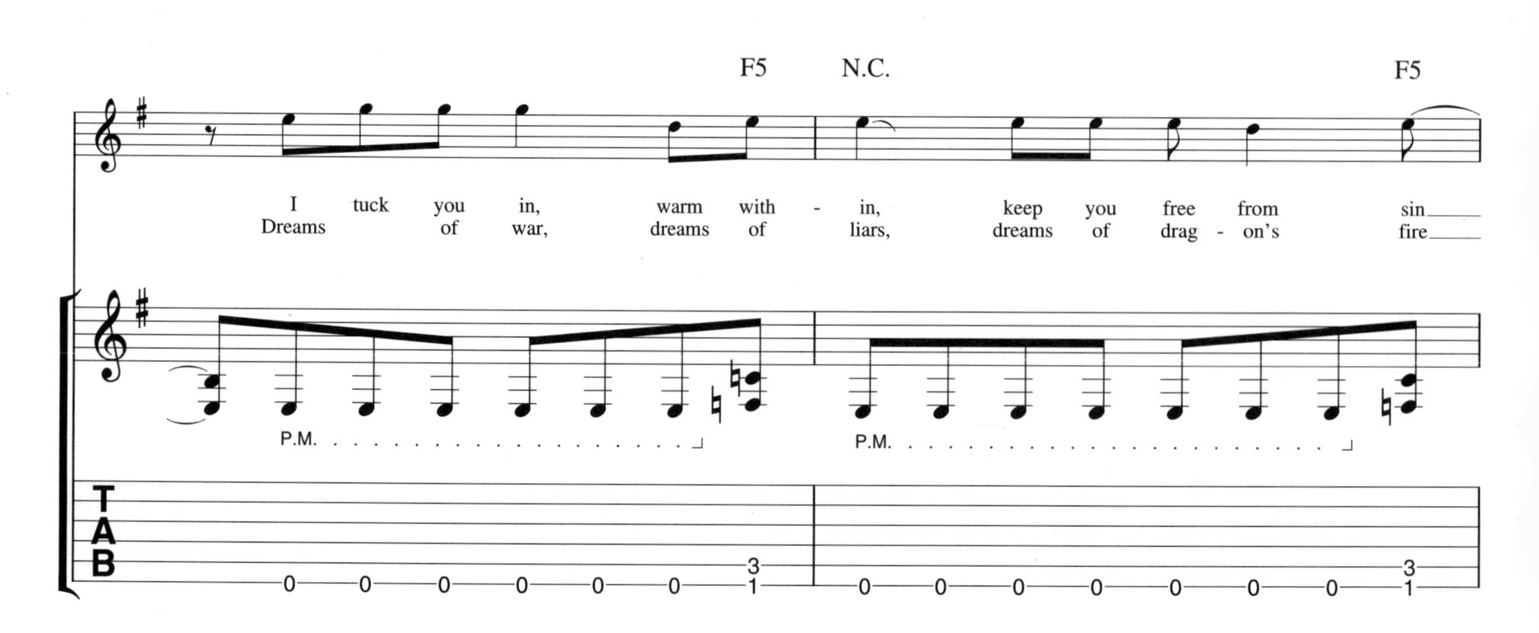
F5
N.C.
F5
I tuck you in, warm with - in, keep you free from sin
Dreams of war, dreams of liars, dreams of drag - on's fire
P.M.
P.M.

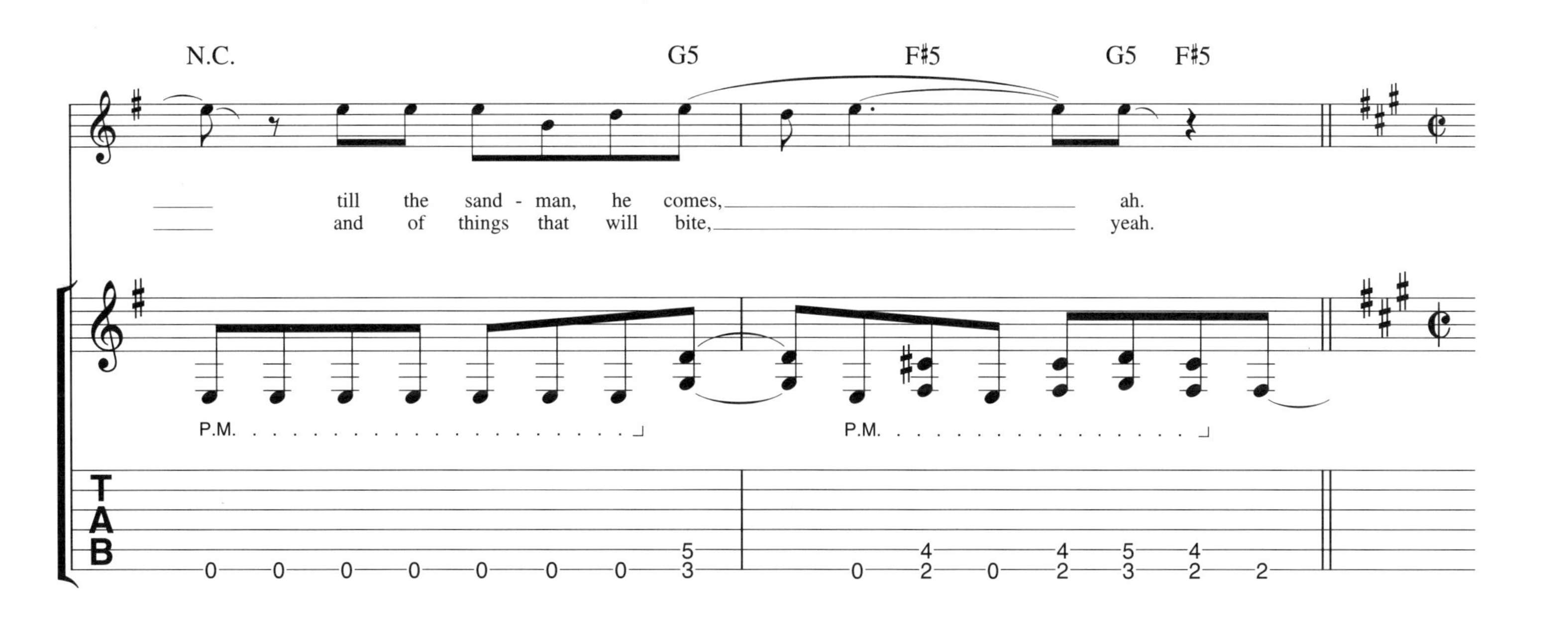

Pre-chorus

Chorus

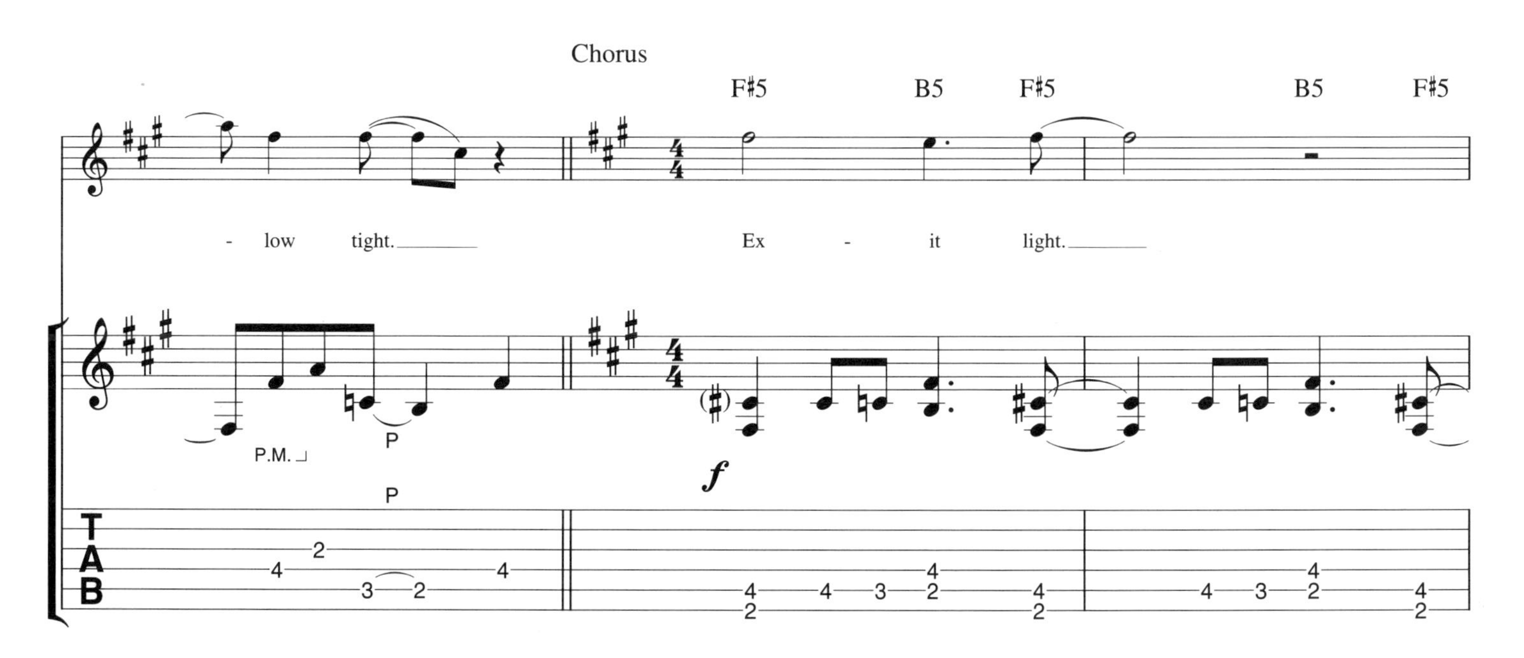

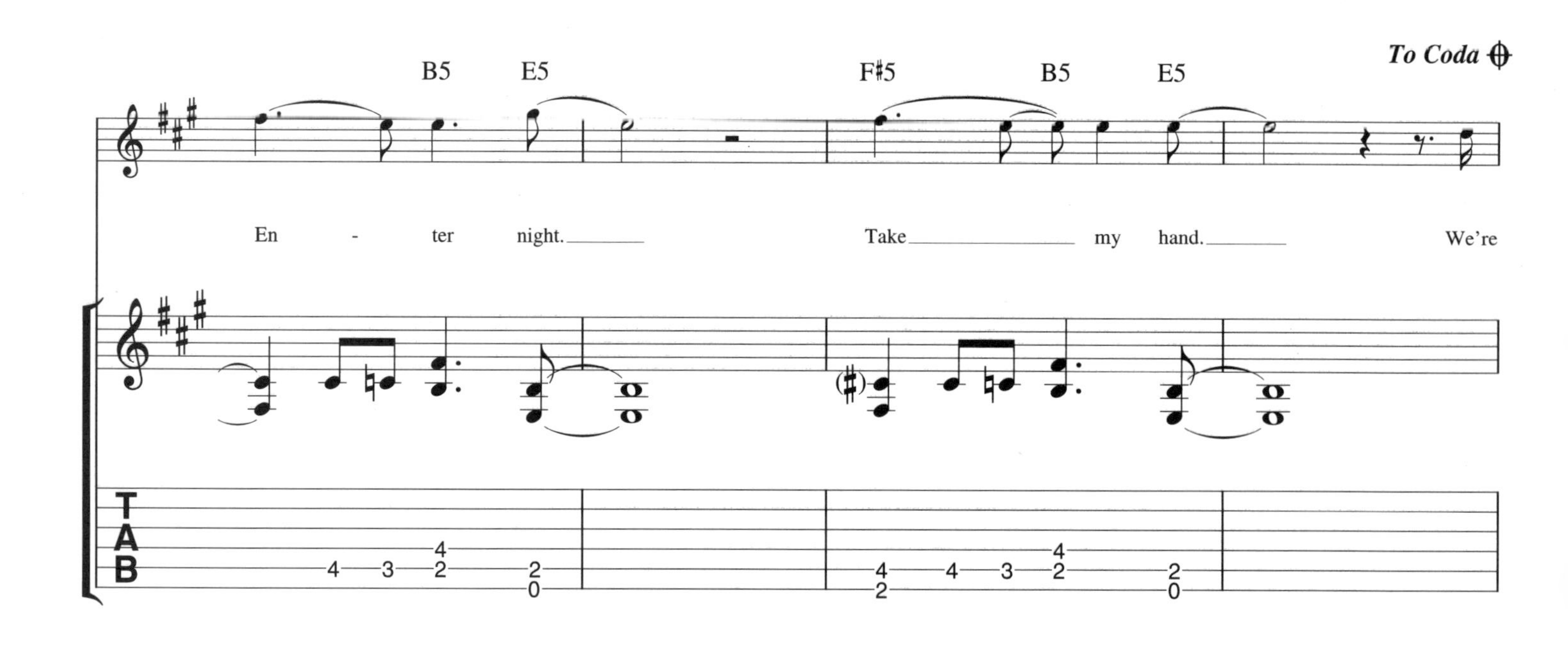
To Coda
B5
E5
F#5
B5
E5
En - ter night.
Take my hand.
We're
T
A
B

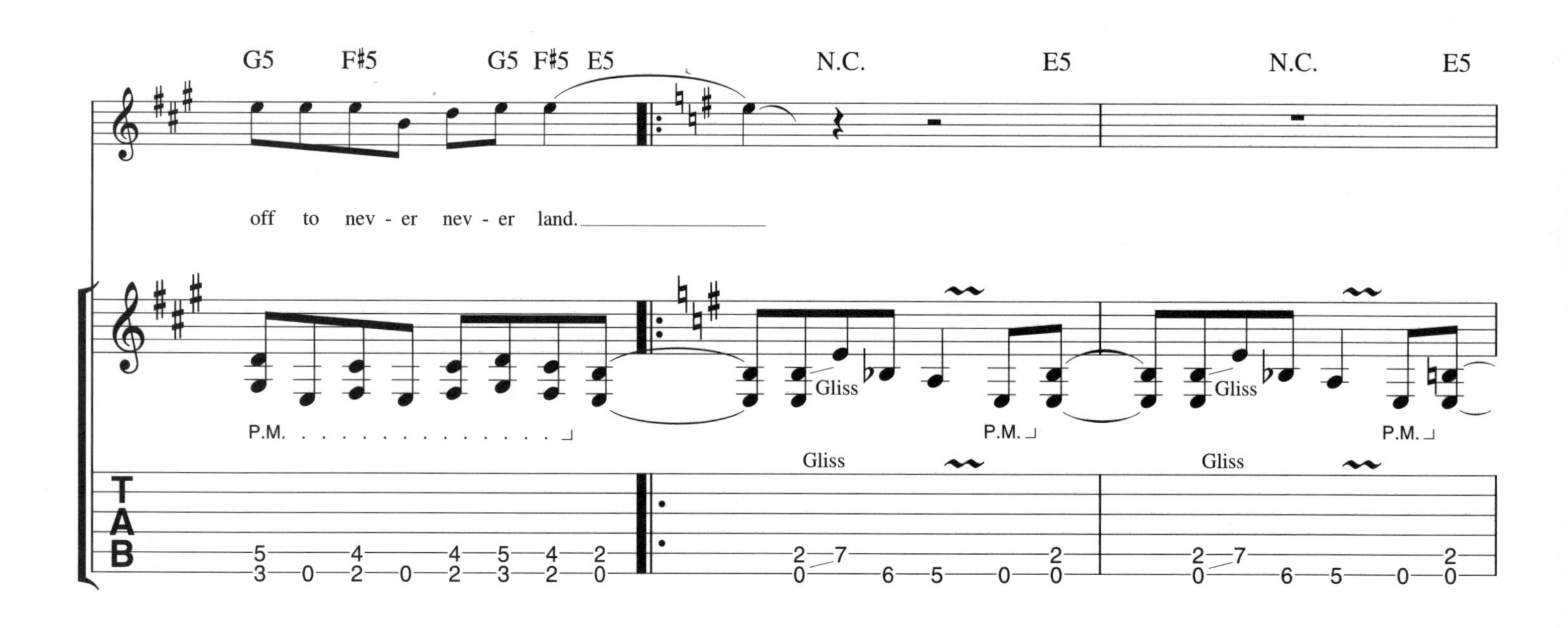
G5
F#5
G5
F#5
E5
N.C.
E5
N.C.
E5
off to nev - er nev - er land.
P.M.
Gliss
Gliss
P.M.
Gliss
Gliss
P.M.
T
A
B

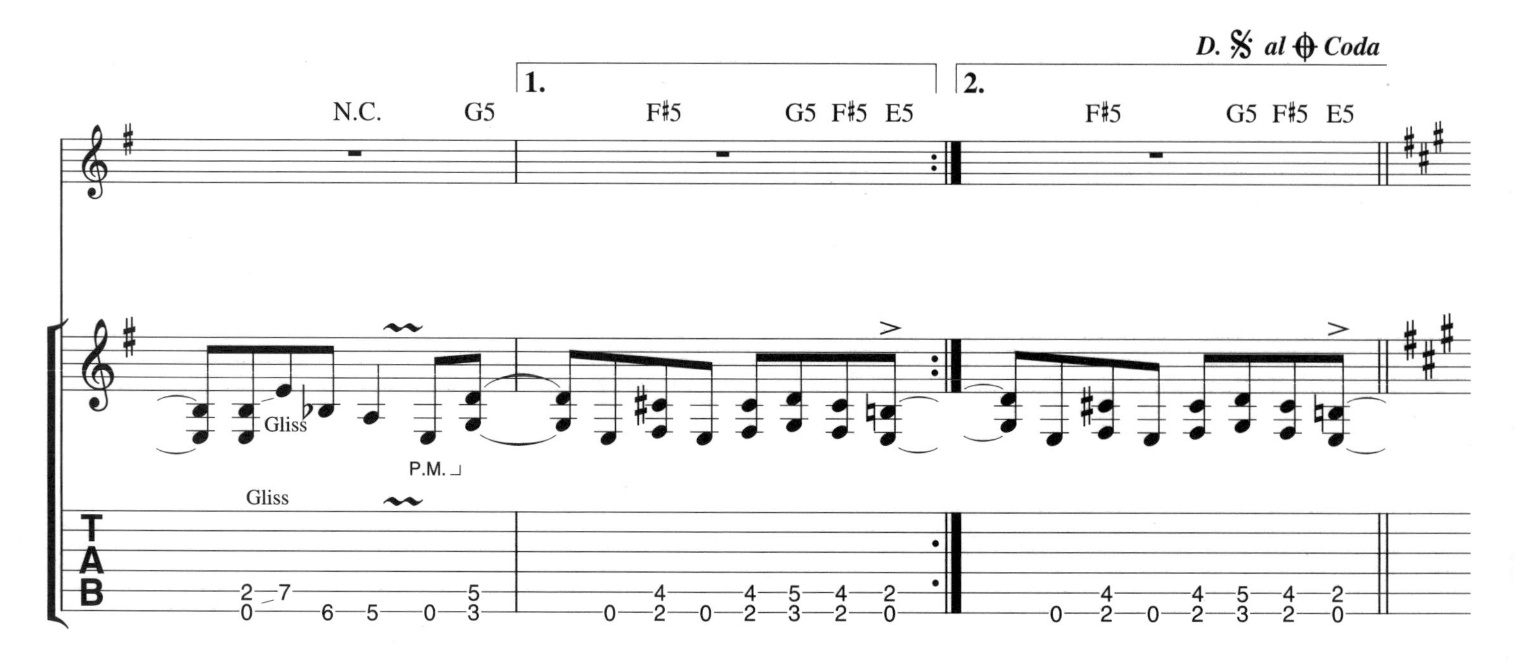
D.S. al Coda
1.
2.
N.C.
G5
F#5
G5
F#5
E5
F#5
G5
F#5
E5
Gliss
P.M.
Gliss
T
A
B

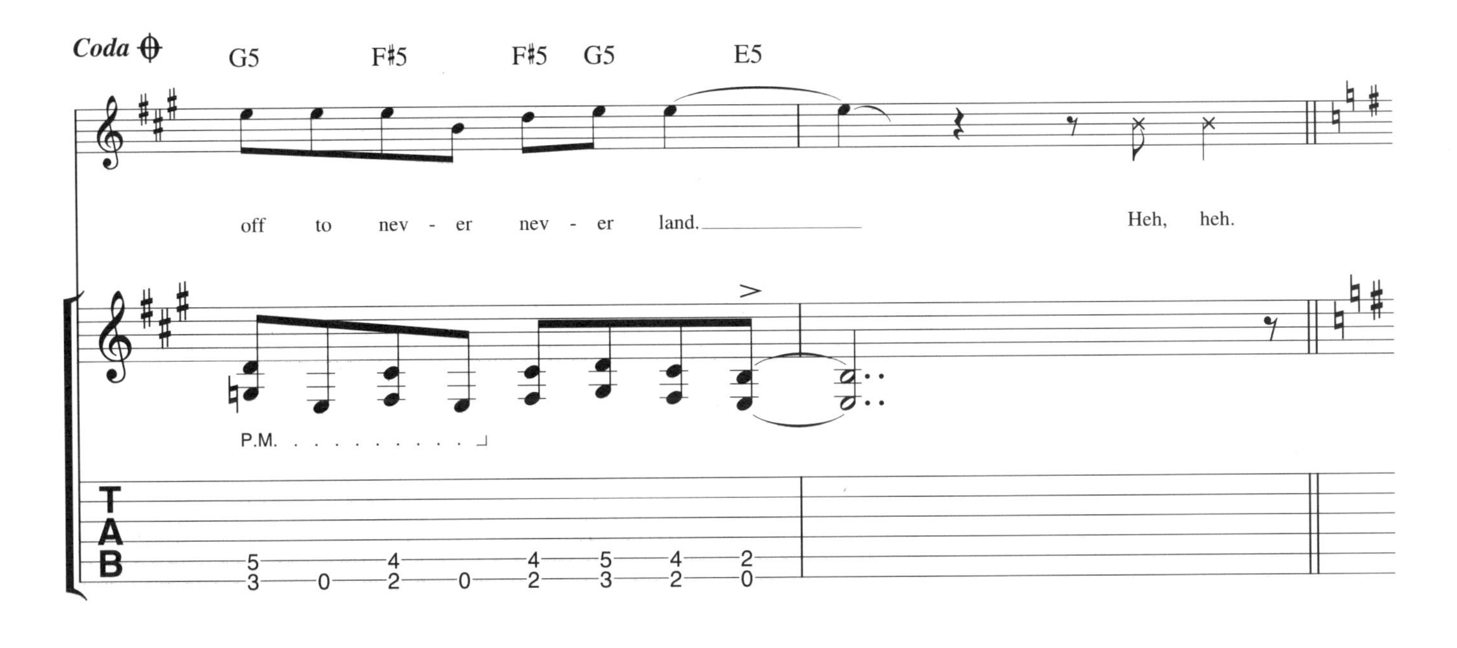
Coda
G5 F♯5 F♯5 G5 E5
off to nev - er nev - er land.
Heh, heh.
P.M.
T
A
B

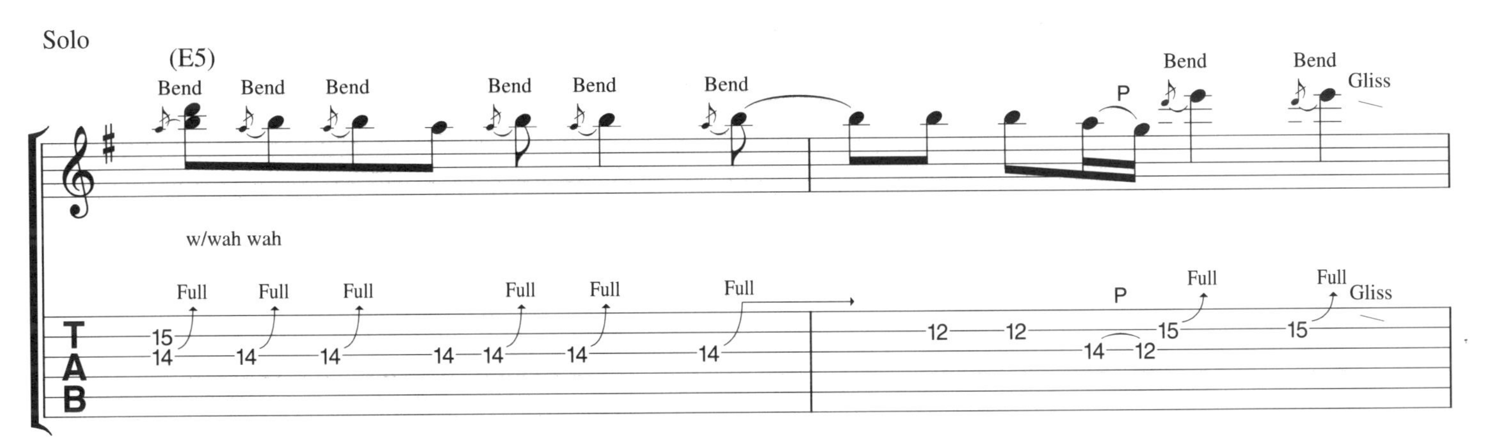
Solo
(E5)
Bend Bend Bend Bend Bend Bend Bend Bend
P
Gliss
w/wah wah
Full Full Full Full Full Full Full Full
T
A
B

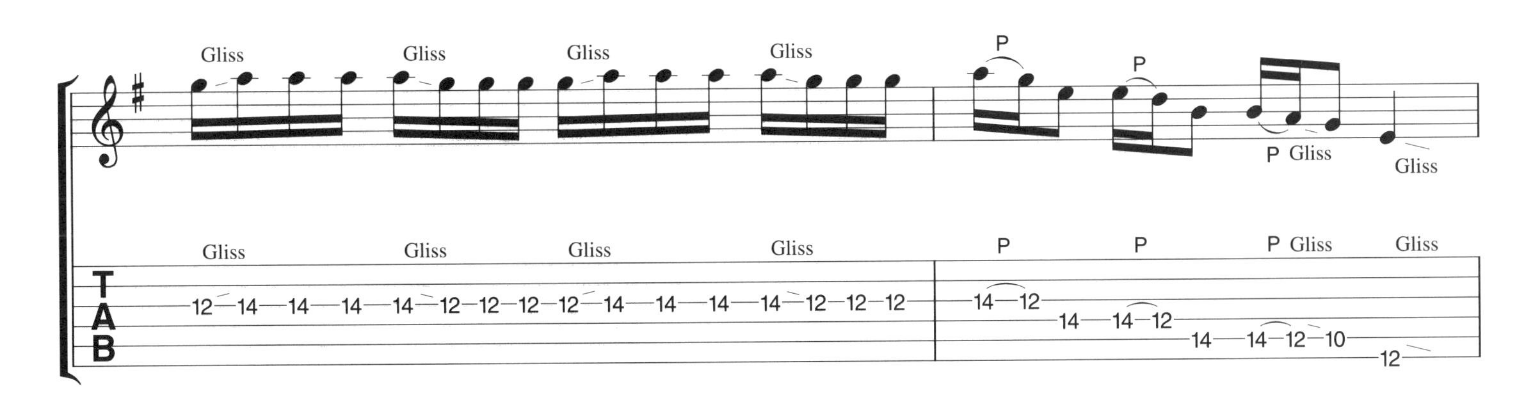
Gliss Gliss Gliss Gliss
P P P Gliss Gliss
T
A
B

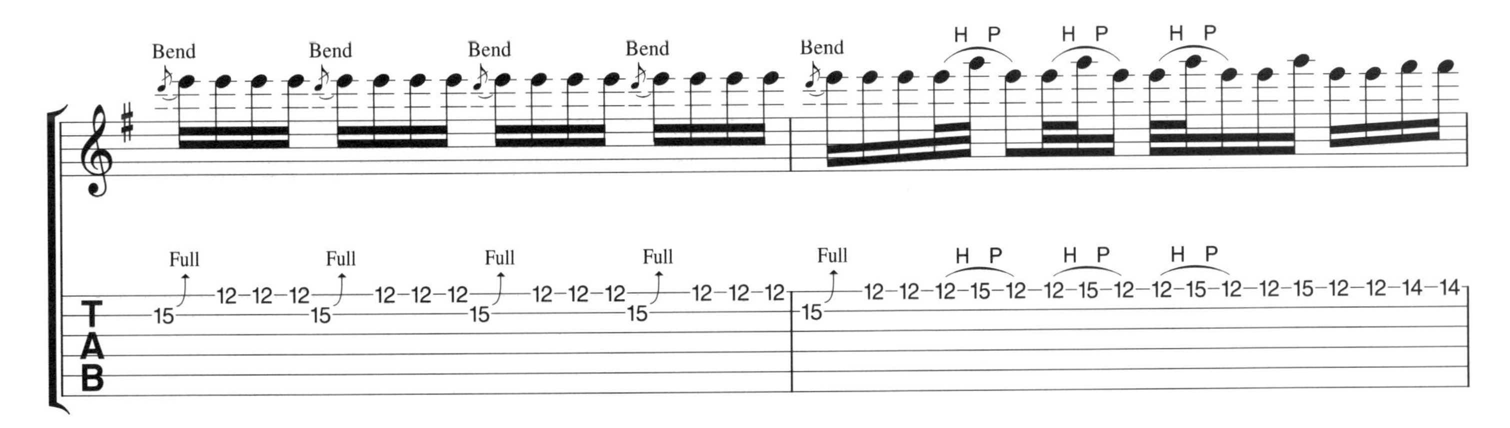
Bend Bend Bend Bend Bend
H P H P H P
Full Full Full Full Full
T
A
B

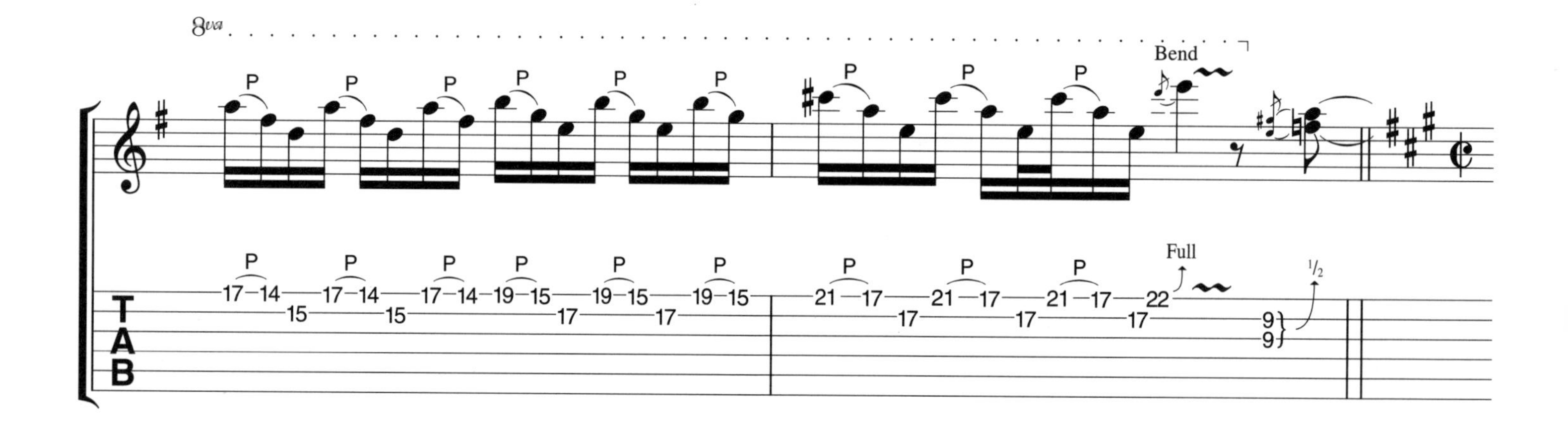
8va
P P P P P P P P P
Bend
Full
½
TAB

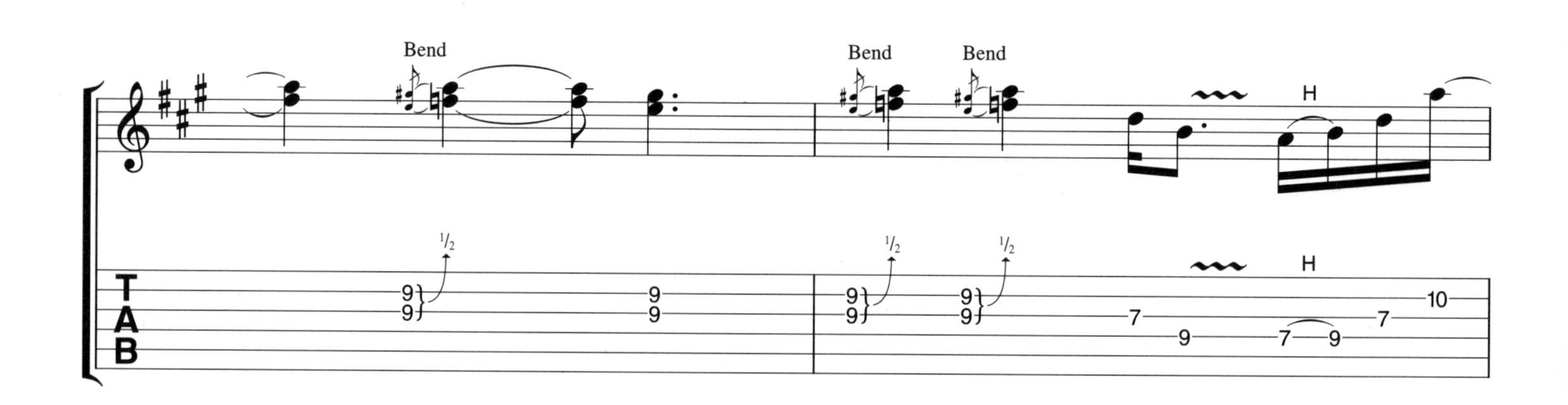
Bend
Bend Bend
H
½ ½ ½
TAB

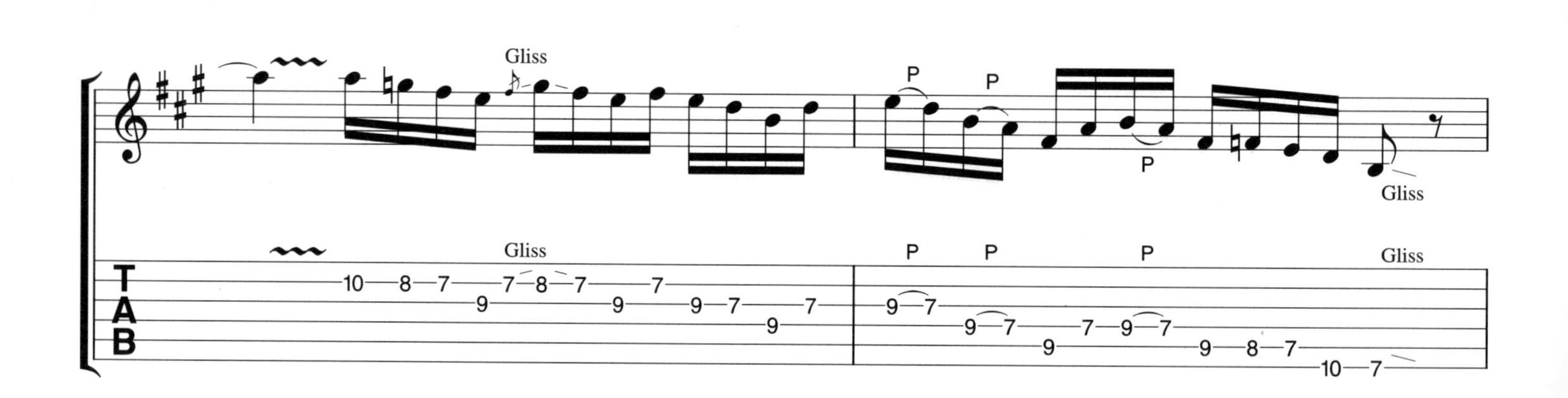
Gliss
P P P
Gliss
TAB

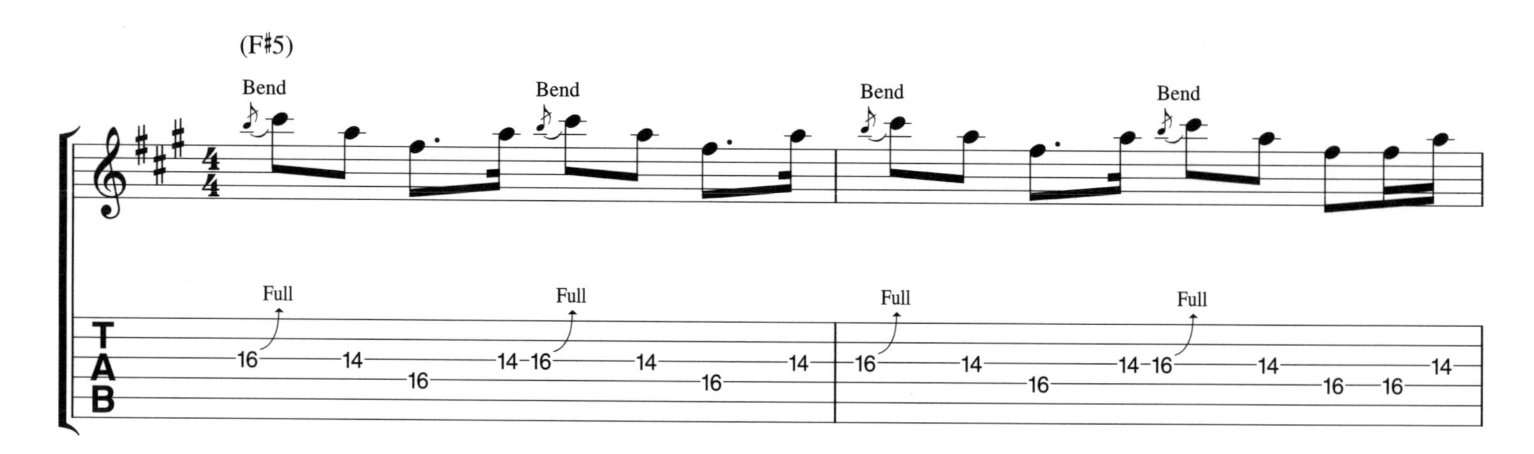
(F♯5)
Bend Bend Bend Bend
Full Full Full Full
TAB

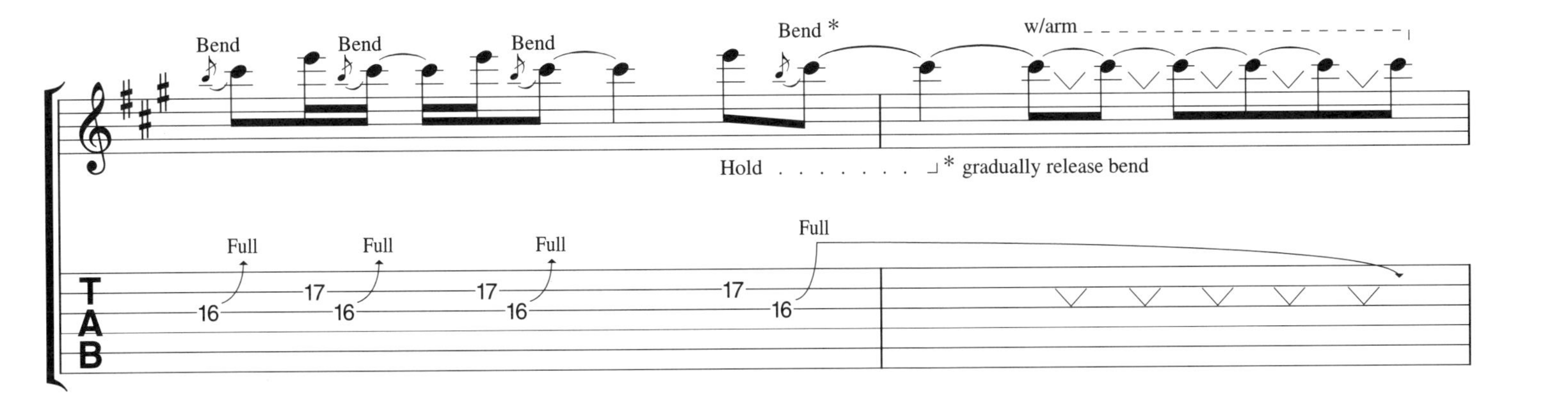
Bend
Bend
Bend
Bend *
w/arm
Hold
* gradually release bend
Full
Full
Full
Full
TAB
16
17
16
17
16
17
16

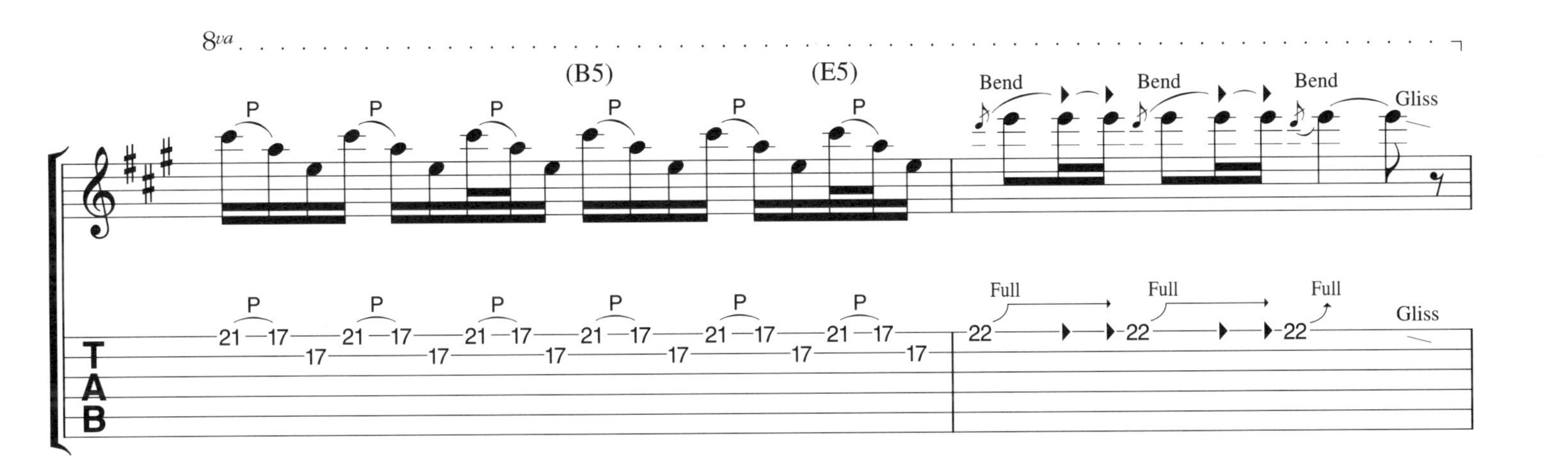
8va
(B5)
(E5)
P
Bend
Bend
Bend
Gliss
Full
Full
Full
TAB
21
17
22

P P
3
P
P
Bend
H
Full
TAB
10
8
7
9
9
7
9
9
7
5
7
5
7
5
7

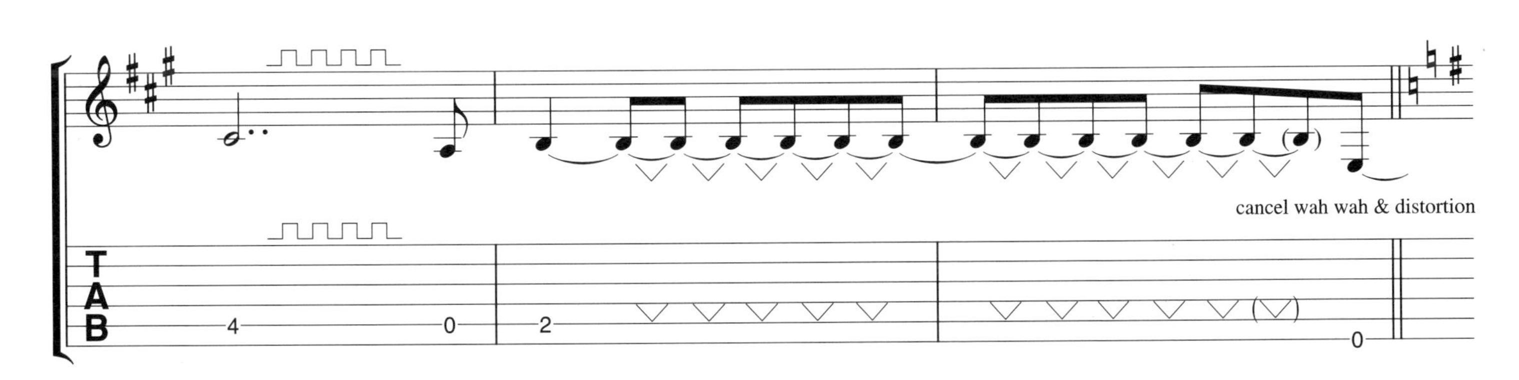
cancel wah wah & distortion
TAB
4
0
2
0

Spoken: 1. Now I lay me down to sleep.
I die before I wake,
(Now I lay me down to sleep.)
(If I die before I wake)
Pray the Lord my soul to keep.
Pray the Lord my soul to take.
mp
w/chorus
T
A
B

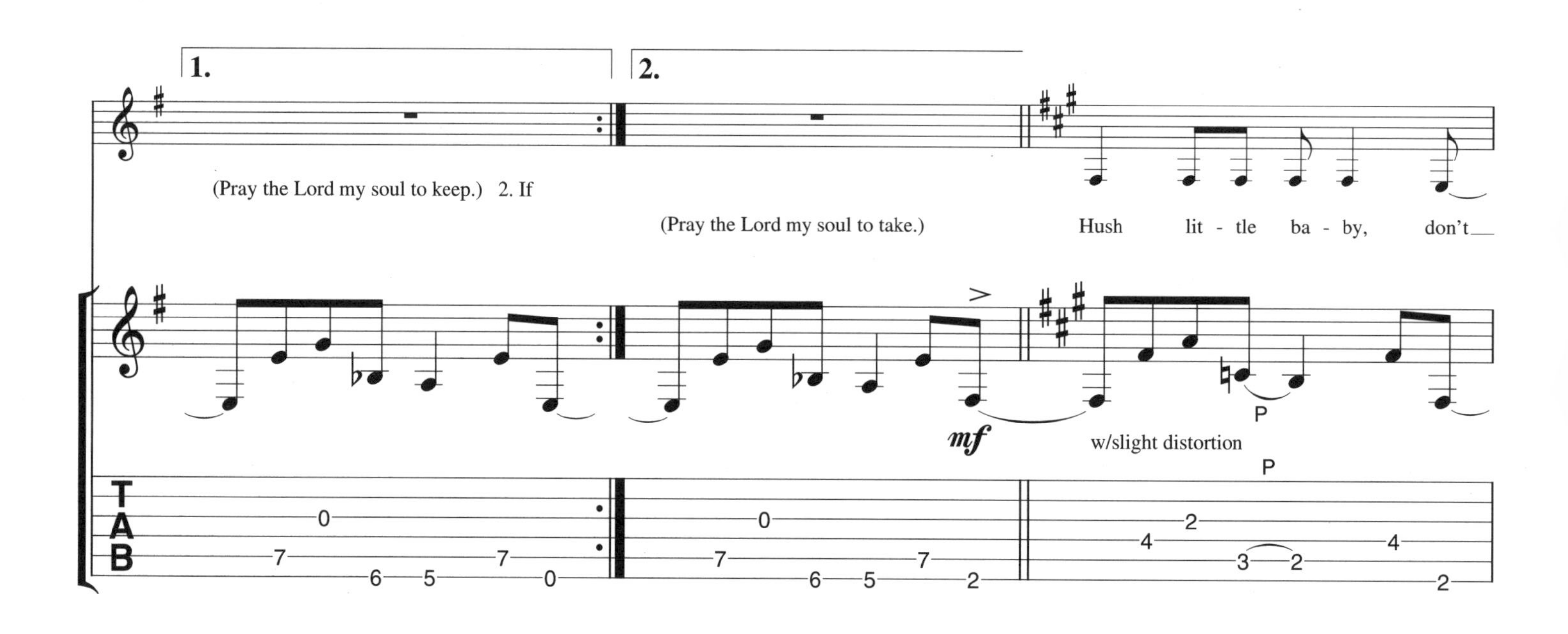
1.
2.
(Pray the Lord my soul to keep.) 2. If
(Pray the Lord my soul to take.)
Hush lit - tle ba - by, don't
mf
w/slight distortion
P
T
A
B

say a word.
And nev - er mind that noise you heard,
P
T
A
B

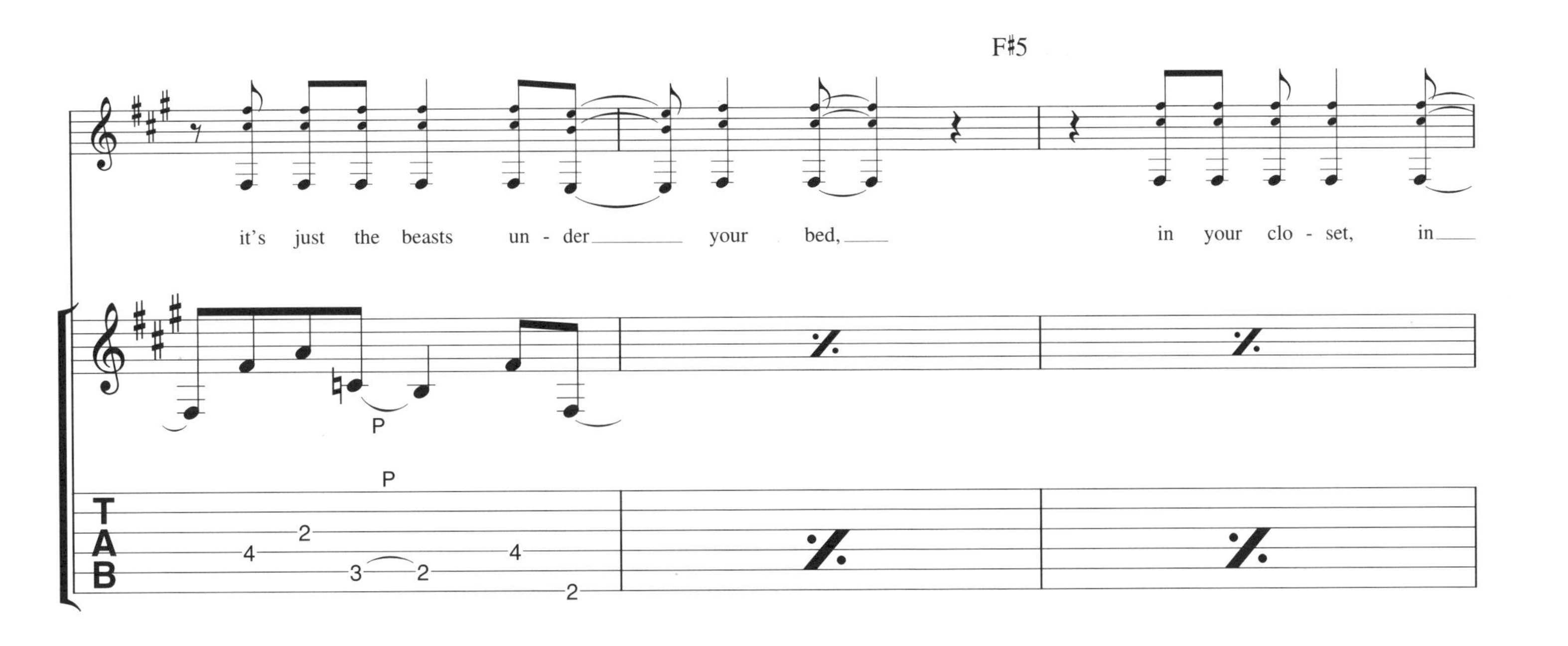
F♯5
it's just the beasts un - der your bed, in your clo - set, in
P
P
T
A
B

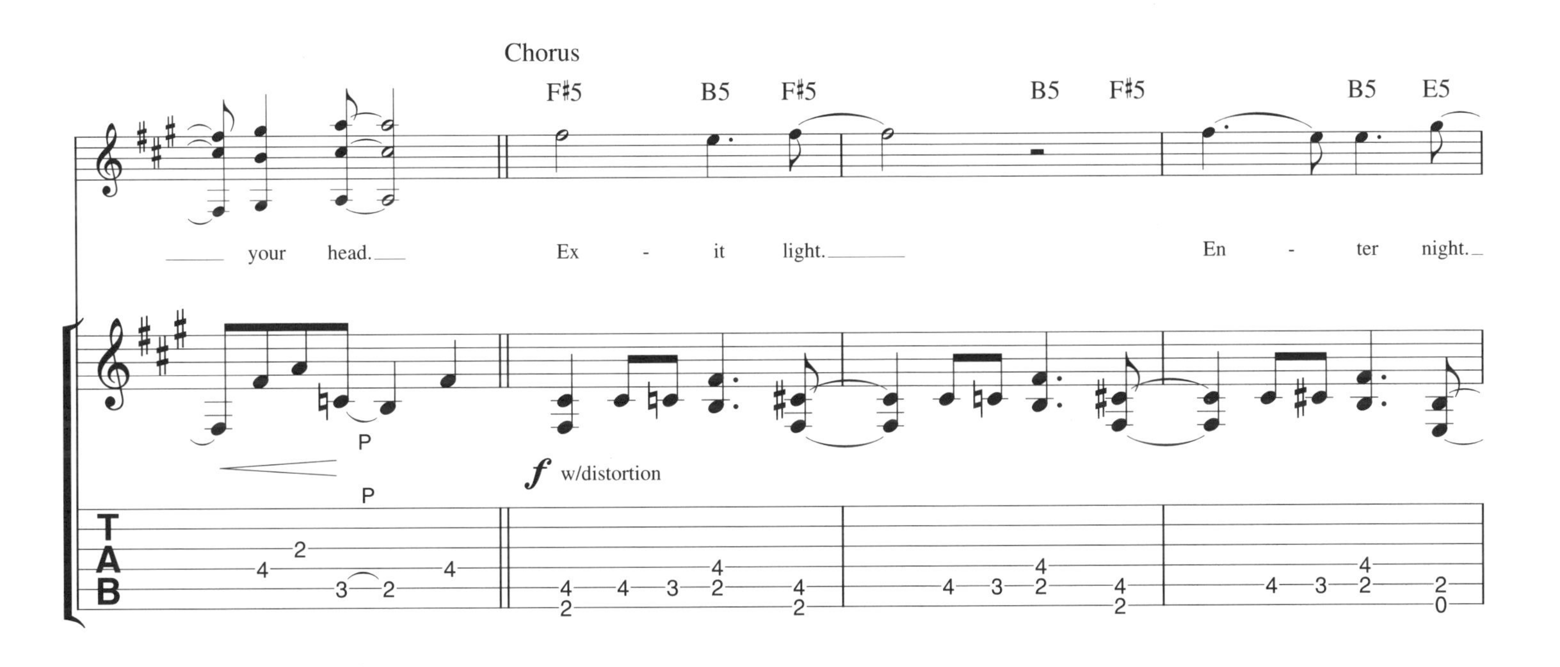
Chorus
F♯5 B5 F♯5 B5 F♯5 B5 E5
your head. Ex - it light. En - ter night.
P
f w/distortion
P
T
A
B

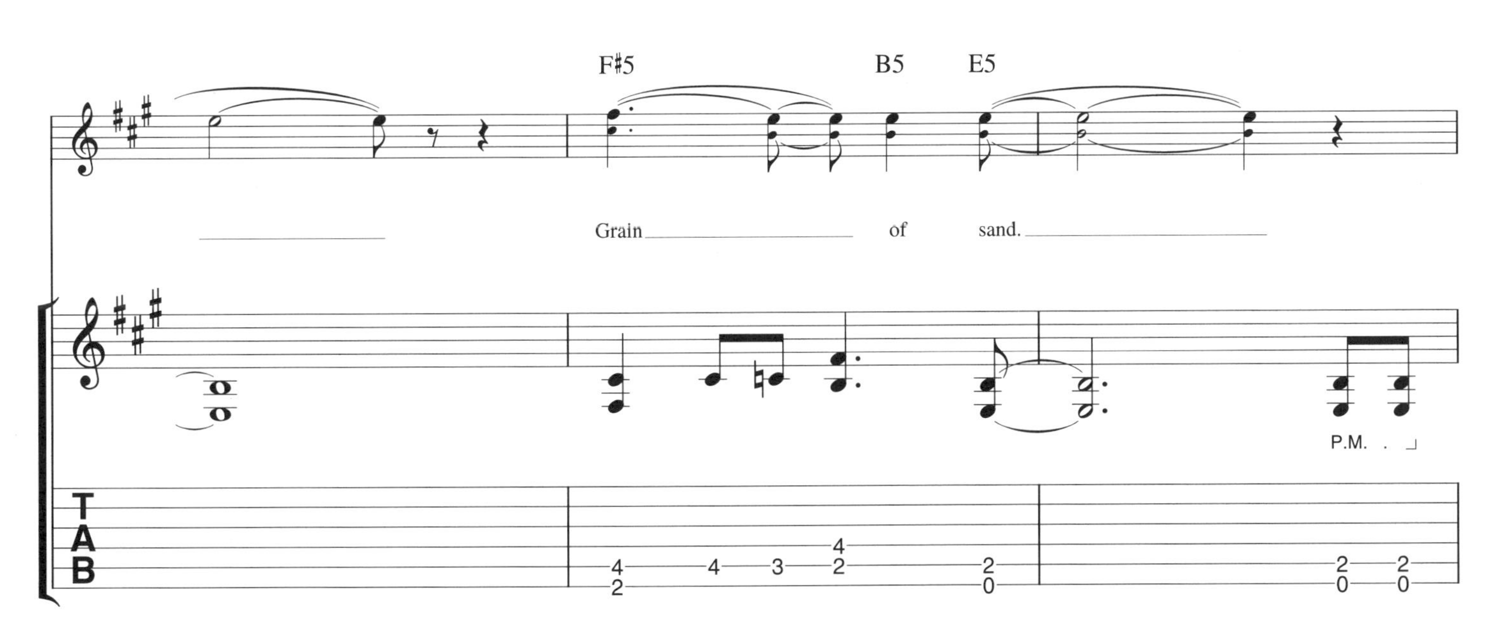
F♯5 B5 E5
Grain of sand.
P.M.
T
A
B

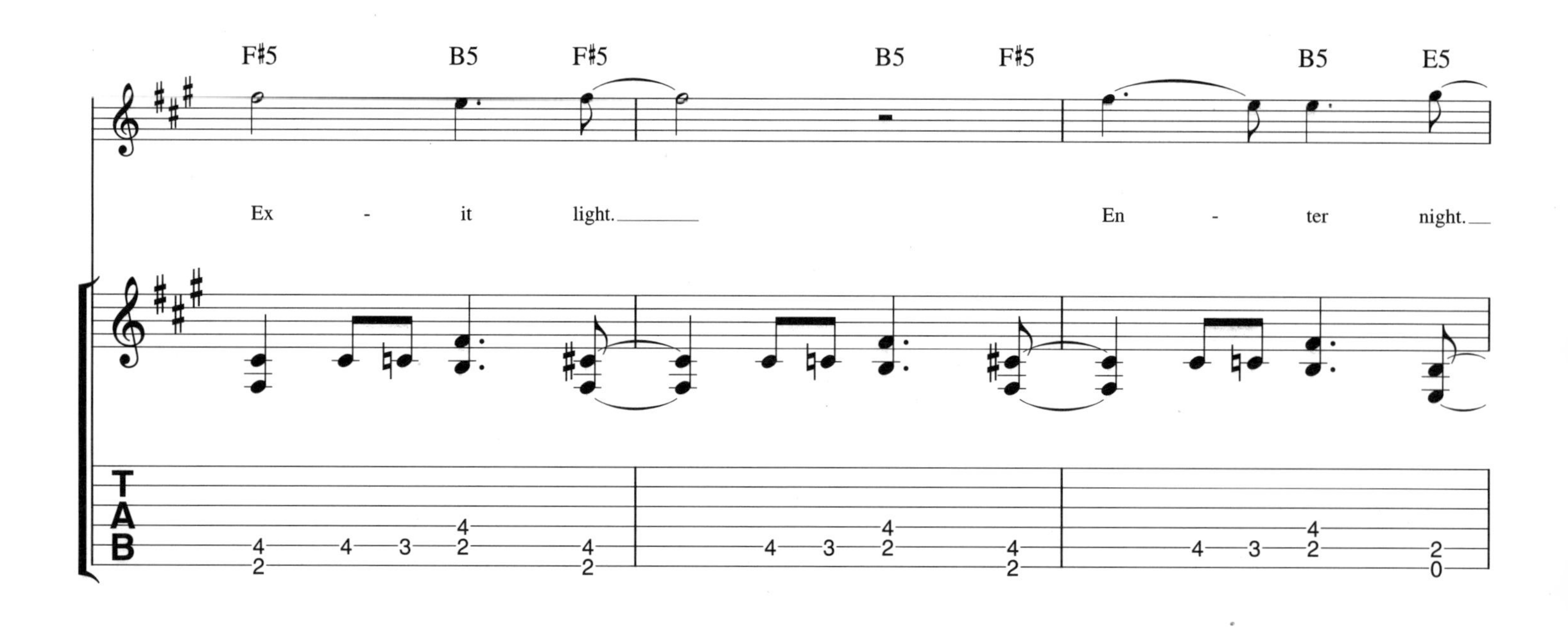
F♯5
B5
F♯5
B5
F♯5
B5
E5
Ex - it light.
En - ter night.

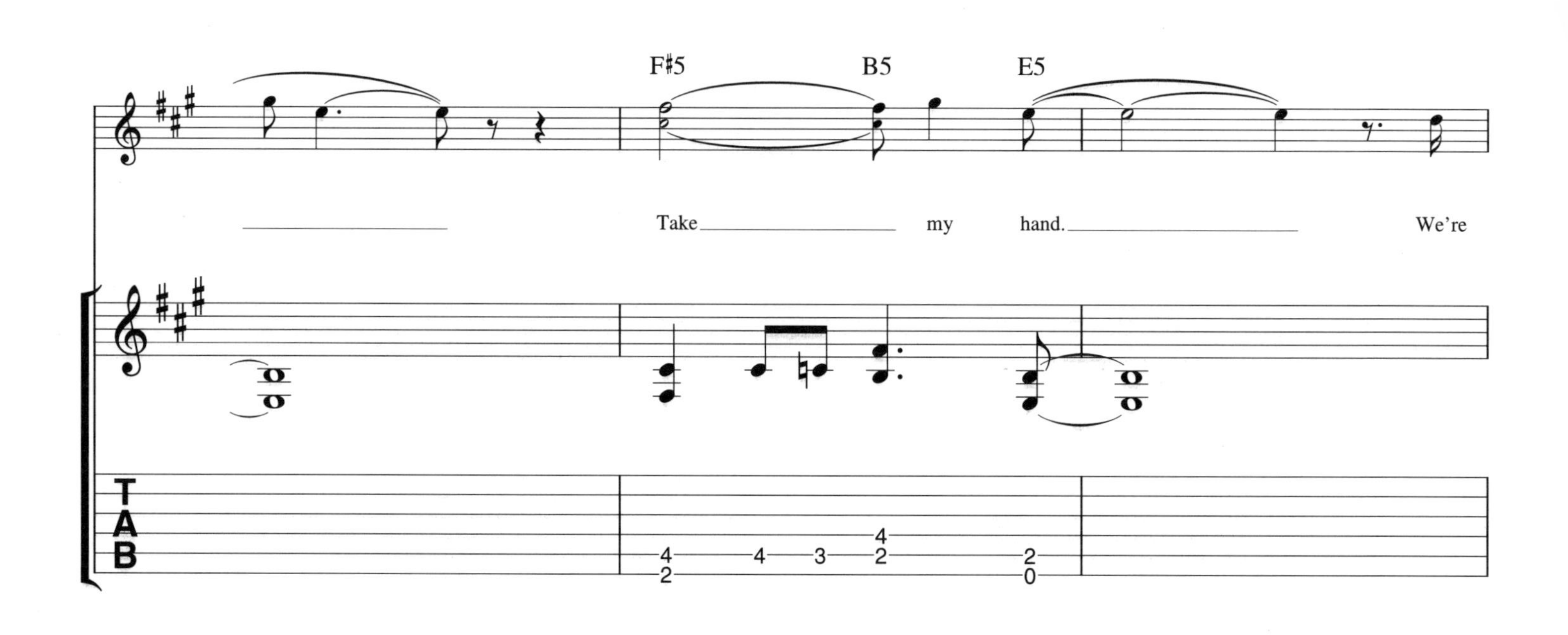
F♯5
B5
E5
Take my hand.
We're

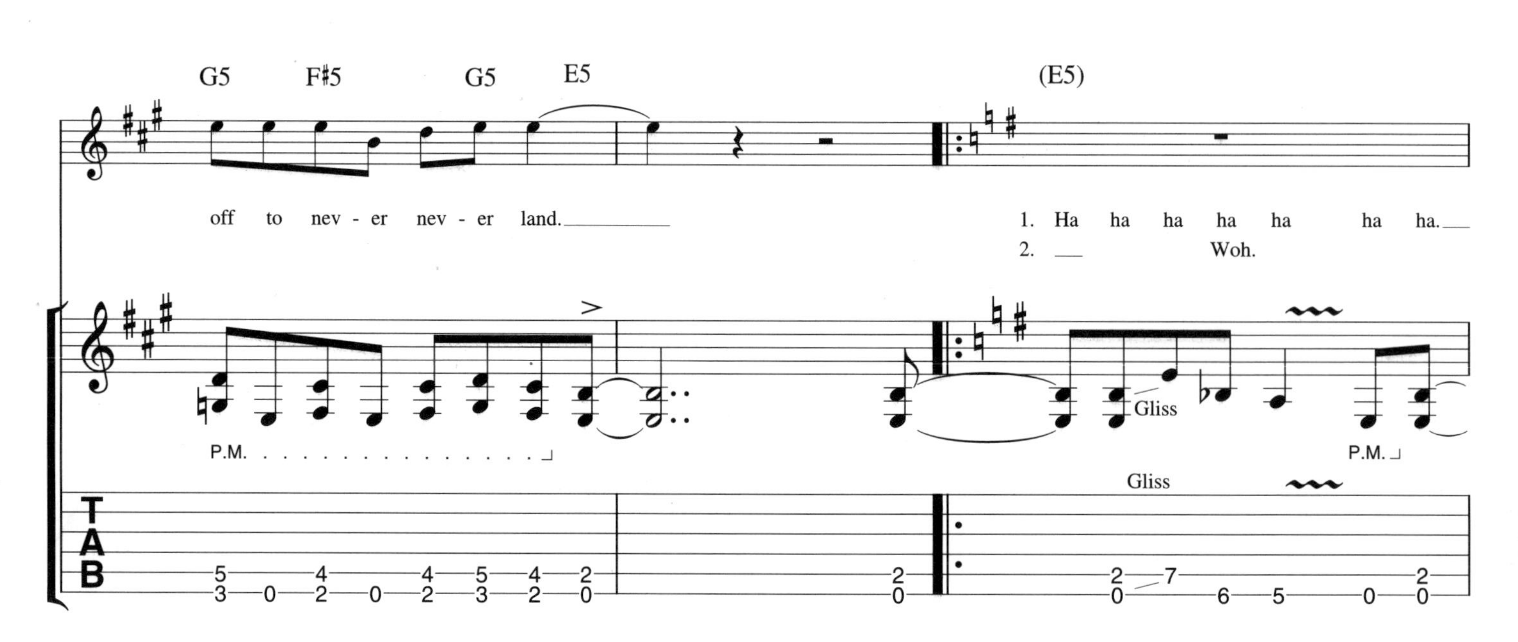
G5
F♯5
G5
E5
(E5)
off to nev - er nev - er land.
1. Ha ha ha ha ha ha ha.
2. Woh.
P.M.
Gliss
P.M.
Gliss

1.
Ooh.
Yeah, yeah!
Yo,
Gliss
P.M.
1°
2°

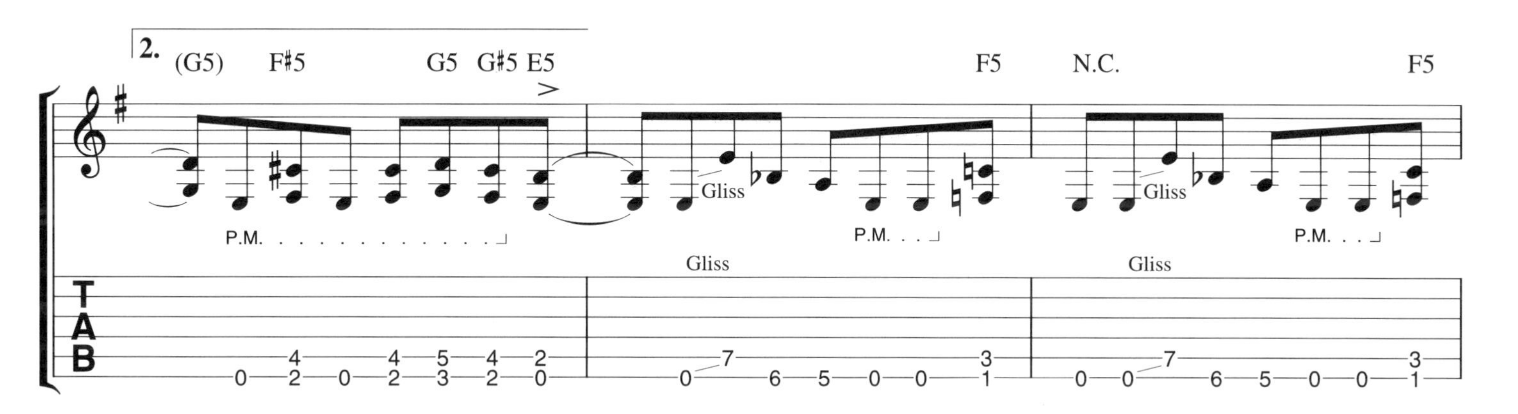
2.
(G5) F♯5 G5 G♯5 E5
F5
N.C.
F5
Gliss
P.M.

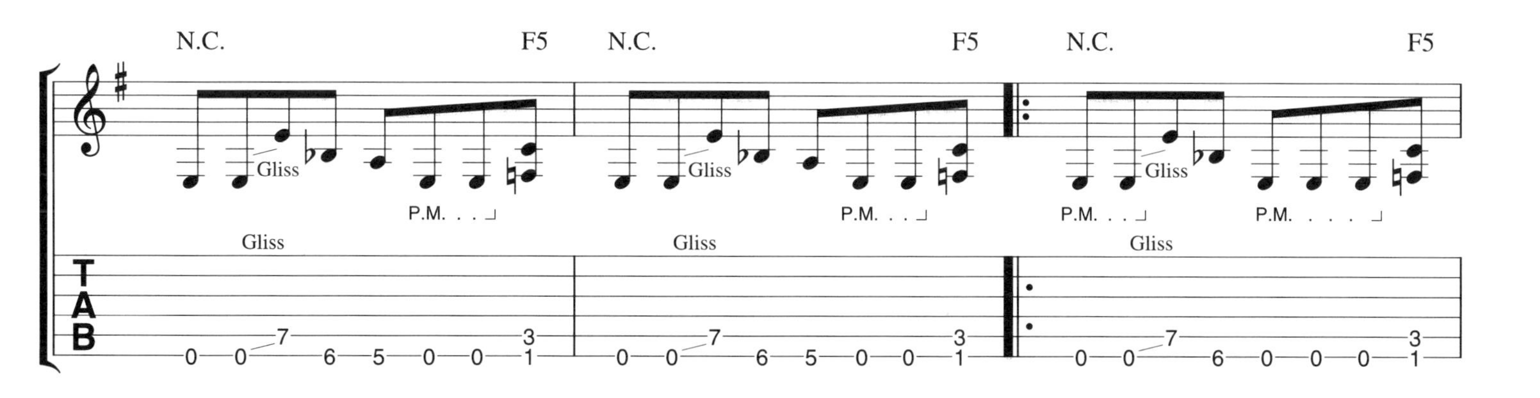
N.C.
F5
N.C.
F5
N.C.
F5
Gliss
P.M.

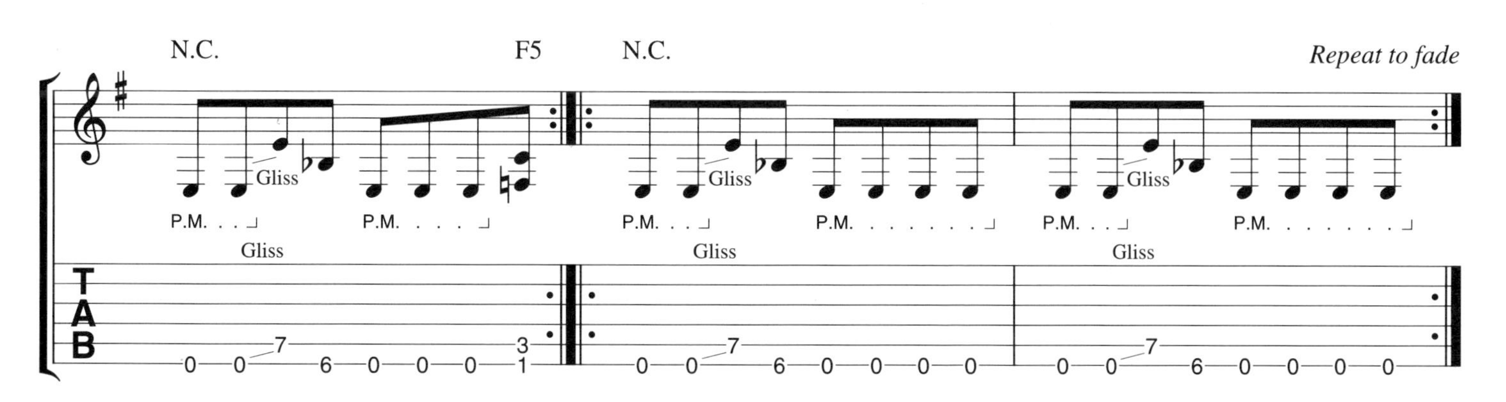
N.C.
F5
N.C.
Repeat to fade
Gliss
P.M.

fat lip

Words & Music by Greig Nori, Deryck Whibley, Steve Jocz & Dave Baksh

A5
3
As a
hang - ing out drink - ing in the back of an El Cam - i - no
Heav - y
what would you ex - pect with a con - science so small?
E5
B5
kid, and no - one knew me by name. Trashed my
was a skid
met - al and mullets, it's how we were raised,
A5
own house par - ty 'cause no - bod - y came. Well I
Maiden and Priest were the gods that we praised. 'Cause
Double tempo
E5
know I'm not the one you thought you knew back in high - school,
we like hav - ing fun at oth - er peo - ple's ex - pense and
P.M.
TAB

C♯5
A5
E5
nev - er go - ing, nev - er show-ing up when we had to (Is it) at - ten - tion that we crave? Don't
cut - ting peo - ple down is just a min - or of - fense then. It's none of your con - cern, I
P.M.
C♯5
A5
tell us to be - have. I'm sick of al - ways hear - ing "Act your age."
guess I nev - er learn. I'm sick of be - ing told to wait my turn.
I don't want to
P.M.
pick scrape
Chorus
E5
B5
C♯m
G♯5
A5
waste my time, be - come an - oth - er cas - u - al - ty of so -
4th string muted . . .
G♯5
A5
E5
B5
C♯m
- ci - e - ty. I'll nev - er fall in line, be - come an - oth - er

1. Half tempo
G♯5
A5
D5
E5
vic - tim of your con - form - i - ty and back down.
1. cont.
N.C.
2. Be - cause you don't
2. Half tempo
* w/echo repeats
down.

Bridge
E5
E5/D♯
C♯m
A5
Don't count on me to let you know when. Don't count on me,
let ring . . .
mp w/clean tone
I'll do it a - gain. Don't count on me, it's the point you're miss - ing.
Don't count on me, 'cause I'm not lis - t'ning.
Well, I'm a
D5
no good nick, low - er mid - dle class brat back packed, and I don't give a shit a - bout no - thing.
You be
ff w/dist.

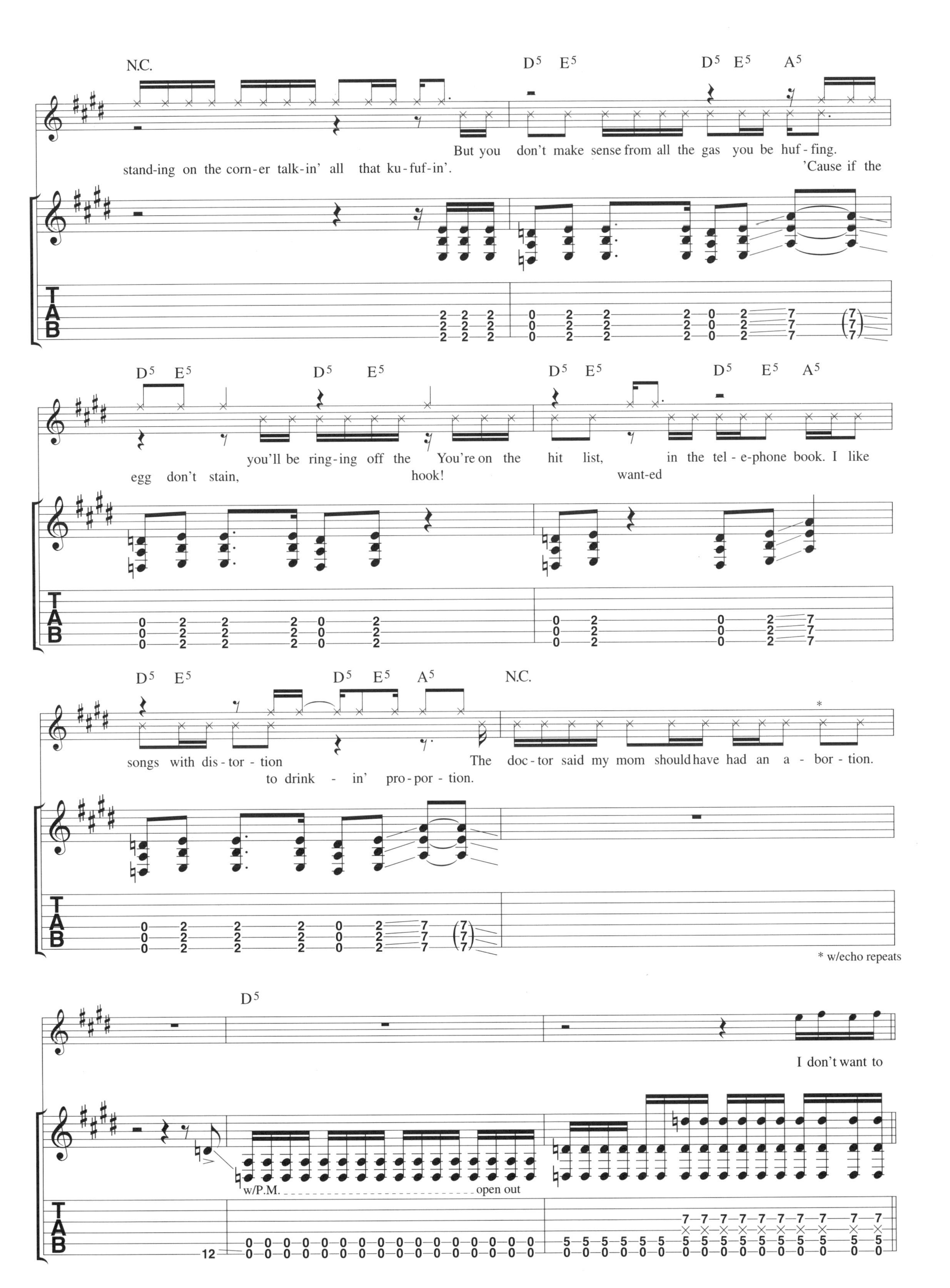
N.C.
D5 E5
D5 E5 A5
But you don't make sense from all the gas you be huf-fing.
stand-ing on the corn-er talk-in' all that ku-fuf-in'.
'Cause if the
D5 E5
D5 E5
D5 E5
D5 E5 A5
you'll be ring-ing off the You're on the hit list, in the tel-e-phone book. I like
egg don't stain, hook! want-ed
D5 E5
D5 E5 A5
N.C.
songs with dis-tor-tion The doc-tor said my mom should have had an a-bor-tion.
to drink-in' pro-por-tion.
* w/echo repeats
D5
I don't want to
w/P.M.
open out

Chorus
Double tempo (♩=♪)

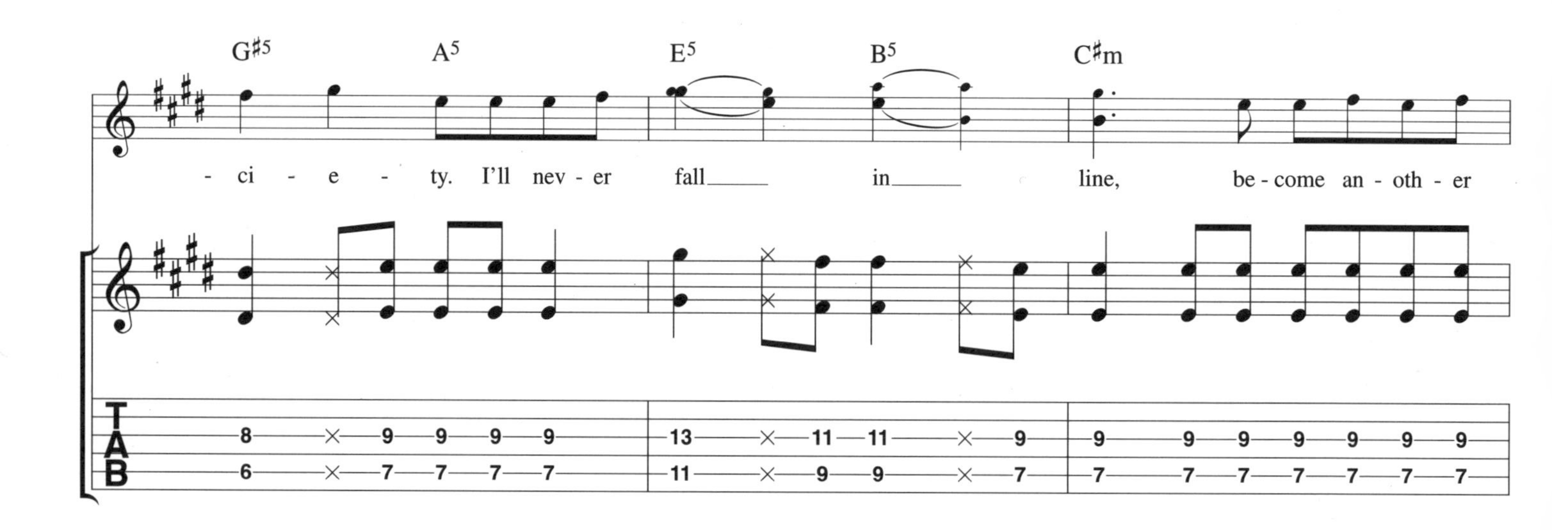

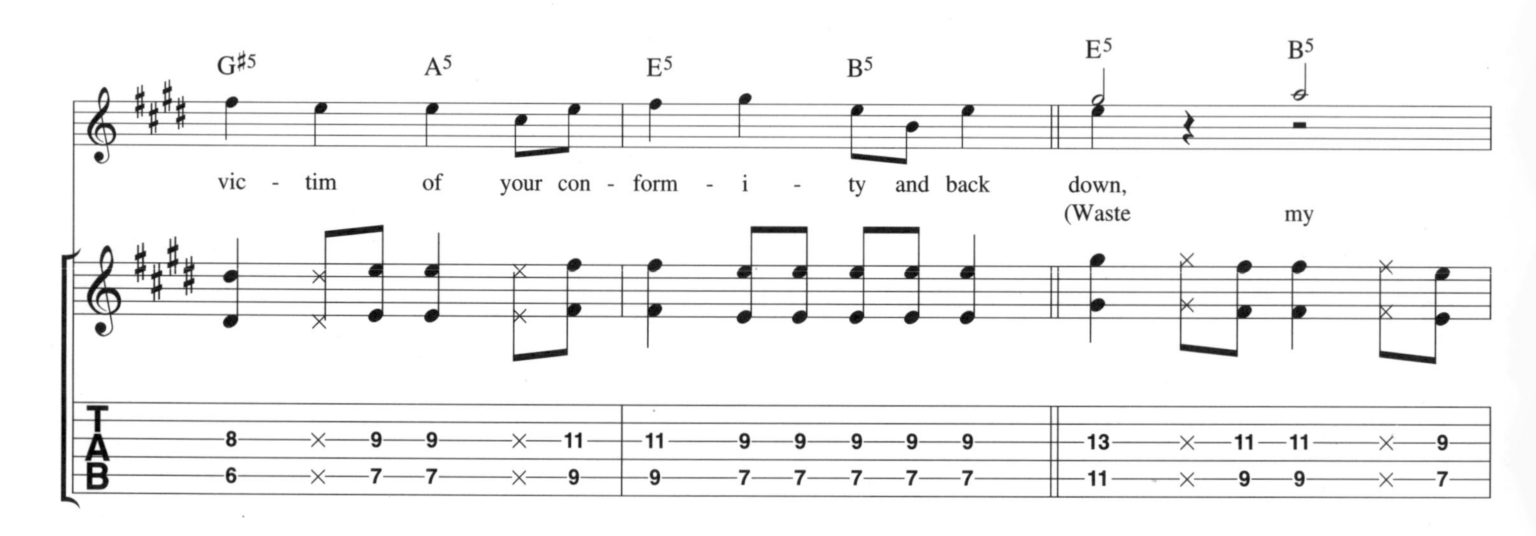

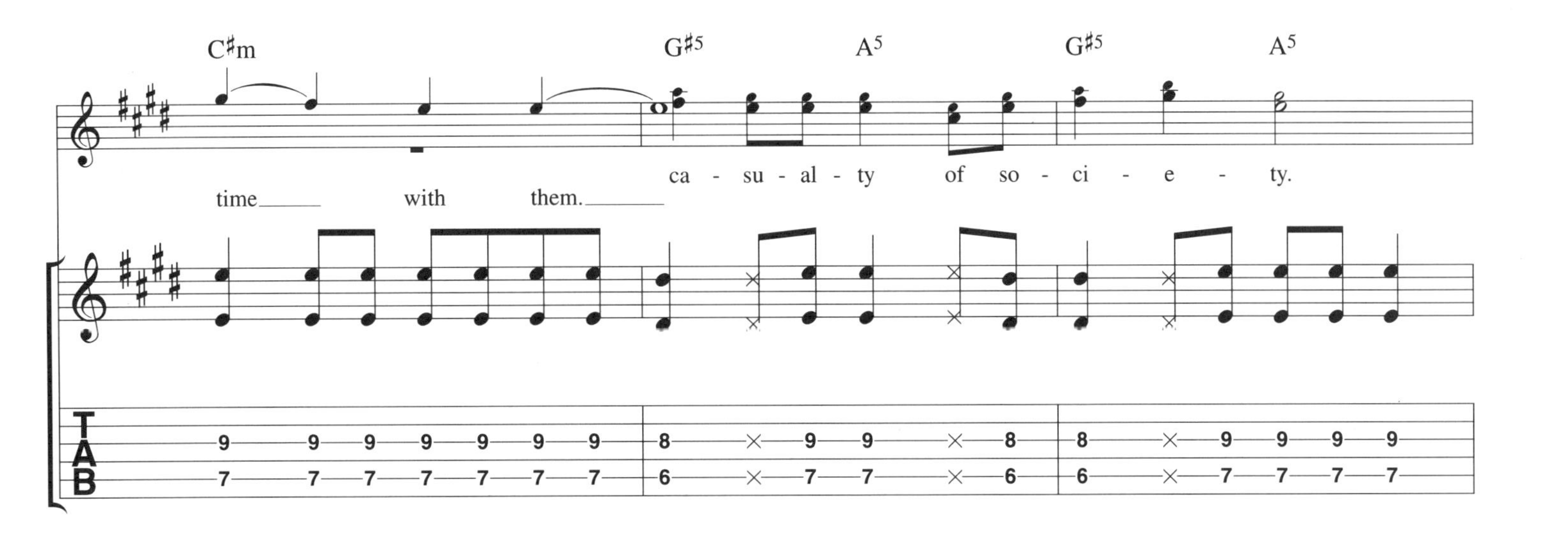
C♯m
G♯5
A5
G♯5
A5
ca - su - al - ty of so - ci - e - ty.
time with them.

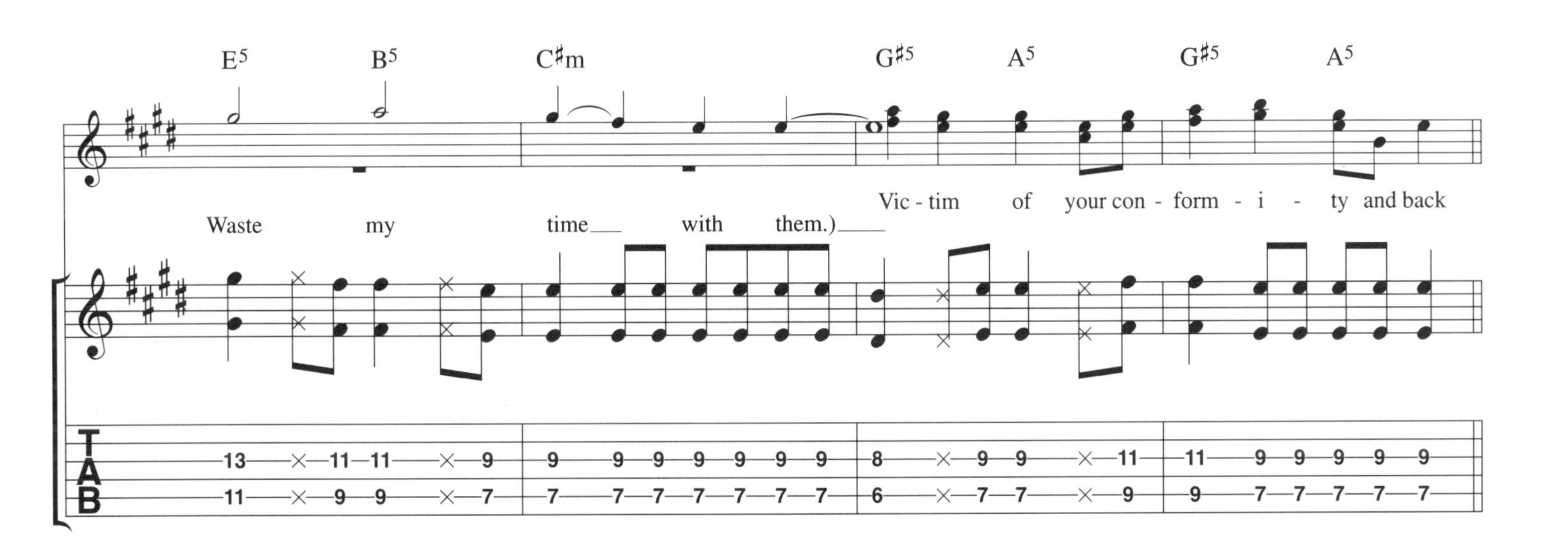
E5
B5
C♯m
G♯5
A5
G♯5
A5
Vic - tim of your con - form - i - ty and back
Waste my time with them.)

Outro
Half tempo
D5 E5 D5 E5 A5 D5 E5 D5 E5 A5 E5
down.
* w/echo repeats

falling away from me

Words & Music by Korn

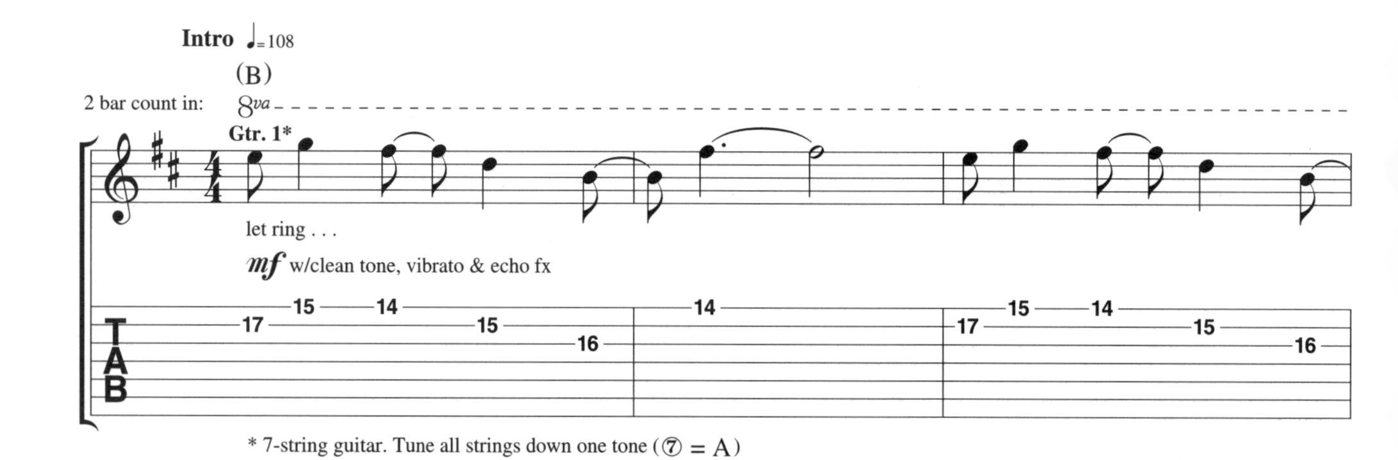

* 7-string guitar. Tune all strings down one tone (⑦ = A)

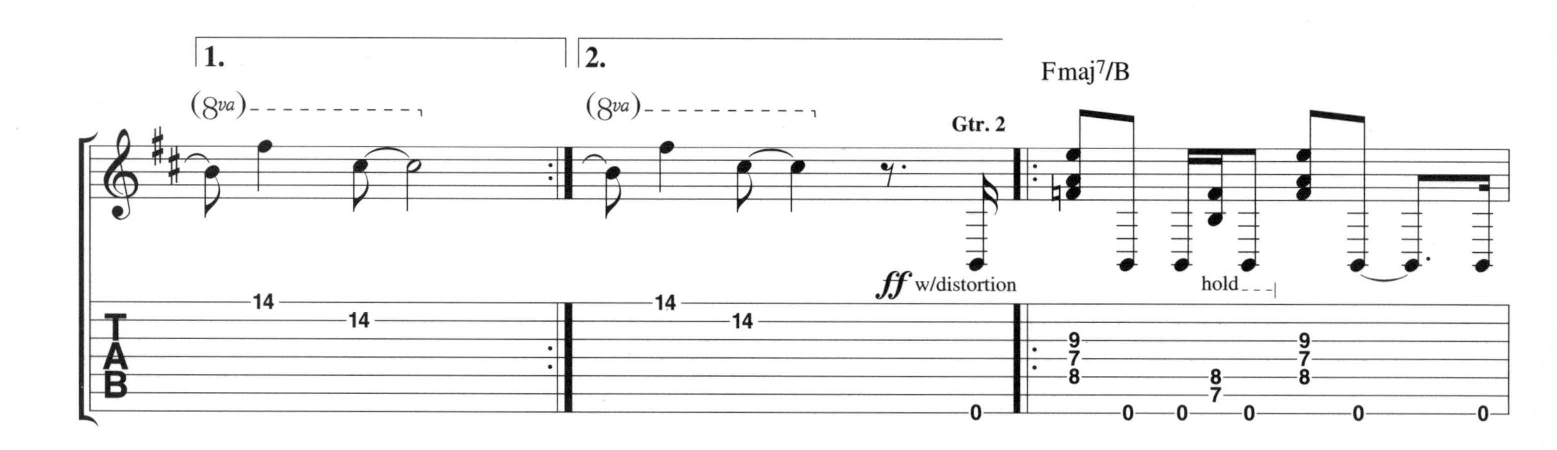

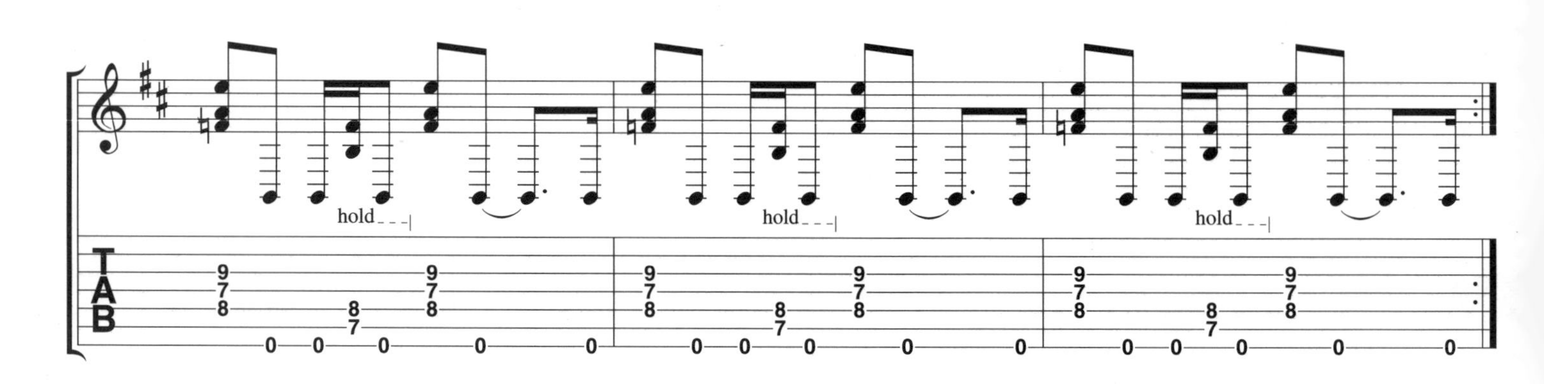

Verse
(B)
1. Hey, I'm feel-ing tired, my time is gone to-day. You're flirt-ing with su-i-cide,
2. Day is here fad-ing, that's when I'm in-sane. I'm flirt-ing with su-i-cide,
8va
Gtr. 1
mf w/clean tone
some-times that's o-kay. Do what oth-ers say, I'm here stand-ing hol-low.
some-times kill the pain. I can't al-ways say, it's gonna be bet-ter to-mor-row.
(8va)
1.
Fmaj7/B
Fall-ing a-way from me fall-ing a-way from me.
(8va)
Gtr. 2
ff w/distortion
hold
1. cont.
hold
hold
hold

2.
Chorus
B5
F♯5
D5
C5
fall - ing a - way from me.
Beat - ing me down, beat - ing me
(8va)
Gtr. 2
ff w/distortion
beat - ing me down,
down.
F5
In - to the ground.
Scream - ing so
sound
beat - ing me
beat - ing me down,
down
in - to the
To Coda
(B)
ground.
8va
mf w/clean tone

Fall - ing a - way from me. It's spin - ning round and
(8va)
T
A
B
14
14
17
15
14
15
16
14

round. Fall - ing a - way from me. It's lost and can't be found. Fall - ing a - way from
(8va)
T
A
B
17
15
14
15
16
14
14
17
15
14
15
16

D.𝄋 al Coda ⊕
me. It's spin - ning round and round. Fall - ing a - way from me slow it down!
(8va)
T
A
B
14
17
15
14
15
16
14
14

Coda
B5
ground.
Gtr. 3
B
½
Bridge
*Bm
F♯
Bm7
E7
Gmaj7
Trust in me then walk a - way.
*Chords implied by harmony
Bm
F♯
Bm7
Em
B
So I pray go a - way
(B)
Life's fall-ing a - way from me.
8va
Gtr. 1
mf w/clean tone

It's fall-ing a - way from me.
Life's fall-ing a - way
from me.
Fall!
(8va)
Fmaj7/B
Gtr. 2
ff w/distortion
hold
Chorus
B5
F♯5
D5
C5
Beat - ing me down
ground. Scream - ing so sound
beat - ing me beat - ing me down,

D5
F5
B5
F♯5
D5
C5
down. In - to the
ground. Beat - ing me down.
ground. Scream - ing so sound,
Beat - ing me
beat - ing me down,
down in - to the
ground.
Gtr. 3
rall.
½
T
A
B

flavor of the weak

Words & Music by Stacy Jones

E♭5
B♭5
F5
best friend on the phone. She'll wash her hair, his dir - ty clothes
G5
E♭5
Pre-chorus
G5
are all he gives to her.
And he's got post -
And he's got pic -
16
B♭5
F5
C5
- ers on the wall of all the girls he wished
- tures on the wall of all the girls he's loved
E♭5
F5
she was, and he means ev - 'ry - thing to her.
be - fore, and she knows all his fav - 'rite songs.

Chorus
B♭5
F5
C5
Her boy - friend, he don't know an - y - thing
E♭5
B♭5
F5
a - bout her. He's too stoned, Nin - ten - do.
C5
E♭5
B♭5
I wish that I could make her see.
B
Full
F5
C5
E♭5
She's just the fla - vor of the weak.
B
Full

B♭5
F5
To Coda
G5
E♭5
D5
E♭5
D5
(%) Yeah!
B
B
hold bend
Pre
Full
Full
Full
Full
Verse
B♭5
F5
G5
2. It's Fri - day night and she's all a - lone.
He's a
P.M.
* optional
E♭5
B♭5
F5
mil - lion miles a - way.
She's dressed to kill but the T. V.'s on.
G5
E♭5
D.% al Coda
He's con - nect - ed to the sound.

Coda
G5
Eb5
D5
F5
Play 3x
B
Full
Solo
Bb5
Pre
ff
C5
hold bend
Her boy - friend, he don't know an - y - thing

B♭5
F5
a - bout__ her. He's___ too___ stoned. He's too___ stoned.
C5
E♭5
Chorus
B♭
He's too___ stoned. He's too___ stoned. Her boy - friend,
B
Full
F5
C5
E♭5
he don't_ know an - y - thing a - bout__ her. He's_
B
Full
B♭
F5
C5
__ too__ stoned, Nin - ten - do. I wish_ that
B
Full
B
Full

E♭5
B♭5
F5
I could make her see.
B
Full
C5
E♭5
B♭5
She's just the fla - vor of the weak.
F5
C5
E♭5
Yeah, she's the fla - vor of the weak,
B♭5
F5
C5
A♭5
and she makes me weak.

get free

Words & Music by Craig Nicholls

N.C.
She nev - er loved me, she nev - er loved me, she nev - er loved me,
P.M.
open out
1/4 1/2 1/2
C5 G5
Chorus
C5 D5 C5 D5 C5 D5 G5 A♭5 F5
why should an - y - one?
I'll take your pho - to for ya.
Come here, come here, come here.
Drive you a - round the cor - ner.
Come here, come here, come here,
You know you real - ly ought - a
move out - ta Cal - i - for - nia.

N.C.
Verse
N.C.(D5)
2. Get (get) me (me) far (far) when
P.M.
open out
C5
G5
N.C.
I've a lot to lose. Save (save) me (me) from
P.M.

Chorus
C5
G5
C5
D5
(from)
here
(here.)
Come here, come here, come here.
P.M. open out
1/4
1/2
1/2
f
G5
A♭5
F5
Come here, come here, come here.
(Ooh,
ah.)
Come here, come here come here.
Bridge
A5
B♭5
When it's breed - ing time,
mf

A5
look in - to your mind a - way.
Verse
N.C.(D5)
3. I'm gon - na get free, I'm gon - na get free, I'm gon - na get free,
1/4 1/2 1/2
C5 G5 N.C.
ride in - to the sun. She nev - er loved me, she nev - er loved me,
she nev - er loved me, why should an - y - one?
Chorus
C5 D5 C5 D5 C5 D5
Come here, come here, come here.

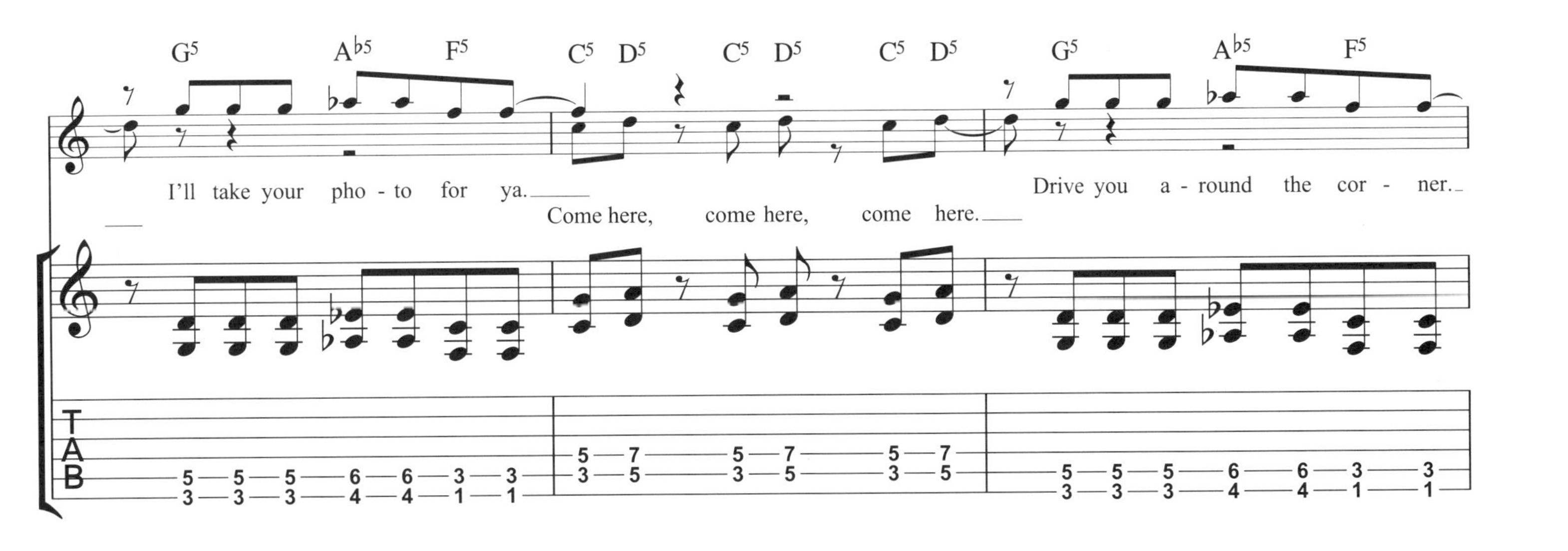
G5 A♭5 F5 C5 D5 C5 D5 C5 D5 G5 A♭5 F5
I'll take your pho - to for ya.
Come here, come here, come here.
Drive you a - round the cor - ner.
T
A
B

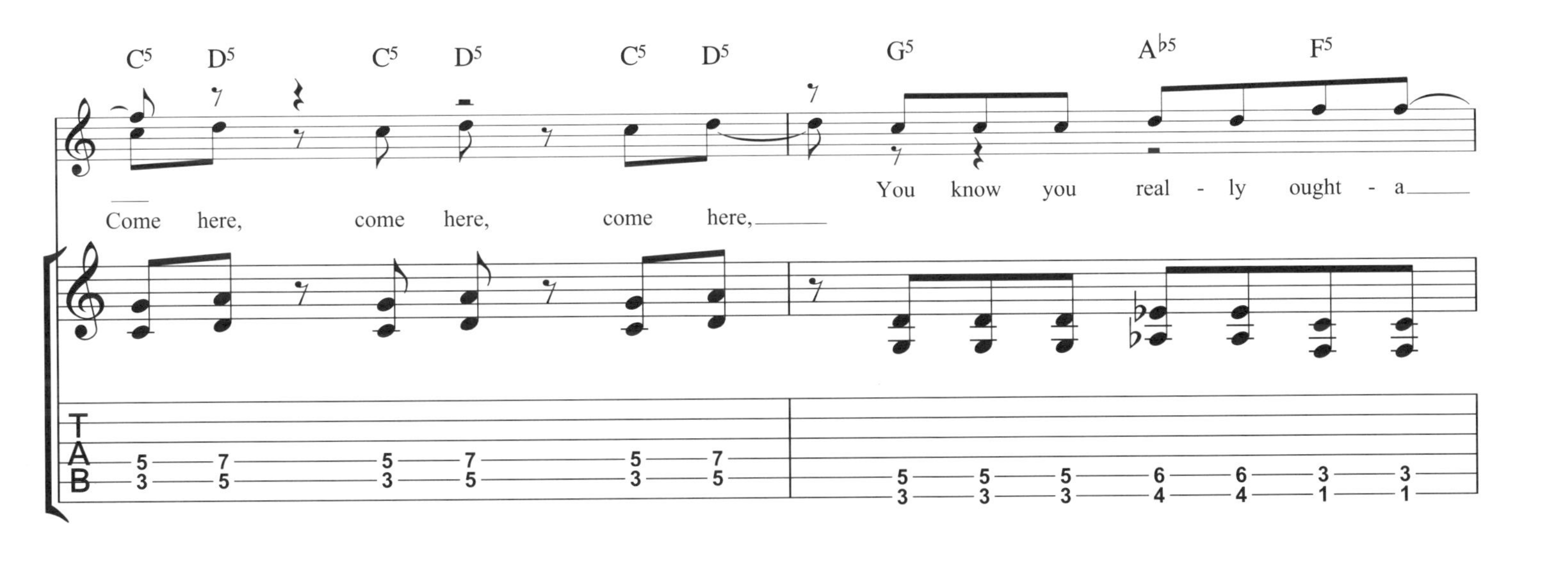
C5 D5 C5 D5 C5 D5 G5 A♭5 F5
Come here, come here, come here,
You know you real - ly ought - a
T
A
B

C5 D5 C5 D5 C5 D5 G5 A♭5 F5
Come here, come here, come here.
move out - ta Cal - i - for - nia.
T
A
B

the fight song

Words & Music by Brian Warner & John Lowery

F♯5 E5 F♯5 A5 F♯5 E5 F♯5 E5 F♯5 E5 F♯5 A5
pas-sin' of ev-'ry - day hu-man e - vents._ And i - so - la - tion is the
F♯5 E5 F♯5 A5 F♯5 E5 F♯5 A5 F♯5 E5 F♯5 E5
ox - y - gen mask,_ you make your child-ren breathe_ in to_ sur - vive._
Chorus
F♯5 E5 F♯5 A5 F♯5 E5 F♯5 A5 F♯5 E5 F♯5 A5
Well, I'm not a slave_ to a god_ that does-n't ex - ist._
ff w/distortion
cont. sim.
F♯5 E5 F♯5 E5 F♯5 E5 F♯5 A5 F♯5 E5 F♯5 A5
Well, I'm not a slave_ to a world_

F♯5 E5 F♯5 A5 F♯5 E5 F♯5 E5 B5
— that does-n't give a shit.— Re-mem-ber when we—
A5 B5 A5
— were good, well just close your eyes.—
D5 B5 A5
So man, we— are bad,— we'll scar your mind.
E5 F5 F♯5 E5 F♯5 A5 F♯5 E5 F♯5 A5
Fight! Fight! Fight! Fight!

Verse
F♯5 E5 F♯5 A5 F♯5 E5 F♯5 E5 F♯5 E5 F♯5 A5
Fight! Fight! Fight! Fight! 2. You'll nev - er grow up to be
mp w/slight crunch
F♯5 E5 F♯5 A5 F♯5 E5 F♯5 A5 F♯5 E5 F♯5 E5
a big rock star, cel - e - bra - ted vic - tim of your fame.
cont. sim.
F♯5 E5 F♯5 A5 F♯5 E5 F♯5 A5 F♯5 E5 F♯5 A5
They'll just cut our wrists like cheap cou - pons and say that death was on
F♯5 E5 F♯5 E5 B5 A5
sale to - day ah. Re - mem - ber when we were good,
ff w/distortion

B5
A5
D5
well just close your eyes.
So man, we
B5
A5
E5
F5
are bad,
we'll scar your mind.
Chorus
F#5
E5
A5
Well I'm not a slave to a god that does-n't ex - ist.
cont. sim.
Well I'm not a slave to a world
TAB

F♯5 E5 F♯5 A5 F♯5 E5 F♯5 E5 C5 D5
that does-n't give a shit.
The death of one is a trad -
A5 C5 A5
- ge - dy ah.
The death of one is a trad - ge - dy ah.
C5 D5 A5 C5
The death of one is a trad - ge - dy ah.
The death of mil - lions just
Chorus
A5 B5 F♯5 E5 F♯5 A5 F♯5 E5 F♯5 A5
a stat - is - tic.
Well I'm not a slave
to a god

F♯5 E5 F♯5 A5 F♯5 E5 F♯5 E5 F♯5 E5 F♯5 A5
that does-n't ex - ist.
Well I'm not a slave
F♯5 E5 F♯5 A5 F♯5 E5 F♯5 A5 F♯5 E5 F♯5 E5
to a world that does-n't give a shit.
F♯5 E5 F♯5 A5 F♯5 E5 F♯5 A5
Fight! Fight! Fight! Fight!
F♯5 E5 F♯5 A5 F♯5 E5 F♯5 E5
Fight! Fight! Fight! Fight!
TAB
TAB
TAB
TAB

last resort

Words & Music by Papa Roach

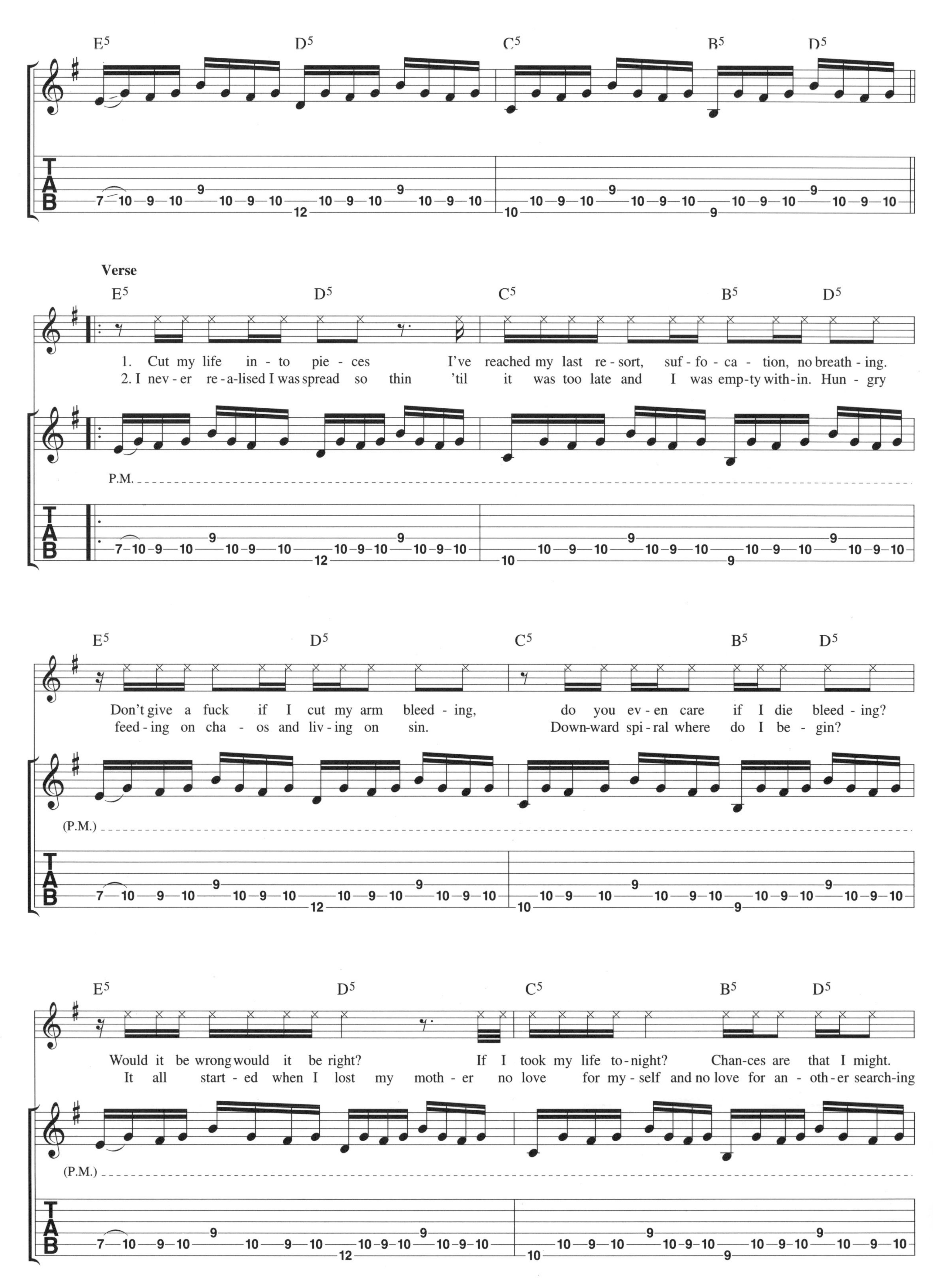
E5 D5 C5 B5 D5
Verse
E5 D5 C5 B5 D5
1. Cut my life in - to pie - ces I've reached my last re - sort, suf - fo - ca - tion, no breath - ing.
2. I nev - er re - a - lised I was spread so thin 'til it was too late and I was emp - ty with - in. Hun - gry
P.M.
E5 D5 C5 B5 D5
Don't give a fuck if I cut my arm bleed - ing, do you ev - en care if I die bleed - ing?
feed - ing on cha - os and liv - ing on sin. Down-ward spi - ral where do I be - gin?
(P.M.)
E5 D5 C5 B5 D5
Would it be wrong would it be right? If I took my life to - night? Chan-ces are that I might.
It all start - ed when I lost my moth - er no love for my - self and no love for an - oth - er search-ing
(P.M.)

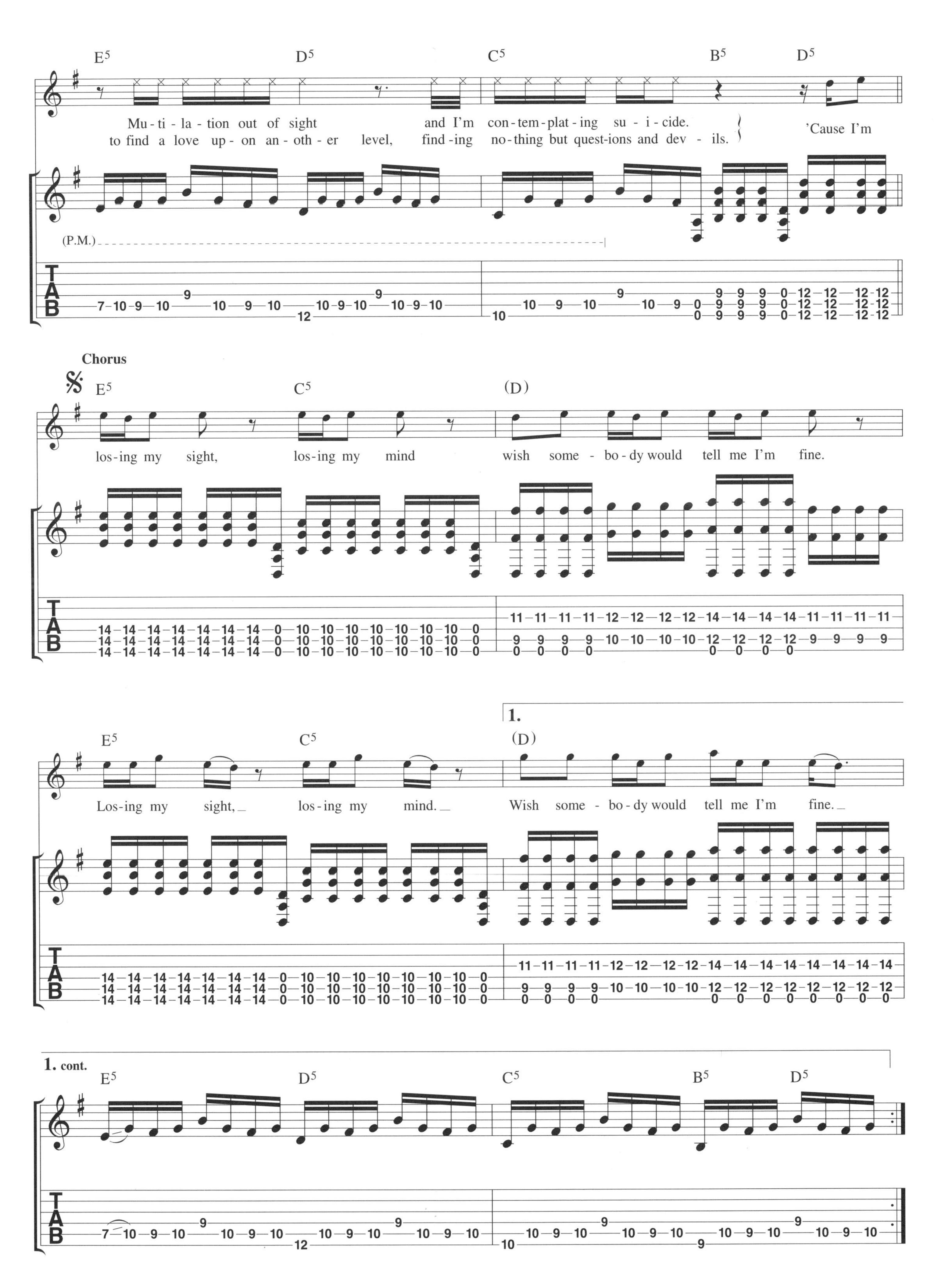
E5
D5
C5
B5
D5
Mu - ti - la - tion out of sight and I'm con - tem - plat - ing su - i - cide.
to find a love up - on an - oth - er level, find - ing no - thing but quest - ions and dev - ils.
'Cause I'm
(P.M.)
Chorus
E5
C5
(D)
los - ing my sight, los - ing my mind wish some - bo - dy would tell me I'm fine.
E5
C5
1.
(D)
Los - ing my sight, los - ing my mind. Wish some - bo - dy would tell me I'm fine.
1. cont.
E5
D5
C5
B5
D5

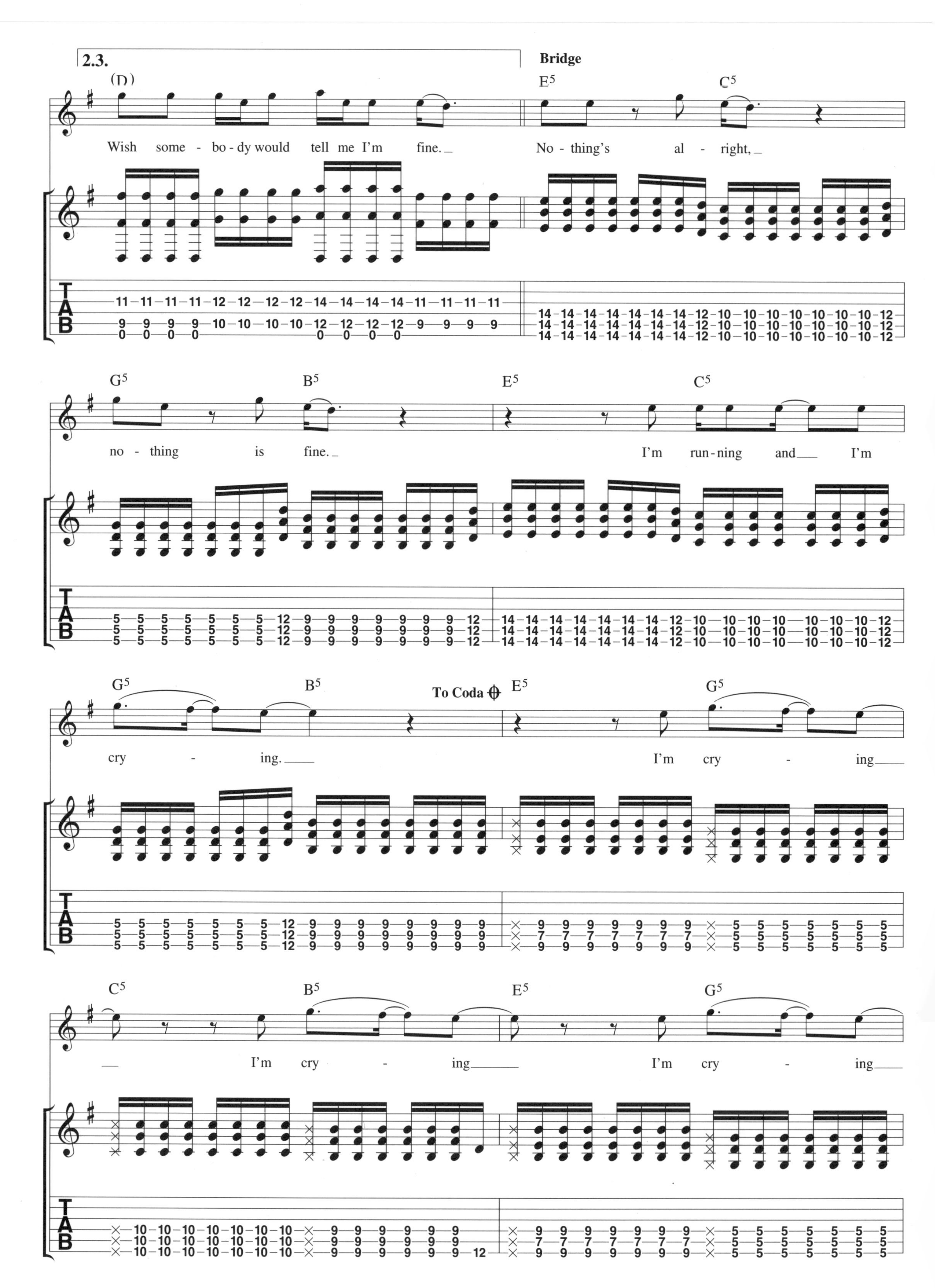
2.3.
Bridge
(D)
E5
C5
Wish some - bo - dy would tell me I'm fine.
No - thing's al - right,
G5
B5
no - thing is fine.
I'm run - ning and I'm
cry - ing.
To Coda
I'm cry - ing
I'm cry - ing
I'm cry - ing
TAB

C5 B5 E5 D5
I'm cry - ing. (Whispered) I can't
C5 B5 D5 E5 D5 C5 B5 D5
go on liv - ing this way.
Verse
E5 D5 C5 B5 D5
3. Cut my life in - to piec - es this is my last re - sort
E5 D5 C5 B5 D5
suf - fo - ca - tion no breath - ing don't give a fuck if I cut my arm bleed - ing.

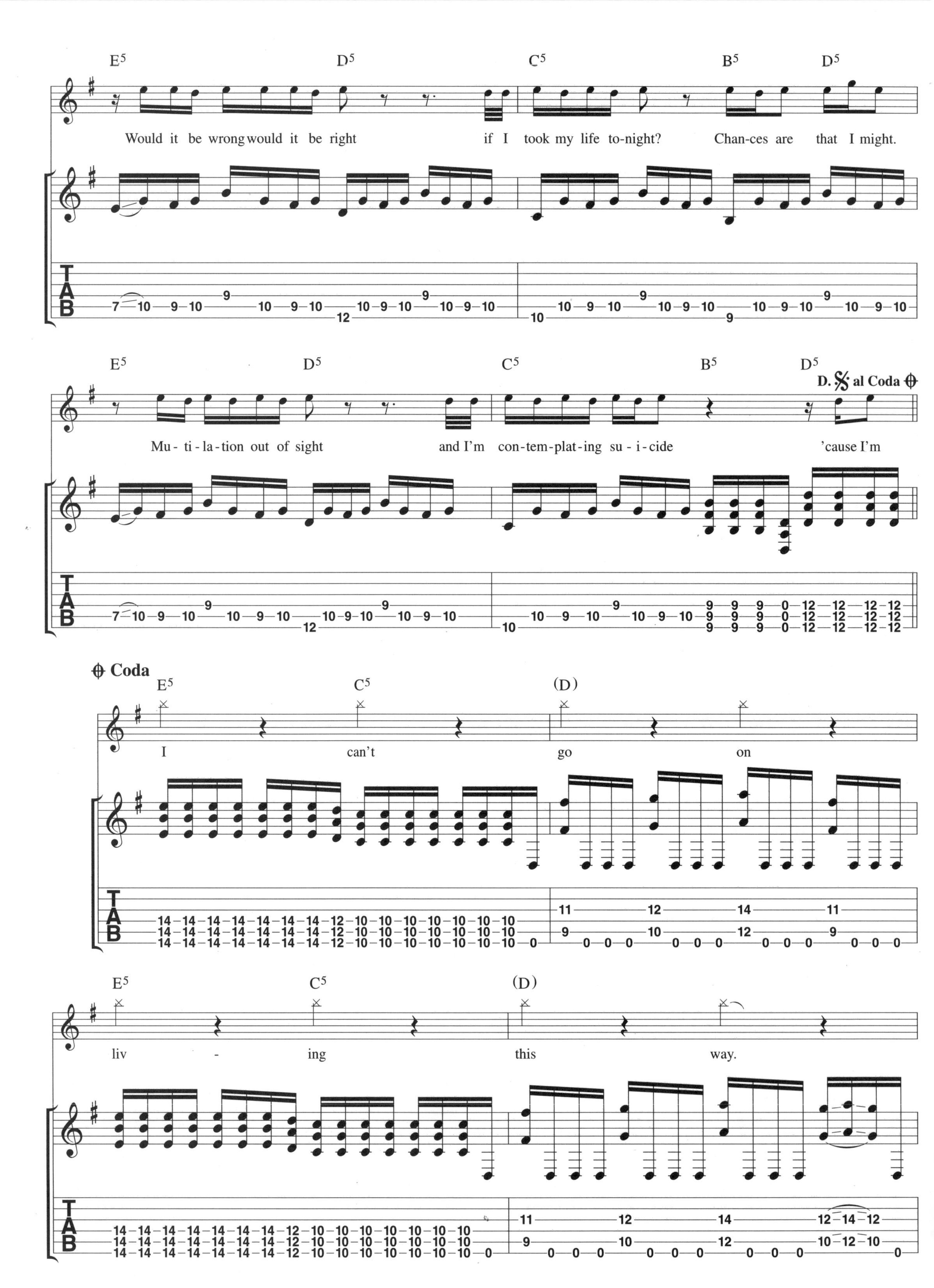
E5
D5
C5
B5
D5
Would it be wrong would it be right if I took my life to-night? Chan-ces are that I might.
Mu-ti-la-tion out of sight and I'm con-tem-plat-ing su-i-cide 'cause I'm
D.𝄋 al Coda
Coda
(D)
I can't go on
liv - ing this way.

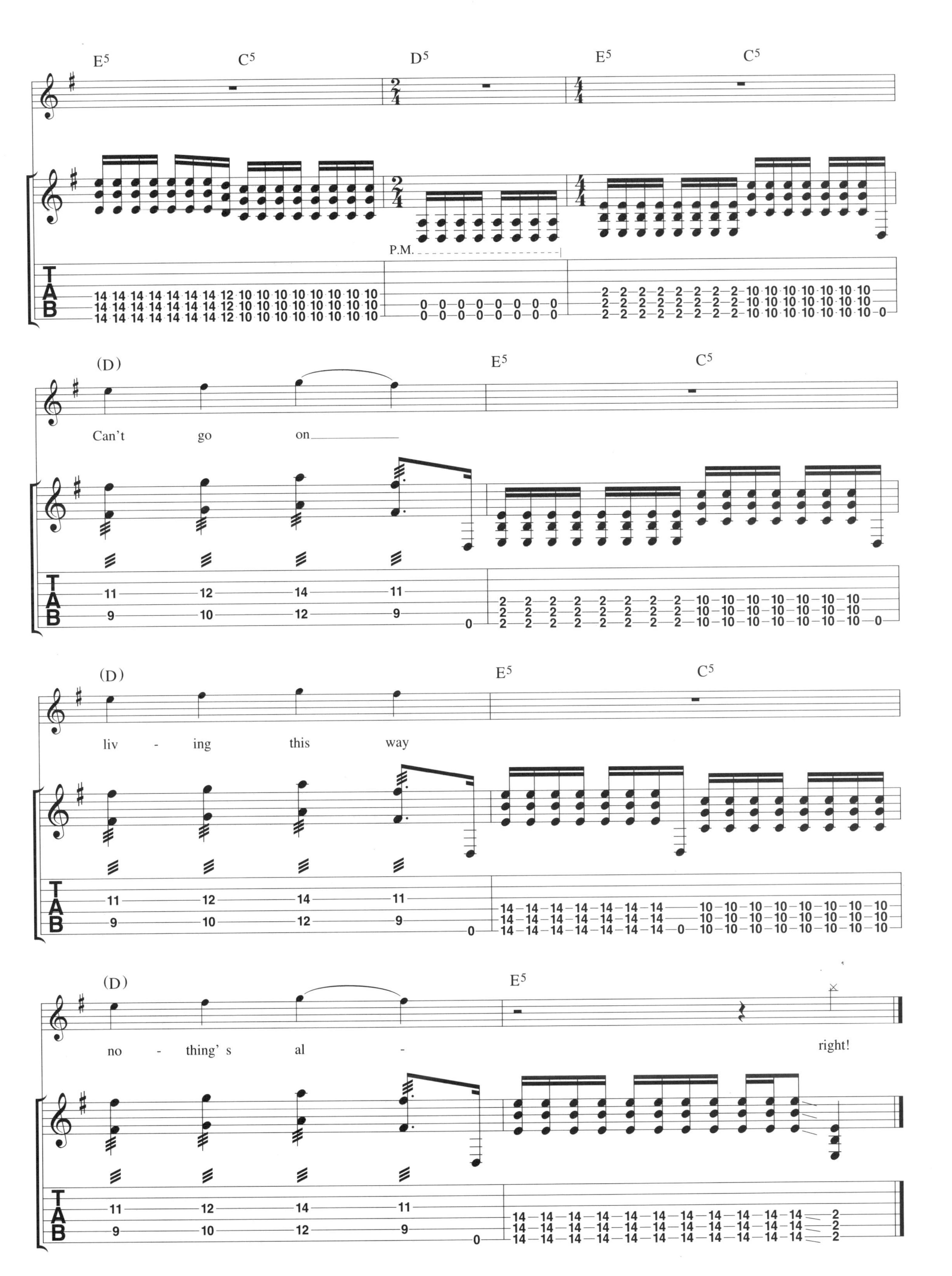
E5
C5
D5
P.M.
(D)
Can't go on
liv - ing this way
no - thing's al - right!
T
A
B

movies

Words & Music by Dryden Mitchell, Terence Corso, Tye Zamora & Mike Cosgrove

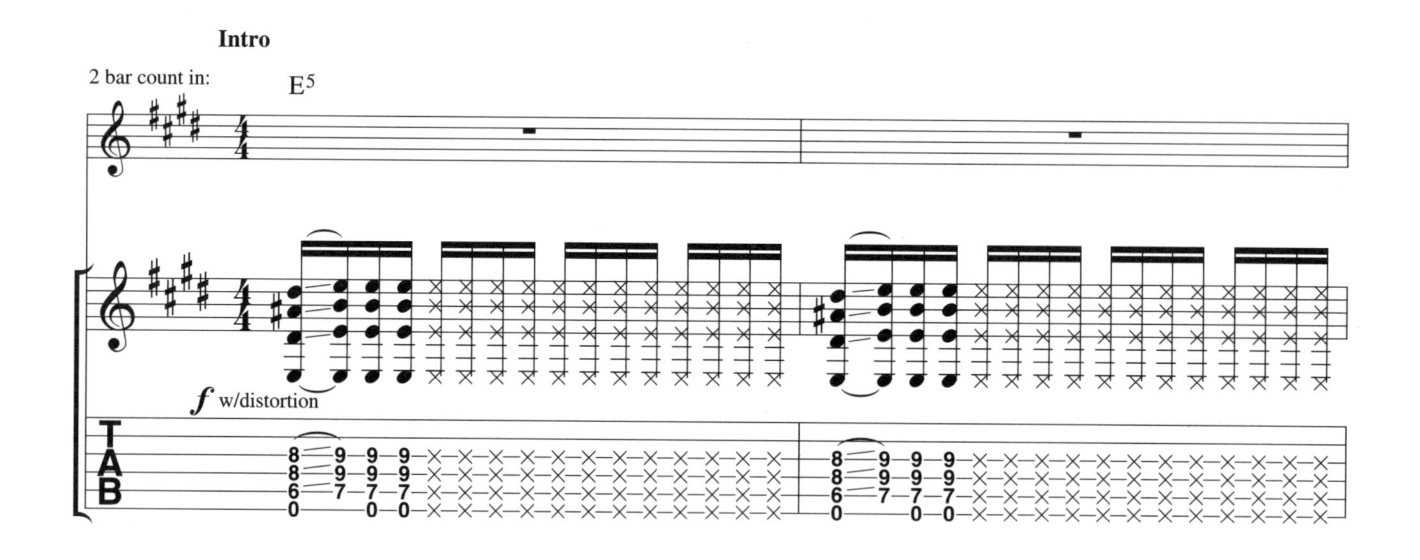

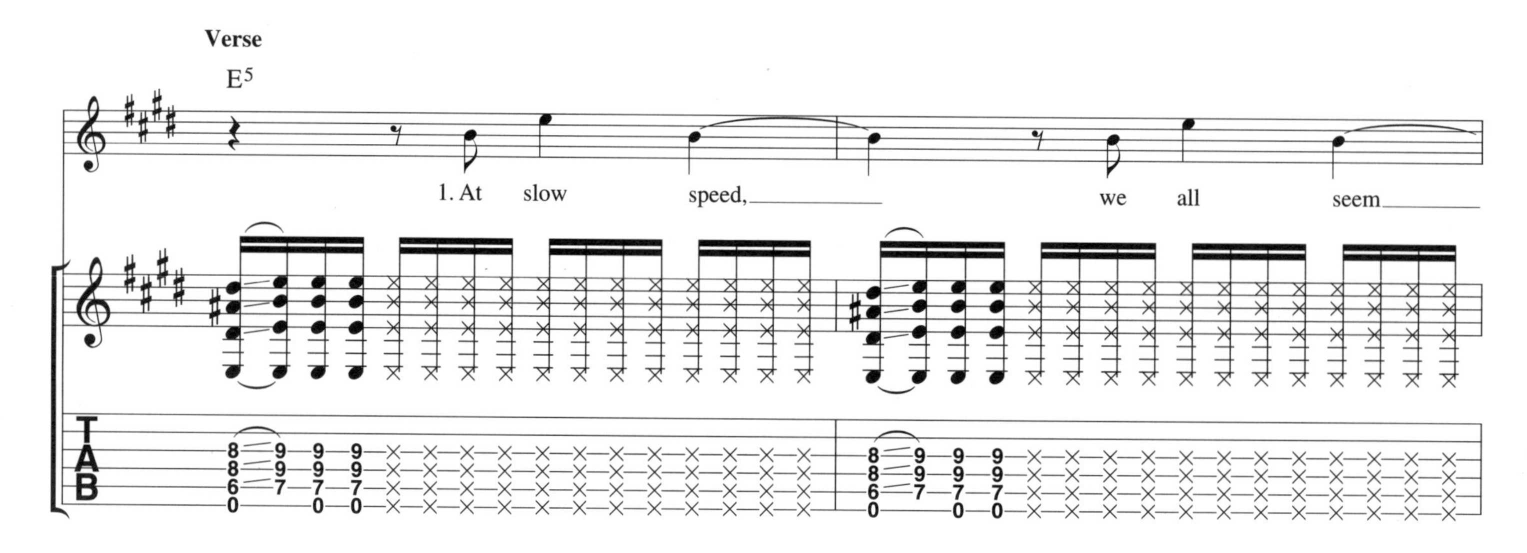

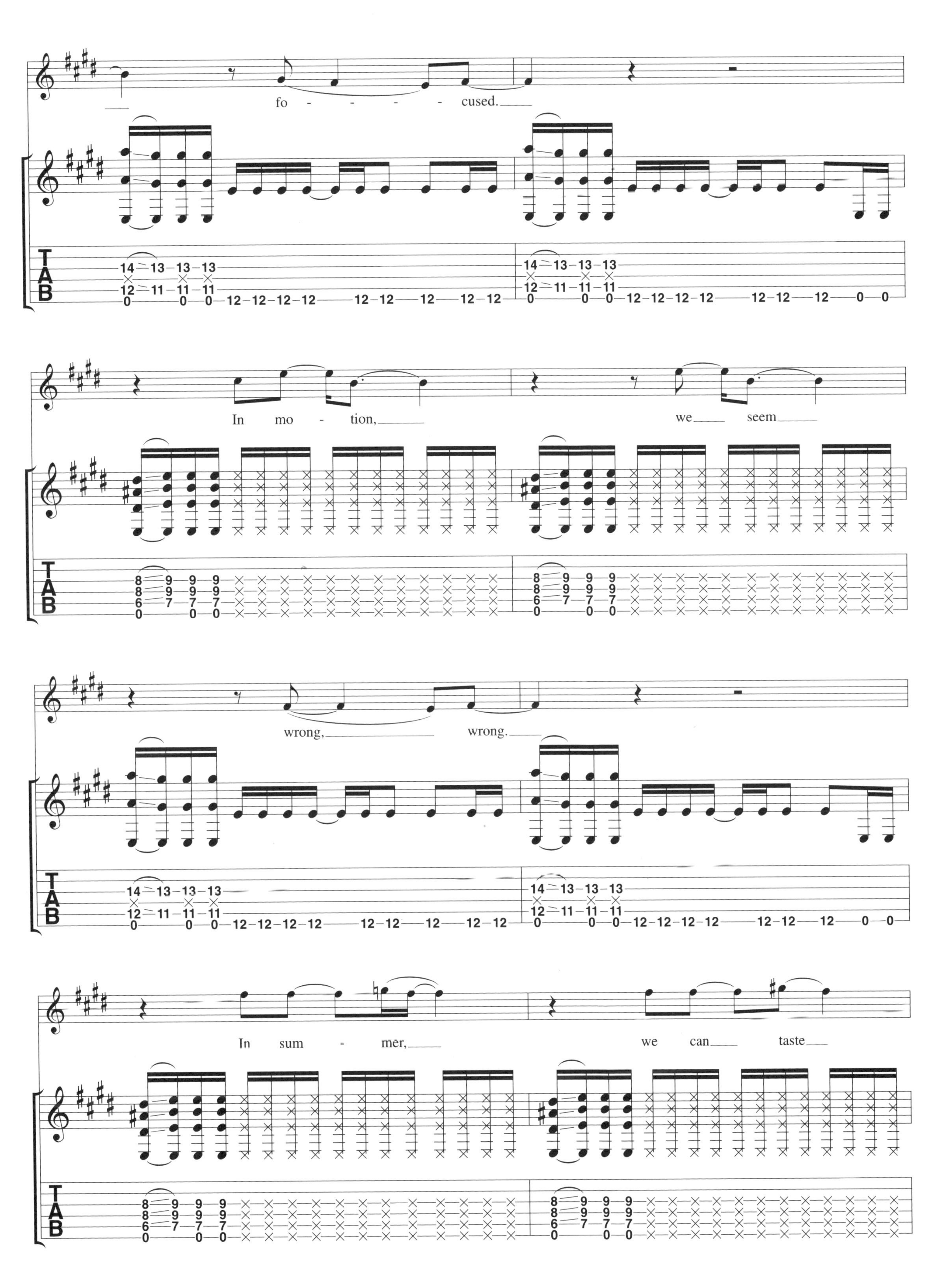
fo - - - - cused.
In mo - tion,
we seem
wrong,
wrong.
In sum - mer,
we can taste
TAB
TAB
TAB
TAB

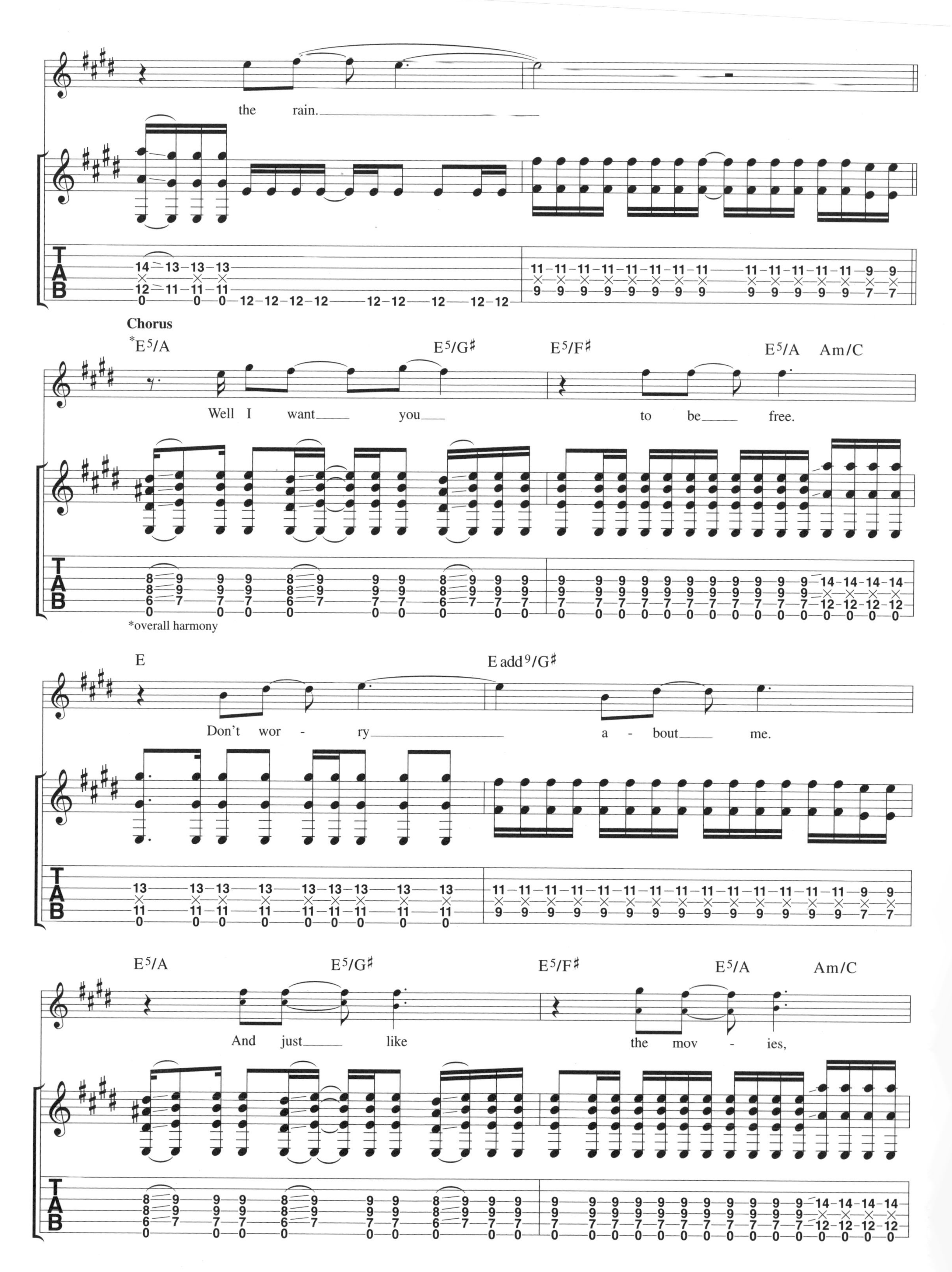
the rain.
Chorus
*E5/A
E5/G♯
E5/F♯
E5/A
Am/C
Well I want you to be free.
*overall harmony
E
E add9/G♯
Don't wor - ry a - bout me.
E5/A
E5/G♯
E5/F♯
E5/A
Am/C
And just like the mov - ies,
TAB

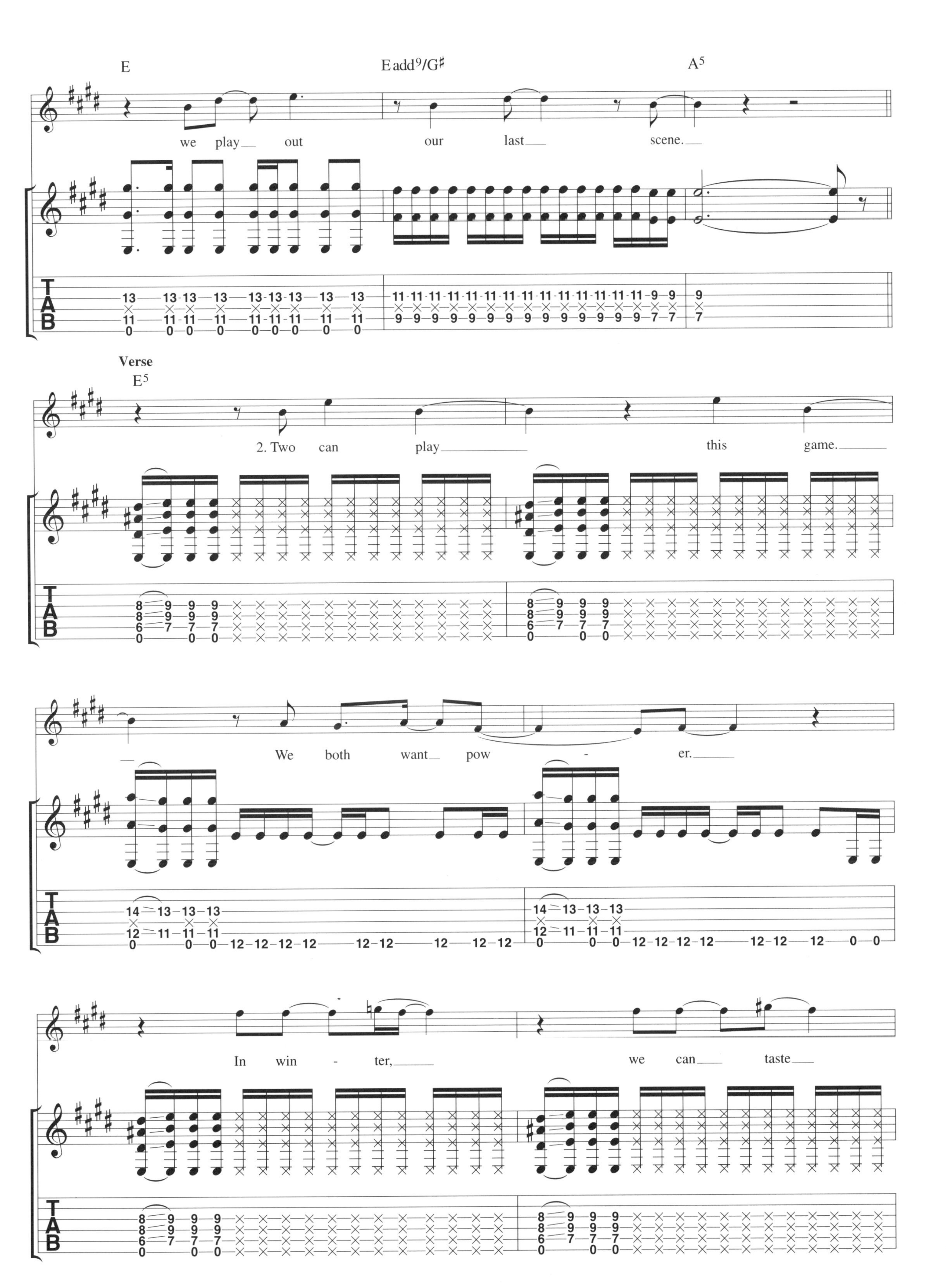
E
Eadd9/G♯
A5
we play out our last scene.
Verse
E5
2. Two can play this game.
We both want pow - er.
In win - ter, we can taste

the pain.
8va
harm.
harmonic fret positions
Bridge
C♯5 E5 B5 C♯5 G♯5
In our short years we come long way
w/P.M.
A5 E5
to treat it bad and throw a - way.
C♯5 E5 B5 C♯5 G♯5
In our short years, we come long way

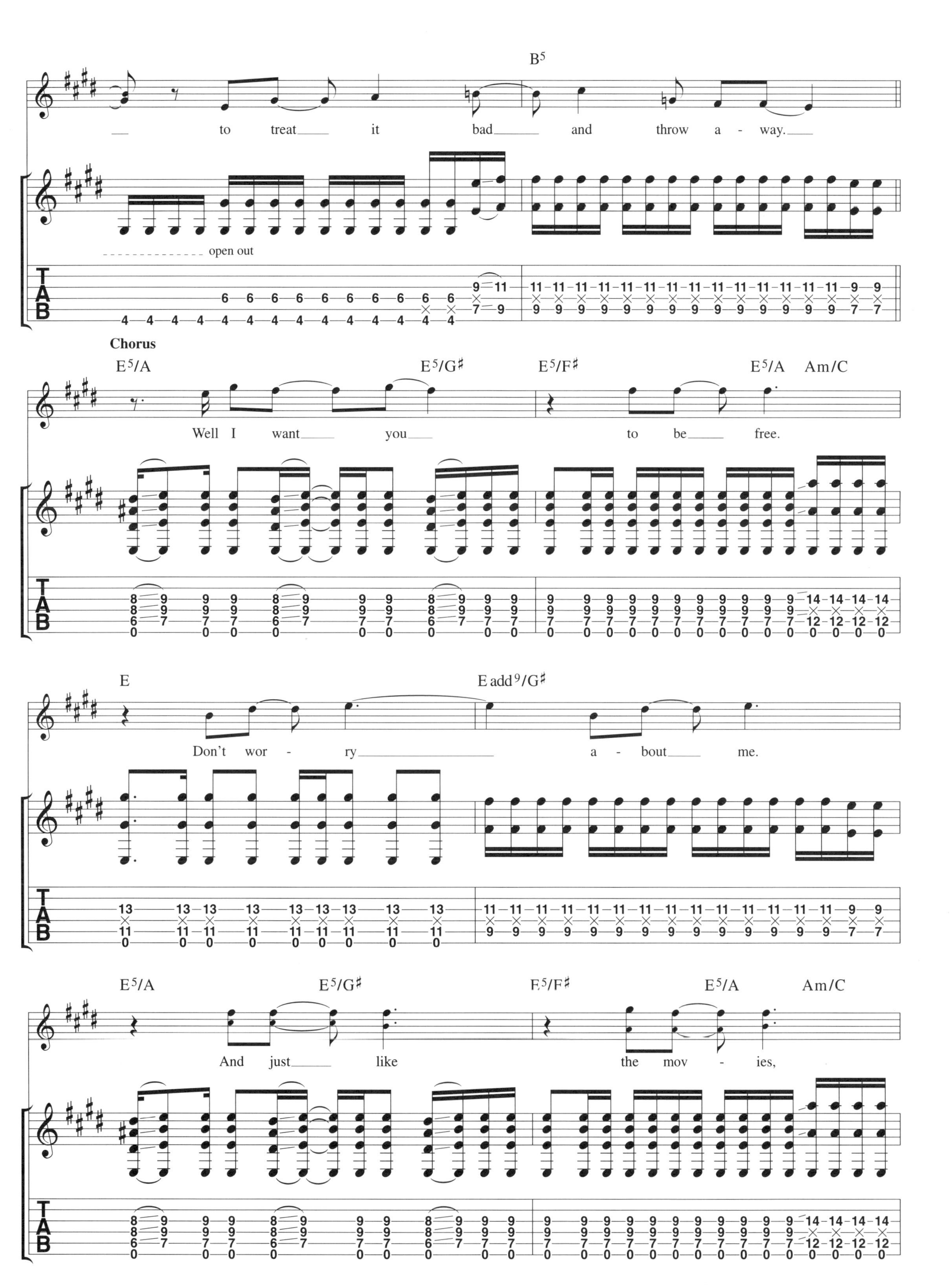
B5
to treat it bad and throw a - way.
open out
Chorus
E5/A
E5/G♯
E5/F♯
E5/A
Am/C
Well I want you to be free.
E
E add9/G♯
Don't wor - ry a - bout me.
E5/A
E5/G♯
E5/F♯
E5/A
Am/C
And just like the mov - ies,

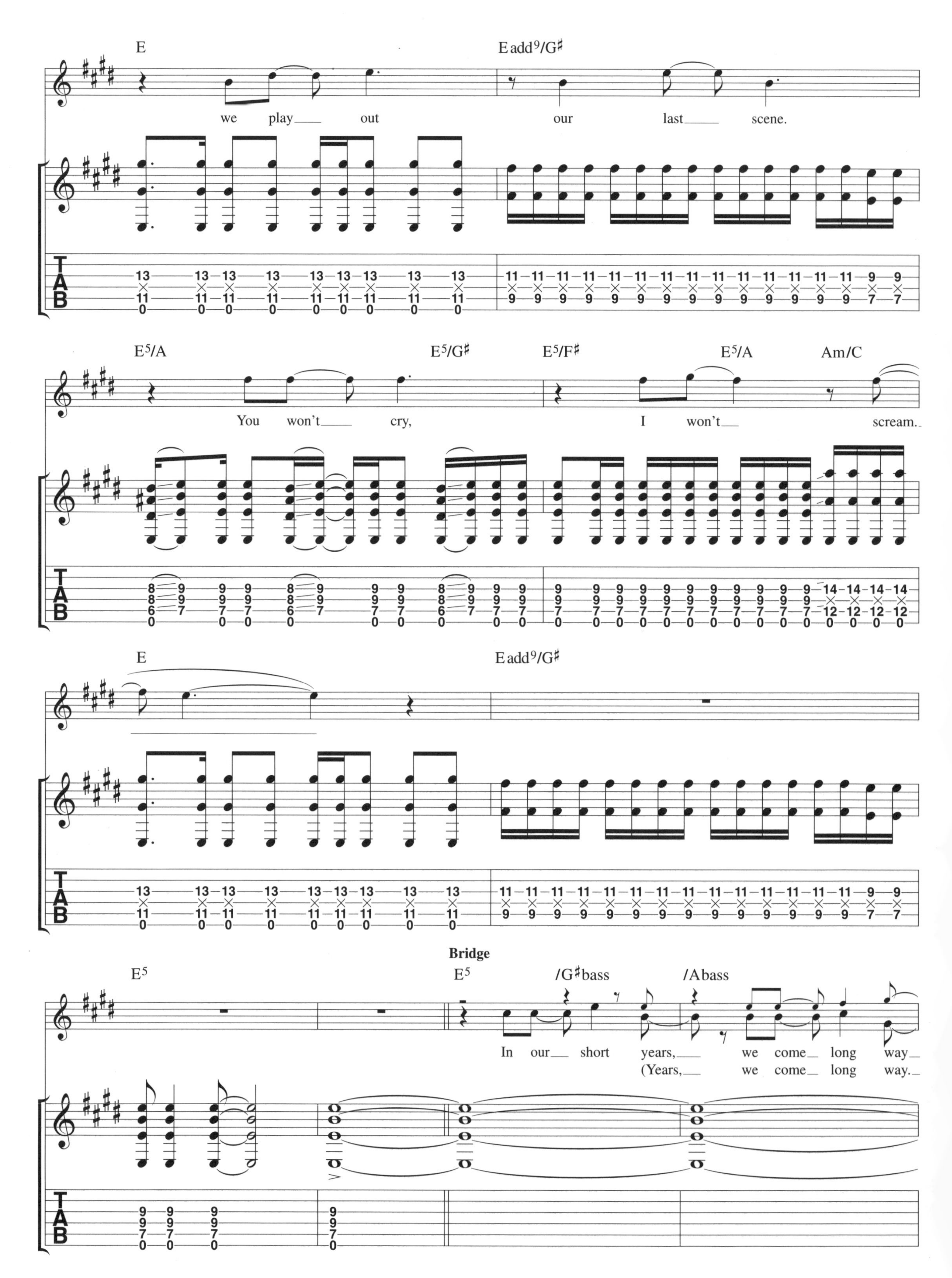
E
Eadd9/G♯
we play out our last scene.
E5/A
E5/G♯
E5/F♯
E5/A
Am/C
You won't cry, I won't scream.
E
Eadd9/G♯
Bridge
E5
E5
/G♯bass
/Abass
In our short years, we come long way
(Years, we come long way.

/E bass
/G♯ bass
C♯5
E5
B5
to treat it bad and throw a-way.
And if we make
+ ad lib feedback
C♯5
G♯5
A5
B5
E5
a lit-tle space, a sci-ence fic-tion show-case.
7
C♯5
/E
/B
C♯5
/G♯
/A
/B
In our short film a love dis-grace, dream a scene
(In our short film, a love dis-grace, dream a
mf w/P.M.
/E
C♯5
to bright-en face. In our short years we come long way
scene to bright-en face.)
P.M.
P.M.

B5
to treat it bad, just to throw it a - way.
Chorus
A5 G♯5 F♯5 A5 C5
I want you to be free.
E5 E add9/G♯
Don't wor - ry a - bout me.
A5 G♯5 F♯5 A5 C5
And just like the mov - - ies,
f
TAB

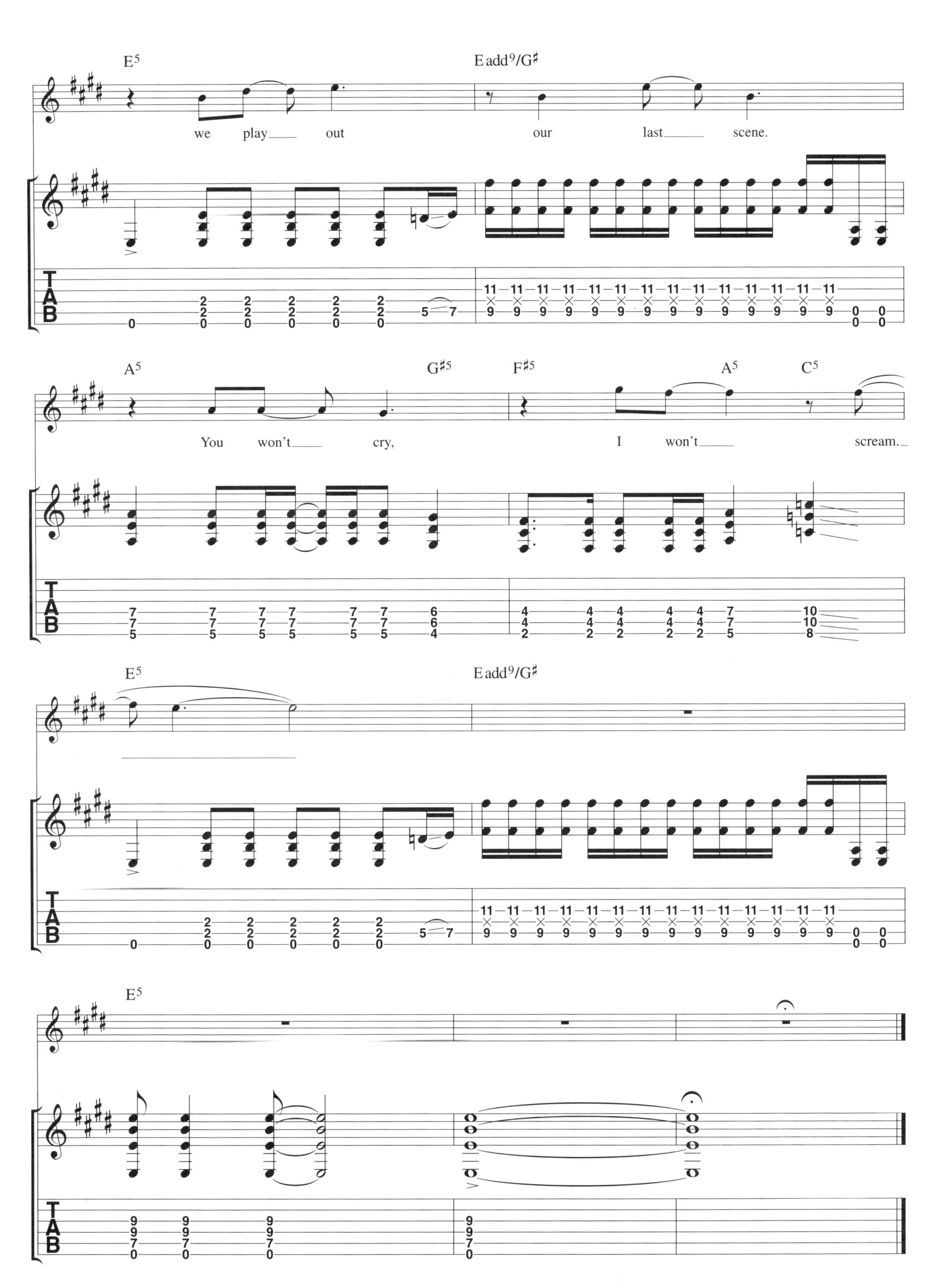
E5
Eadd9/G♯
we play out our last scene.
A5
G♯5
F♯5
A5
C5
You won't cry, I won't scream.
E5
Eadd9/G♯
E5

muscle museum

Lyrics & Music by Matthew Bellamy

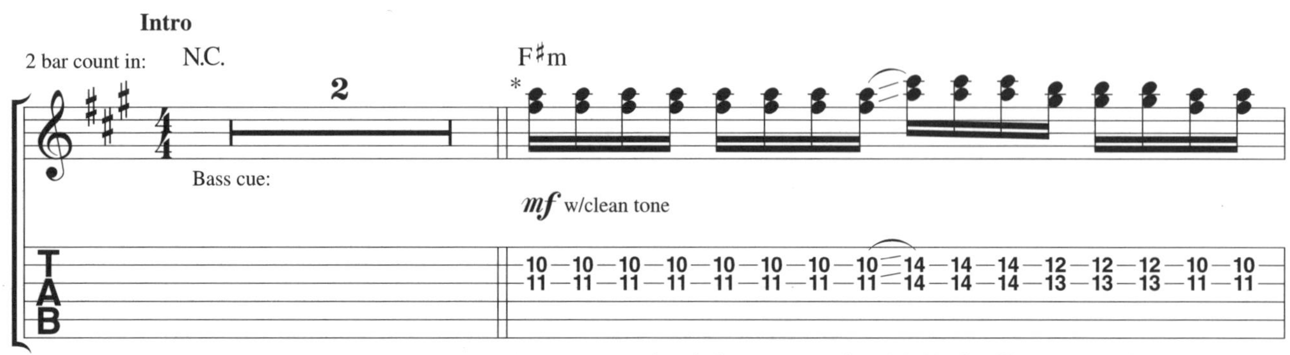

* Top notes optional - harmony can be added by intelligent harmoniser

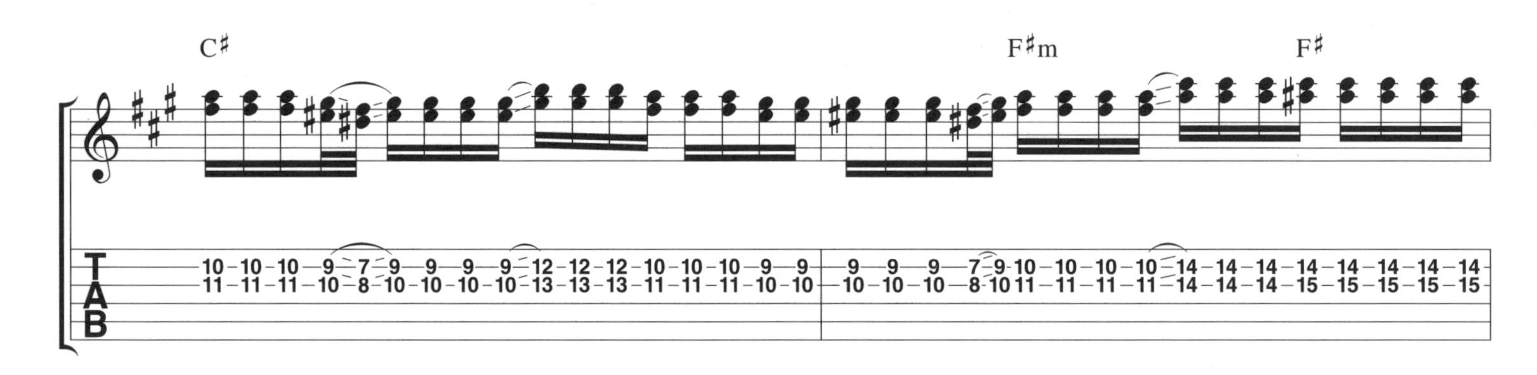

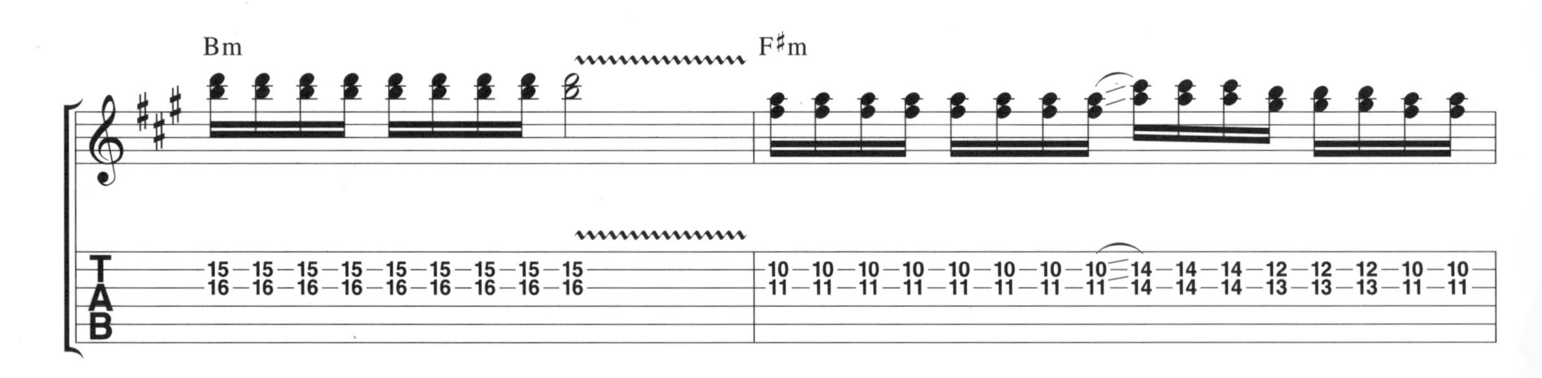

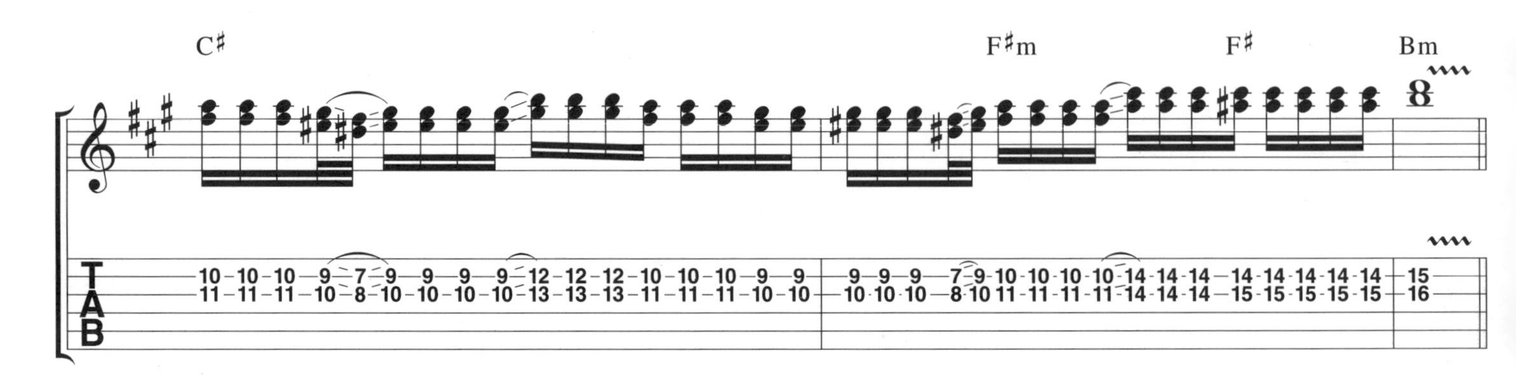

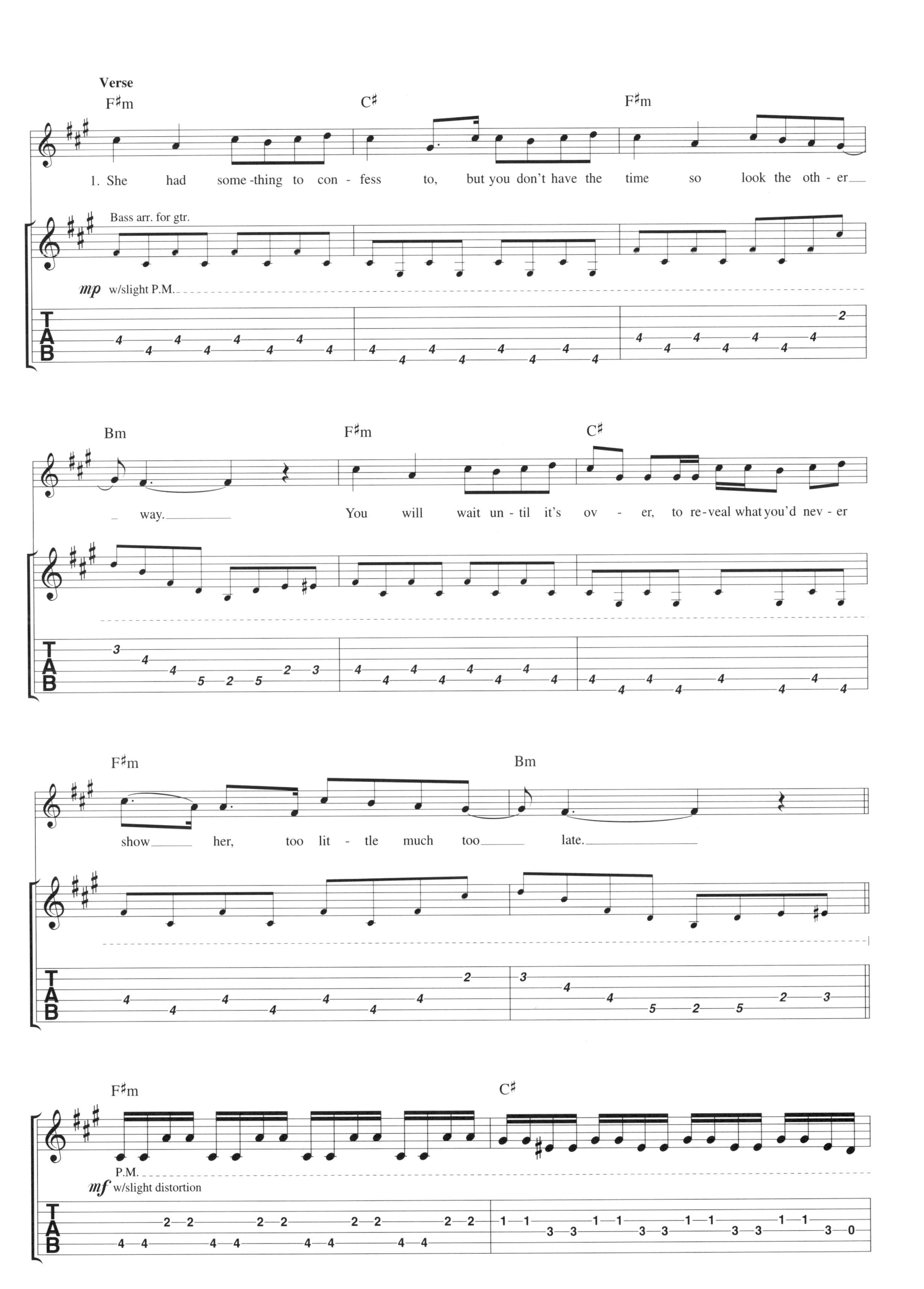
Verse
F♯m
C♯
F♯m
1. She had some-thing to con - fess to, but you don't have the time so look the oth - er
Bass arr. for gtr.
mp w/slight P.M.
Bm
F♯m
C♯
way.
You will wait un - til it's ov - er, to re-veal what you'd nev - er
F♯m
Bm
show her, too lit - tle much too late.
F♯m
C♯
P.M.
mf w/slight distortion

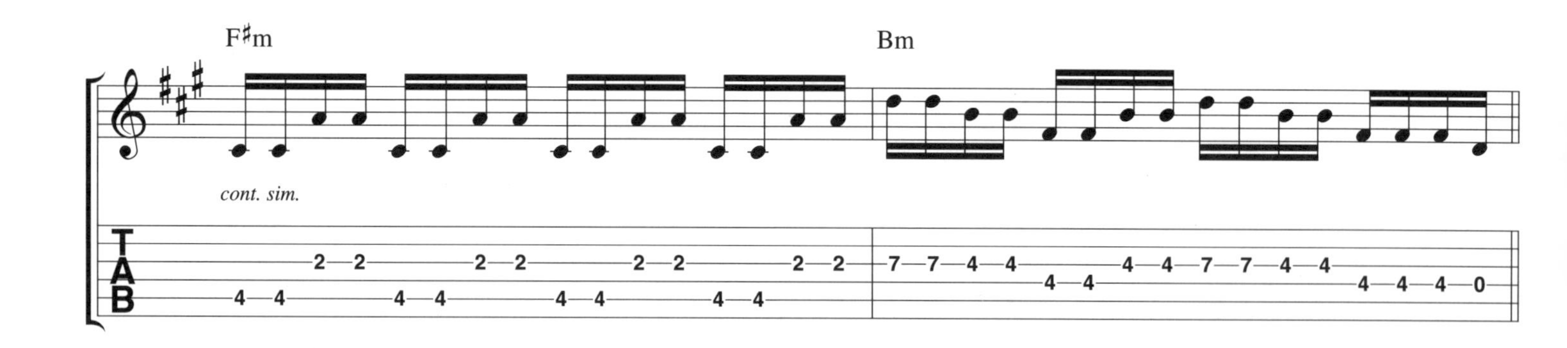
F♯m
Bm
cont. sim.
TAB

F♯m
C♯
2. Too long, try - ing to re - sist it, you've just gone and
TAB

F♯m
Bm
missed it. It's es - caped your world.
TAB

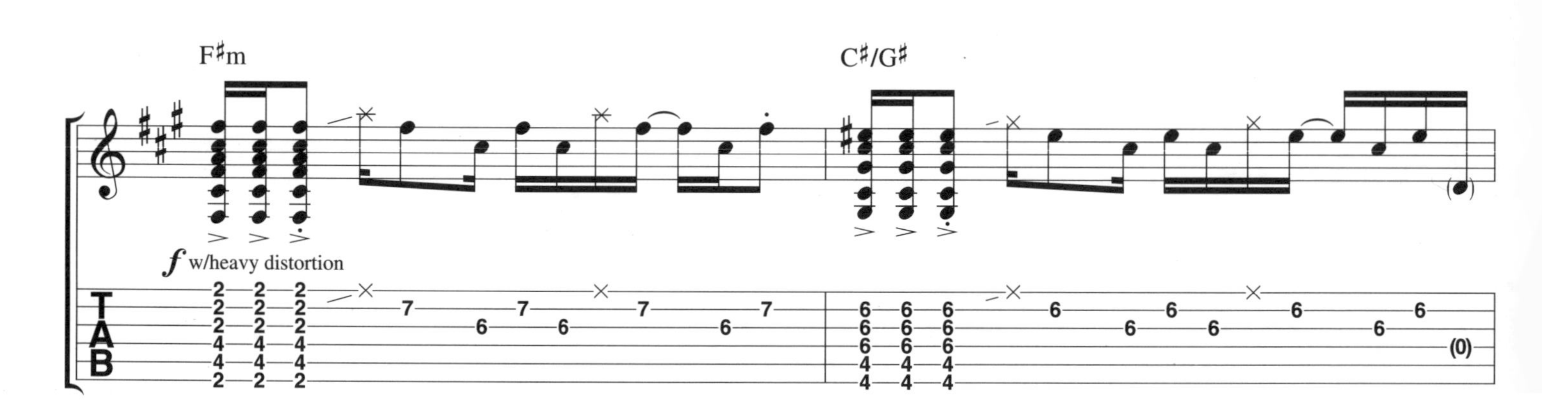
F♯m
C♯/G♯
f w/heavy distortion
TAB

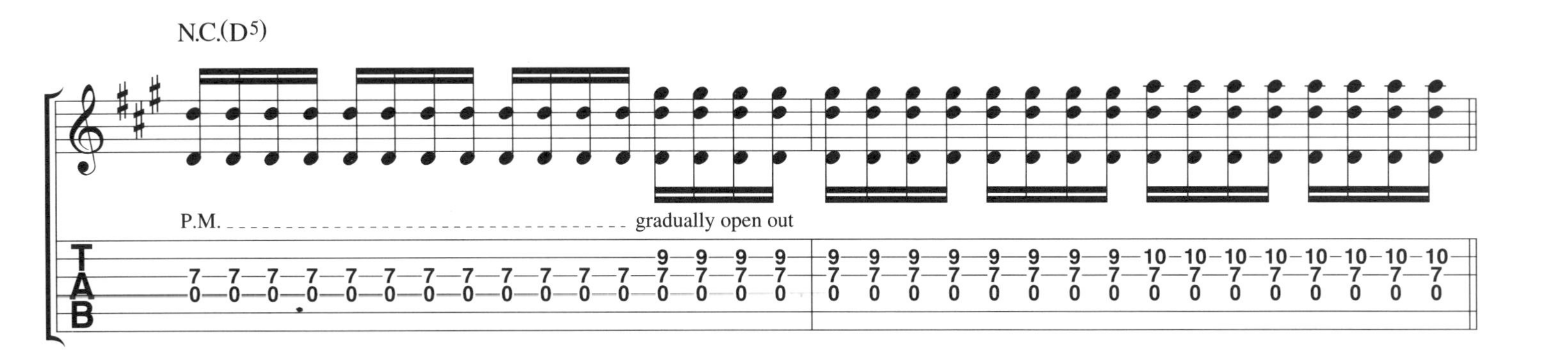
N.C.(D5)
P.M.
gradually open out

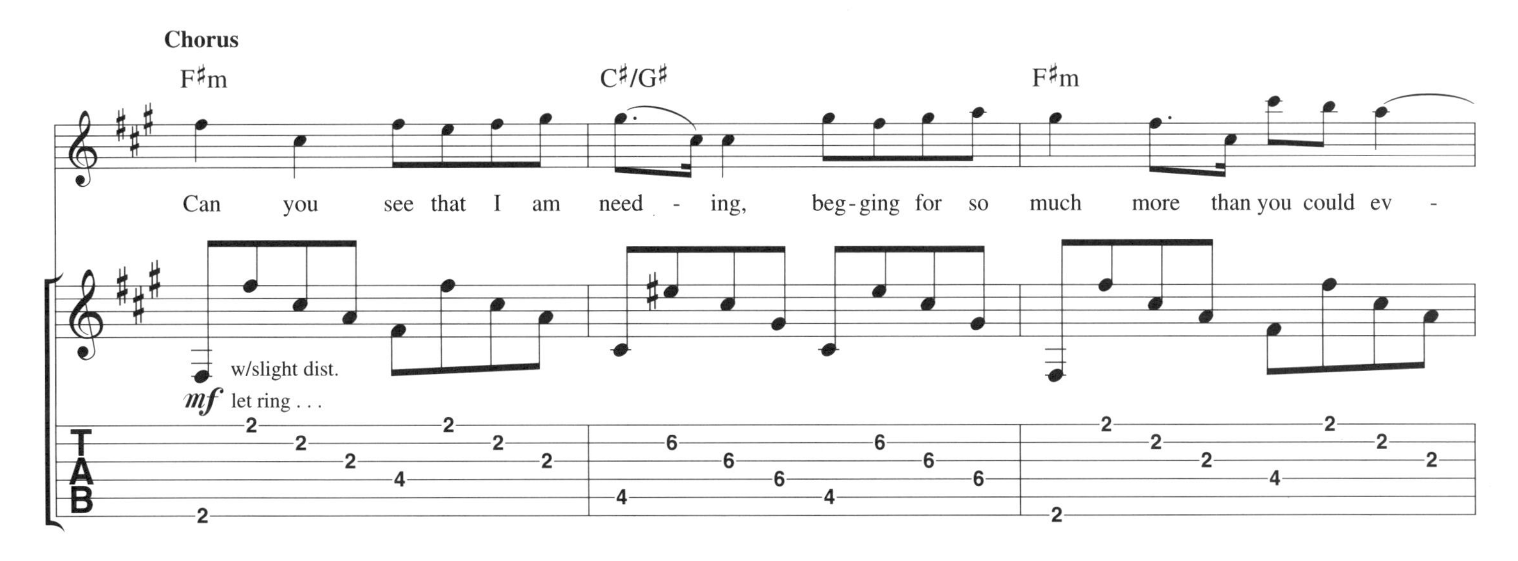
Chorus
F♯m
C♯/G♯
F♯m
Can you see that I am need - ing, beg-ging for so much more than you could ev -
w/slight dist.
mf let ring . . .

Bm
F♯m
C♯/G♯
- er give. And I don't want you to a - dore me, don't want you to ig -

F♯m
Bm
E
- nore me when it pleas - es you. Yeah and I'll do

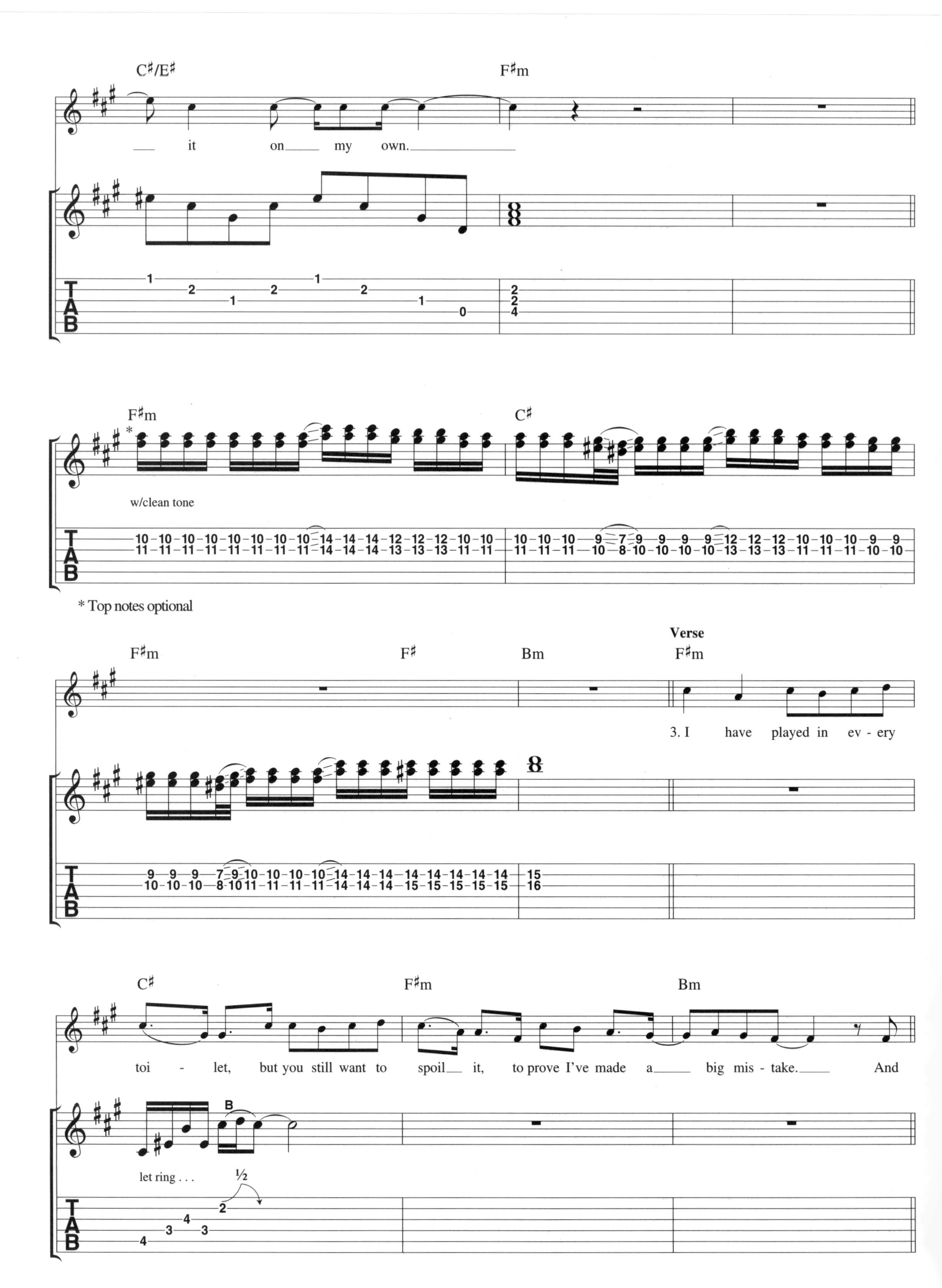
C♯/E♯
F♯m
it on my own.
F♯m
C♯
* Top notes optional
w/clean tone
F♯m
F♯
Bm
Verse
F♯m
3. I have played in ev - ery
C♯
F♯m
Bm
toi - let, but you still want to spoil it, to prove I've made a big mis - take. And
let ring . . .
B
½

F♯m
C♯
too long, try - ing to re - sist it, you've just gone and
P.M. . . .
TAB

F♯m
Bm
missed it. It's es - caped your world.
TAB

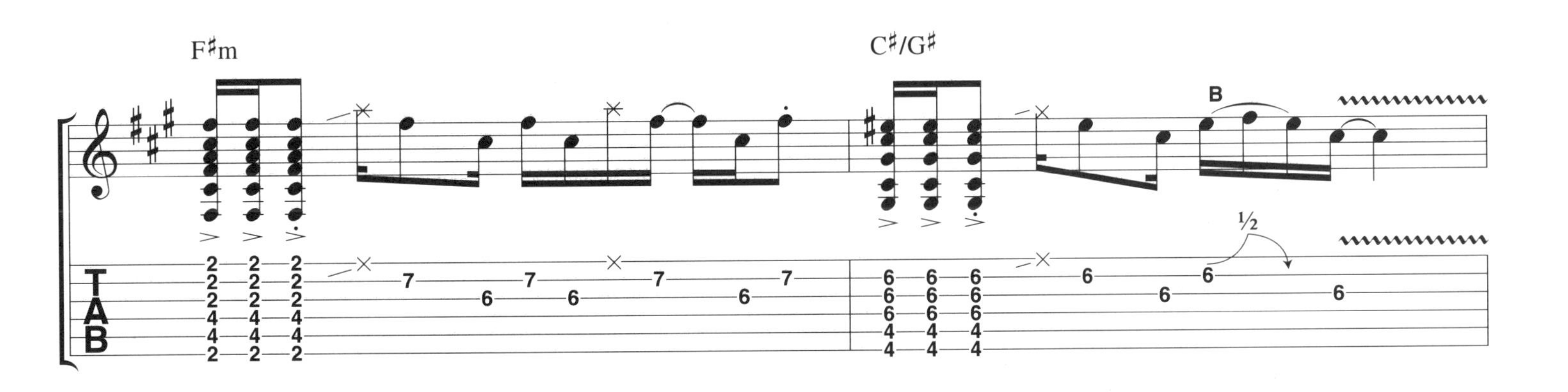
F♯m
C♯/G♯
B
½
TAB

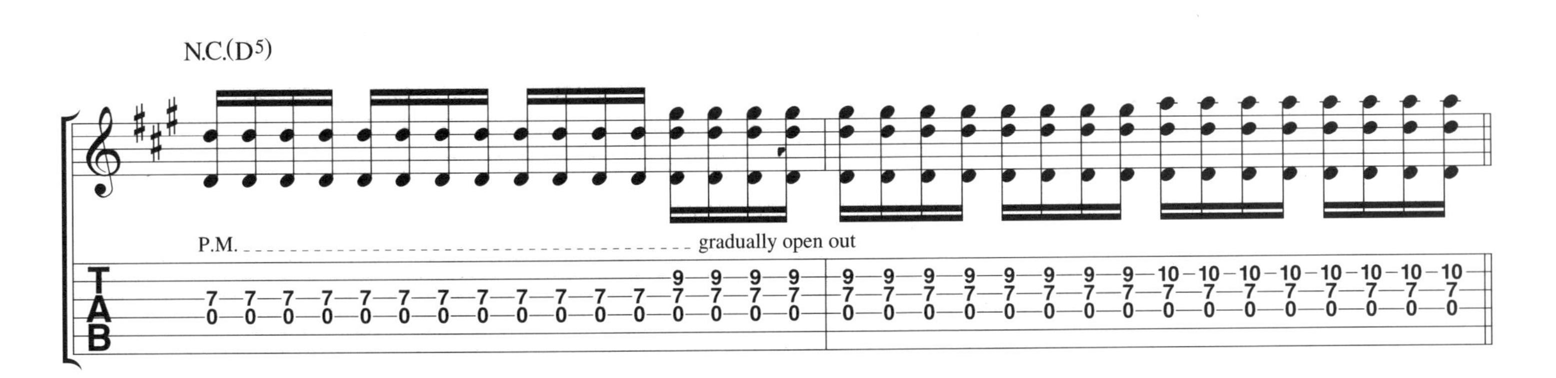
N.C.(D5)
P.M.
gradually open out
TAB

F♯m
C♯/G♯
F♯m
Can you see that I am need - ing, beg-ging for so much more than you could ev -
w/slight dist.
mf let ring . . .
Bm
F♯m
C♯/G♯
- er give.___ And I don't want you to a - dore___ me, don't want you to ig -
F♯m
Bm
- nore___ me when it pleas - es you. Yeah___
w/vocal fx
E
C♯/E♯
F♯m
F♯m/E
___ and I'll___ do___ it on___ my own.___
w/vocal fx

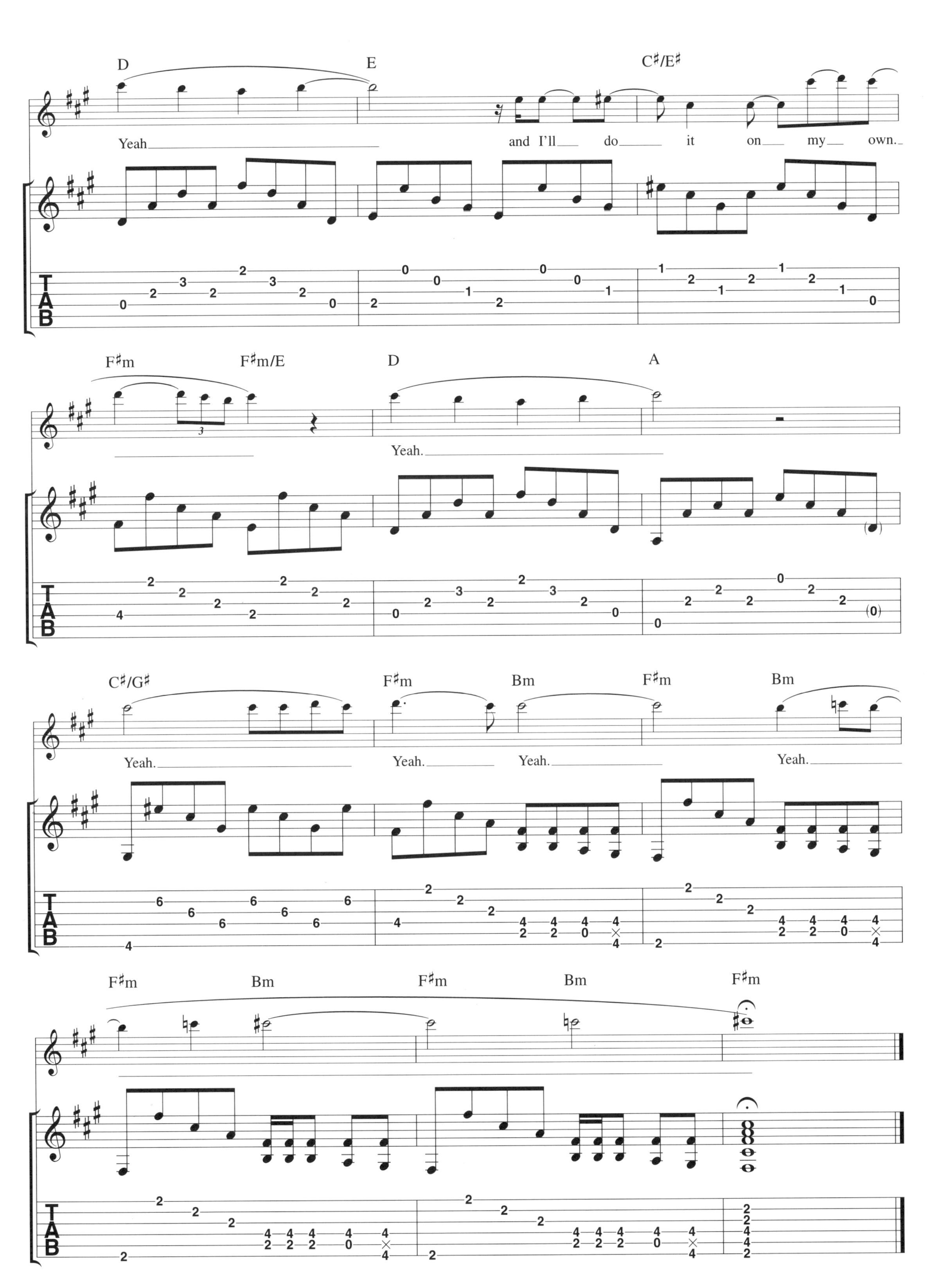
D
E
C♯/E♯
Yeah
and I'll
do
it
on
my
own.
F♯m
F♯m/E
D
A
Yeah.
C♯/G♯
F♯m
Bm
F♯m
Bm
Yeah.
Yeah.
Yeah.
Yeah.
F♯m
Bm
F♯m
Bm
F♯m

no one knows

Words & Music by Josh Homme, Nick Oliveri & Mark Lanegan

Tune gtr. 2 tones lower

⑥ = C ③ = E♭

⑤ = F ② = G

④ = B♭ ① = C

Intro (♫ = ♩♪ triplet)

2 bar count in:

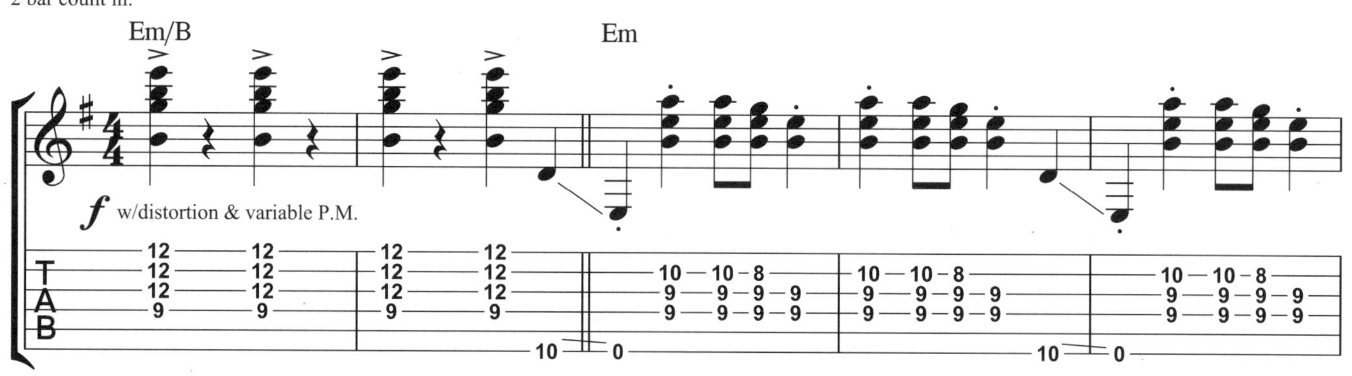

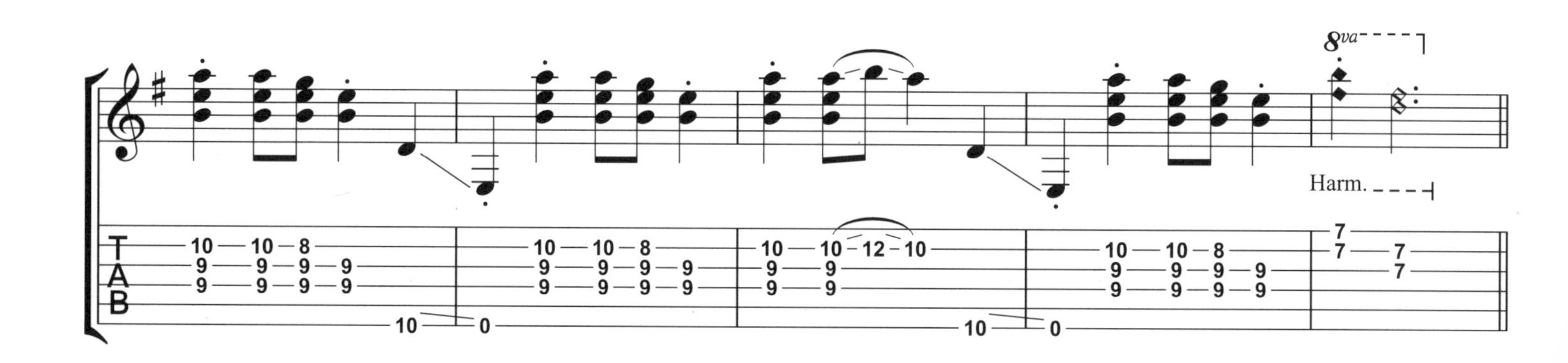

that and this, these and those.
how they stick in your throat.
Fig. 1
B7
D♯
No - one knows.
Taste like gold.
1.
Em
1/2
2.
Em
Oh, what you do

B7
D♯
to me,
no - one knows.
Em
I
full
Bridge
N.C.
B5
re - a - lise you're mine.
cont. sim.
In - deed a fool of
N.C.

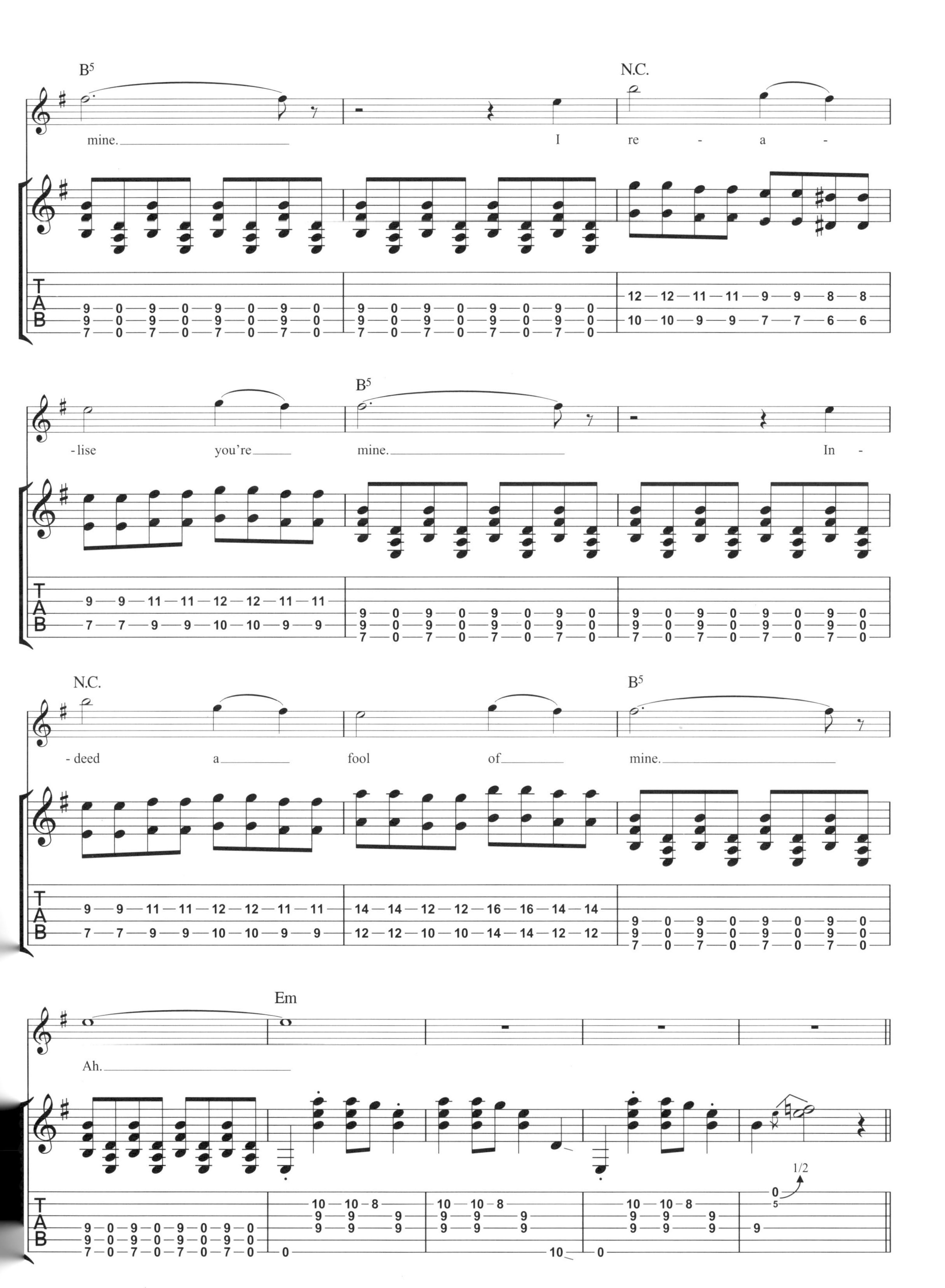
B5
N.C.
mine.
I re - a -
lise you're
mine.
In -
deed a fool of
mine.
Em
Ah.
1/2

Verse
Em
3. I jour - neyed through the des - ert
4. I drift a - long the o - cean,
of the mind with no hope.
dead life - boats in the sun.
2° w/Fig. 1
B7
D#
I found low.
And come un - done.
1. Em
8va
Harm.

2. Em
Plea - sant - ly cav -
B7
- ing in.
D♯
I come un - done.
Em
And I
full
Bridge
N.C.
re - a - lise
cont. sim.
you're
B5
mine.

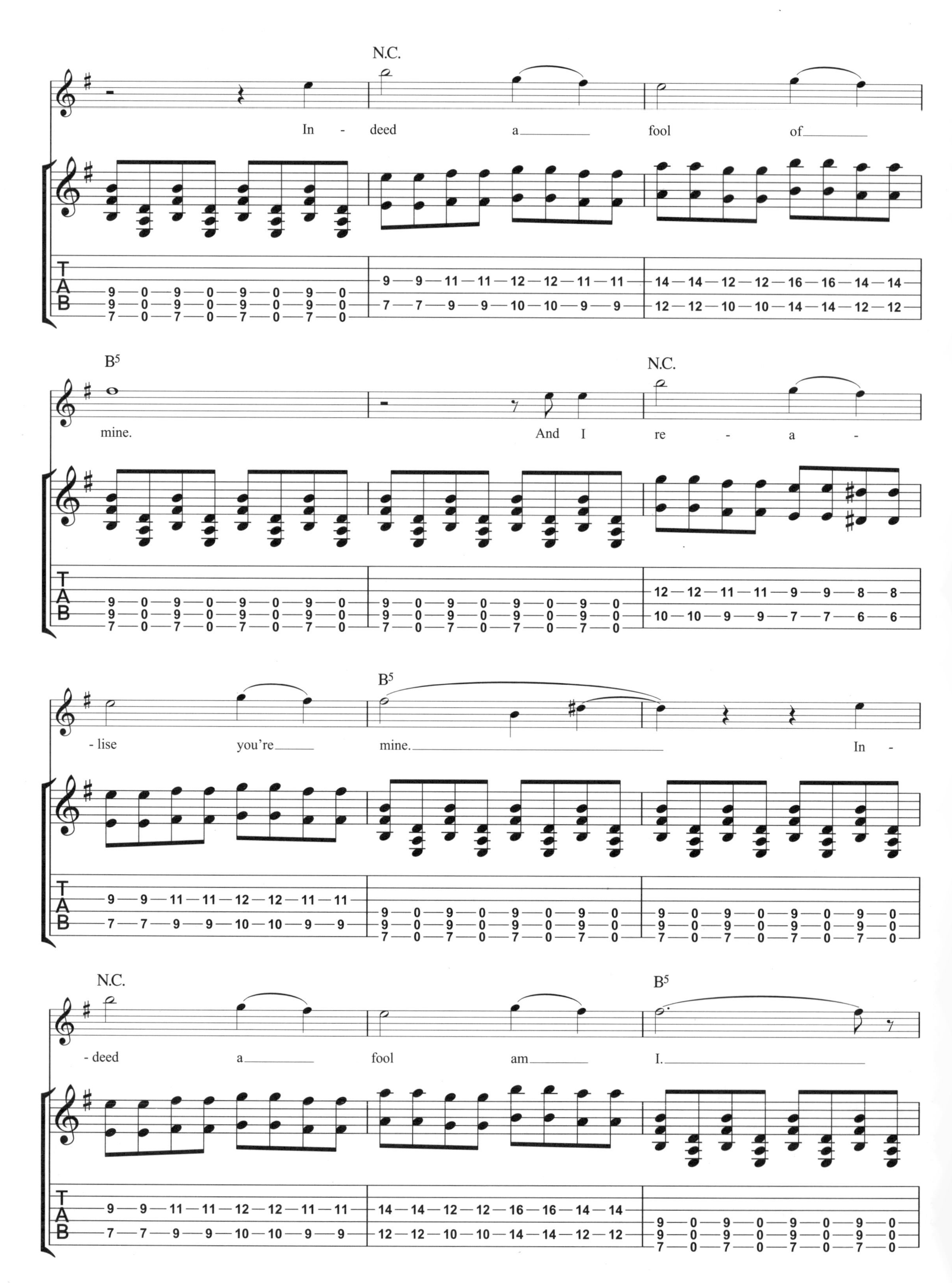
N.C.
In - deed a fool of
mine.
B5
N.C.
And I re - a -
- lise you're mine.
B5
In -
N.C.
- deed a fool am I.
B5

(Em)
Ah.
cont. sim.
B5 C5 D#5 B5 A5 B5
E5
Bass solo
Solo
(E5)
ff
let ring . . .
(A5)/Ebass
(B5)/Ebass
(E5)

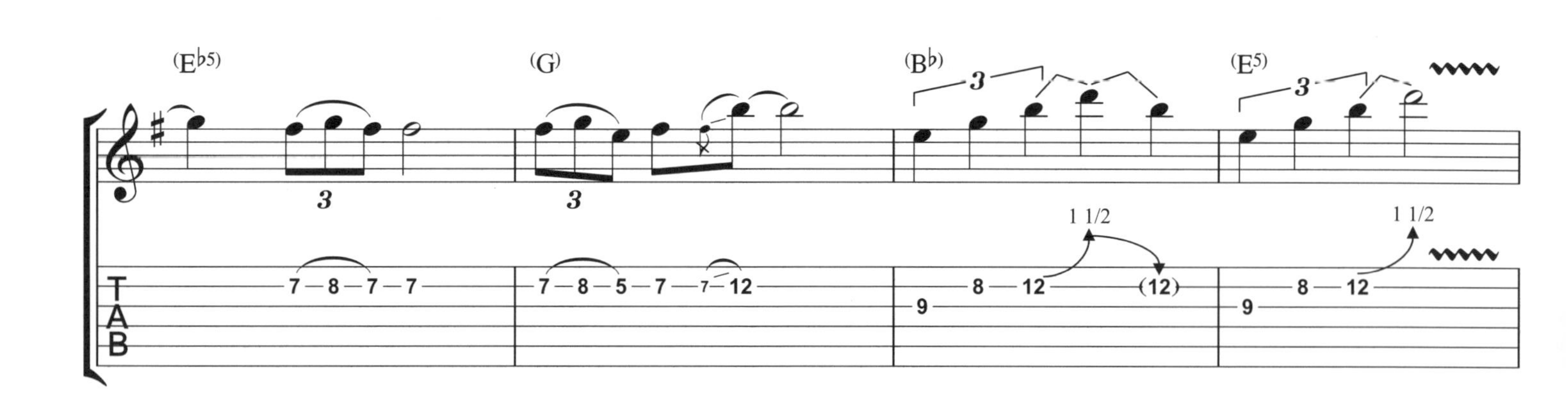
(E♭5)
(G)
(B♭)
(E5)
1 1/2
1 1/2

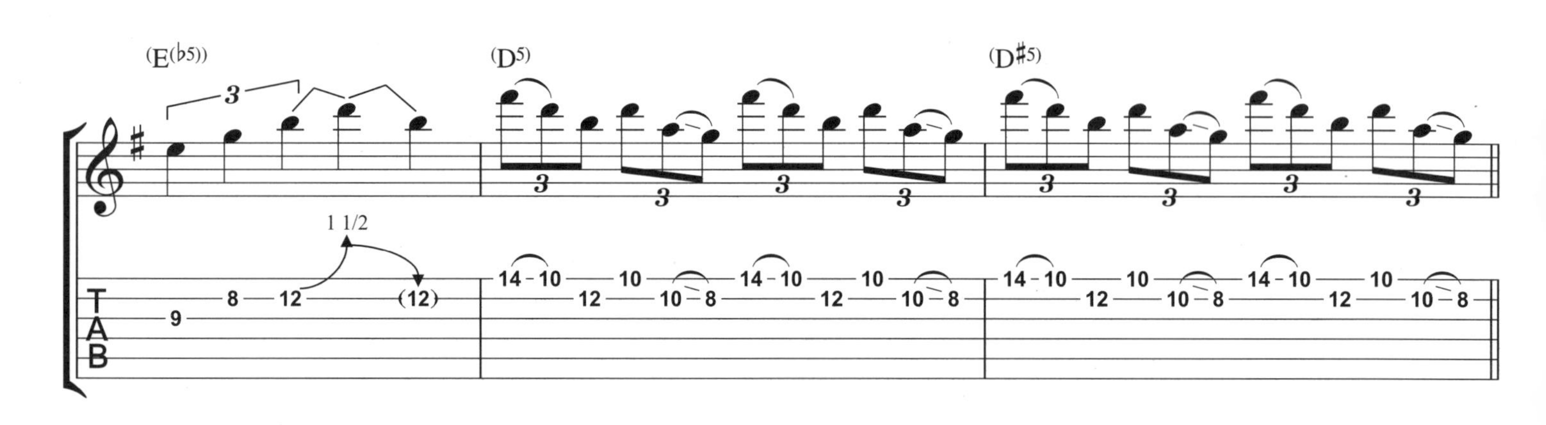
(E(♭5))
(D5)
(D♯5)
1 1/2

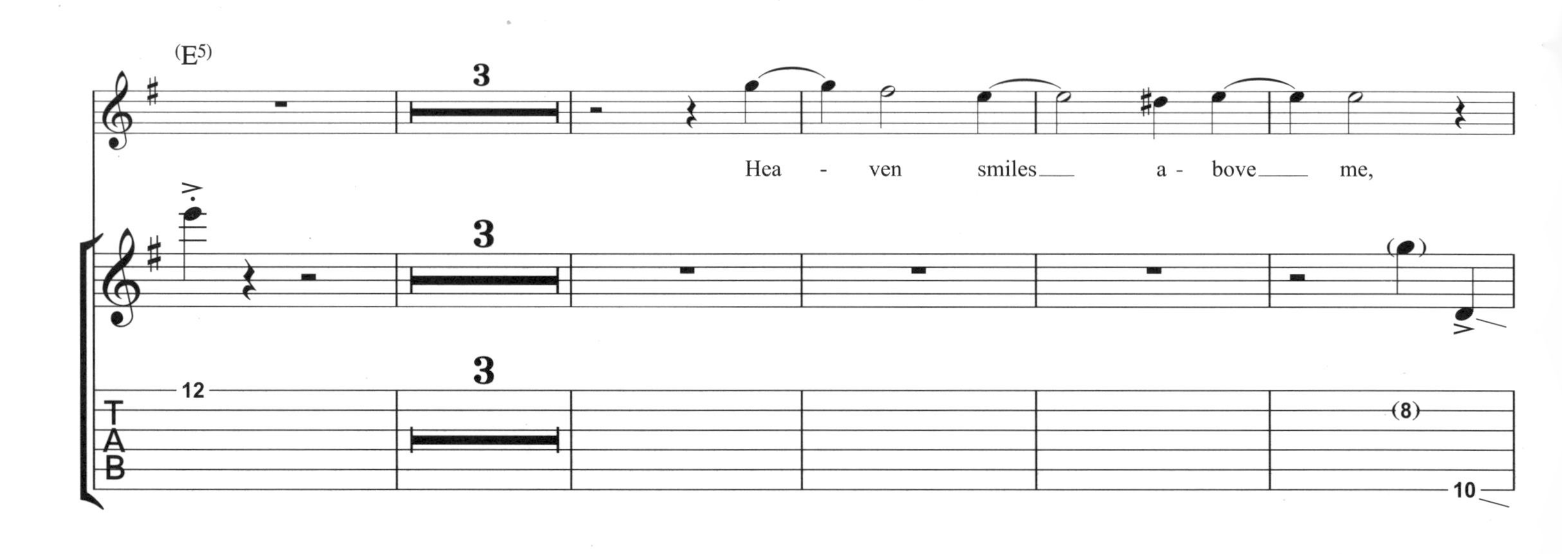
(E5)
Hea - ven smiles a - bove me,

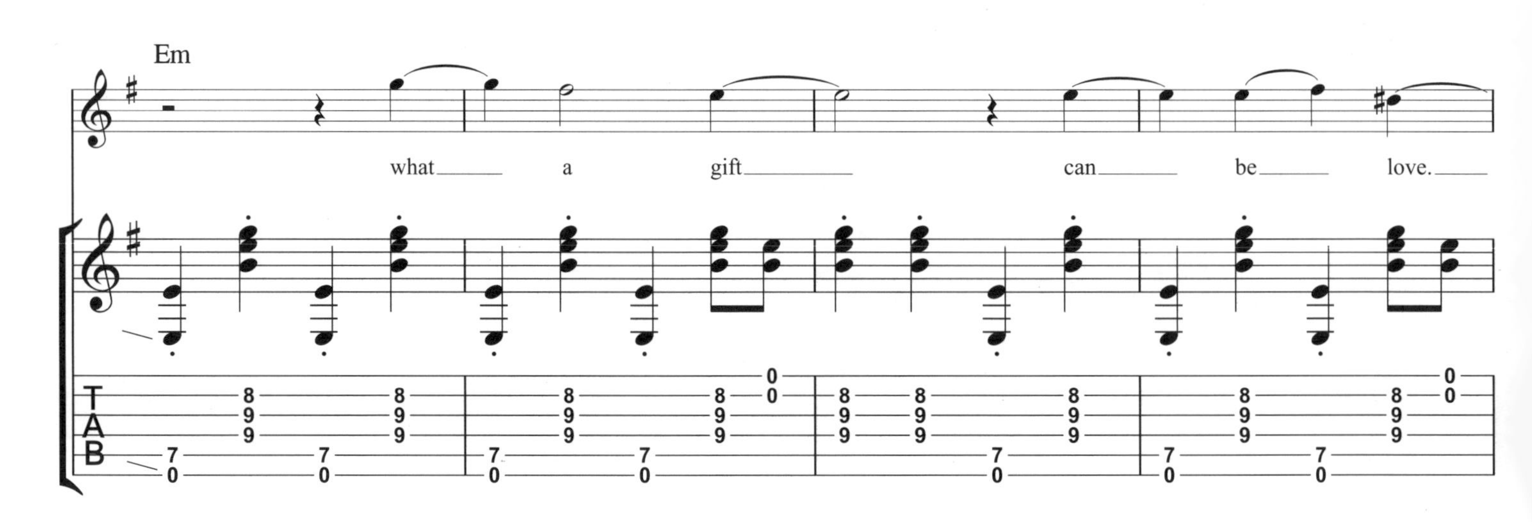
Em
what a gift can be love.

B7
D♯
But no - one knows.
(A) gift that you give
8va
Harm.
B
D♯
to me.
No -
light P.M.
open out
Em
- one knows.

paranoid

Words & Music by Ozzy Osbourne, Tony Iommi, Terry 'Geezer' Butler & Bill Ward

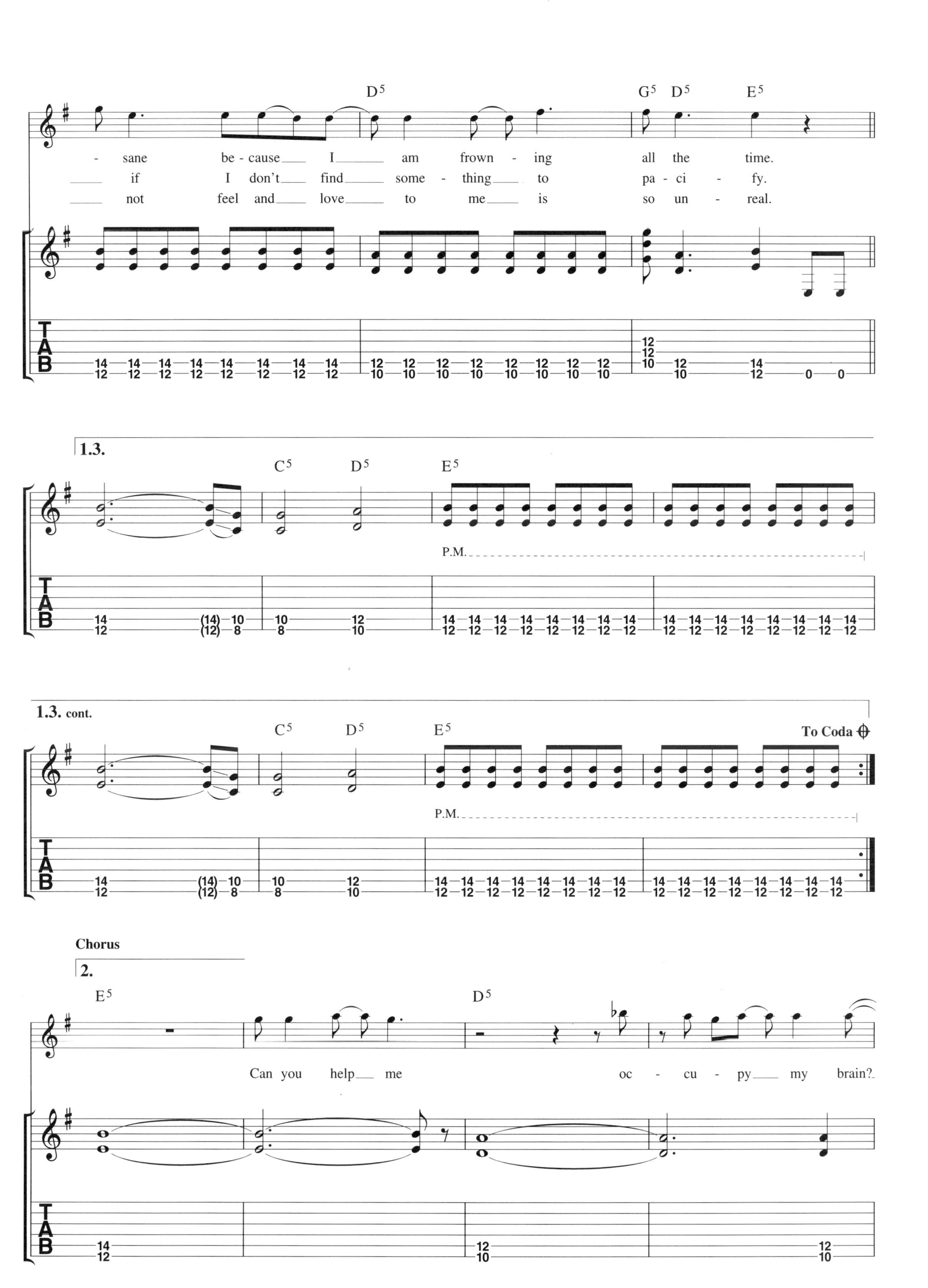
D5
G5 D5 E5
- sane be - cause I am frown - ing all the time.
if I don't find some - thing to pa - ci - fy.
not feel and love to me is so un - real.
1.3.
C5 D5 E5
P.M.
1.3. cont.
C5 D5 E5
To Coda
P.M.
Chorus
2.
E5 D5
Can you help me oc - cu - py my brain?

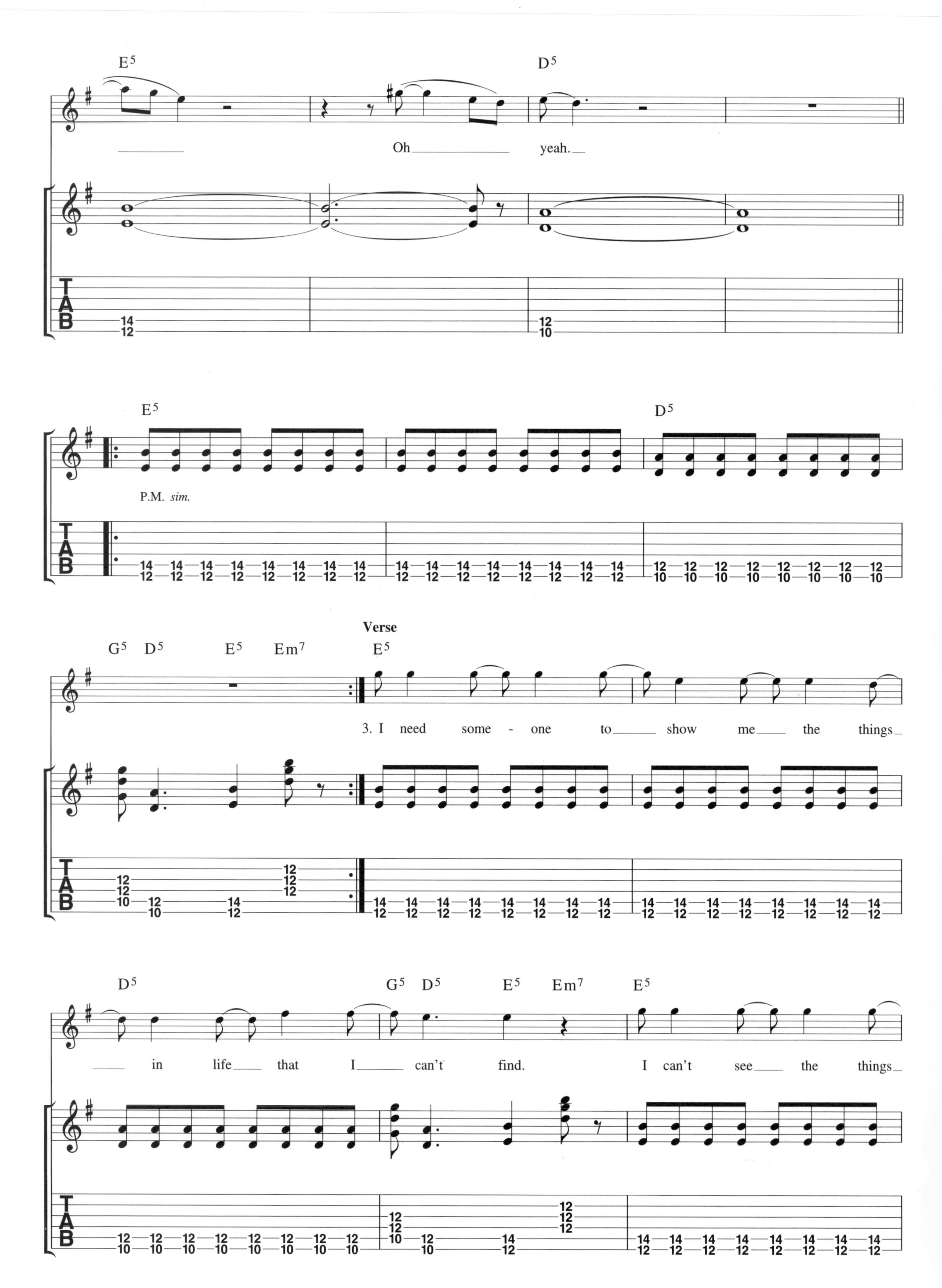
E5
D5
Oh yeah.
E5
D5
P.M. sim.
G5 D5 E5 Em7
Verse
E5
3. I need some - one to show me the things
D5
G5 D5 E5 Em7 E5
in life that I can't find. I can't see the things

D5
G5 D5 E5 Em7
that make true hap - pi - ness, I must be blind.
TAB

Solo
E5
Pre
D5
w/distortion & ring mod fx
1½
TAB

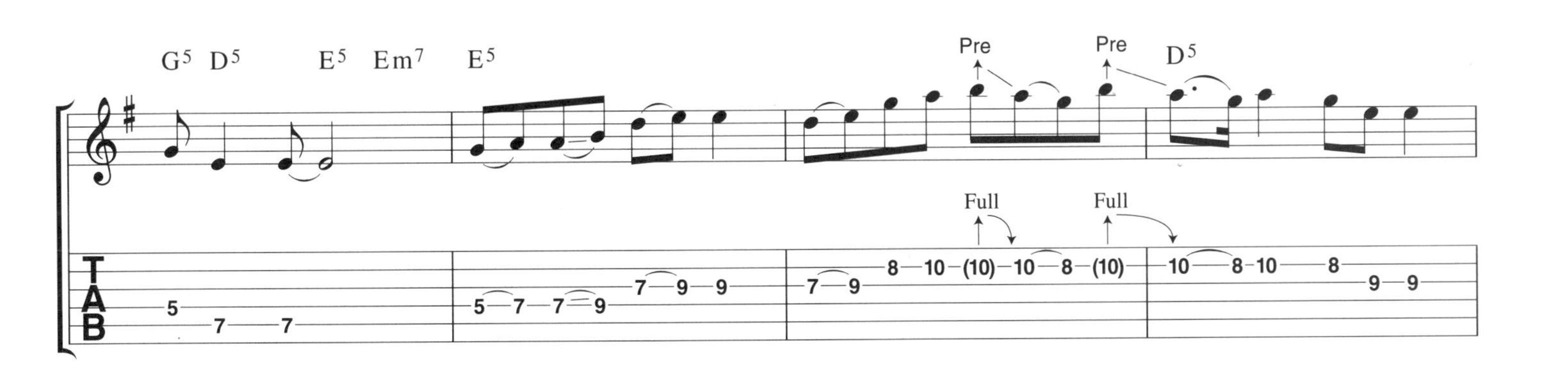
G5 D5 E5 Em7 E5
Pre
Pre
D5
Full
Full
TAB

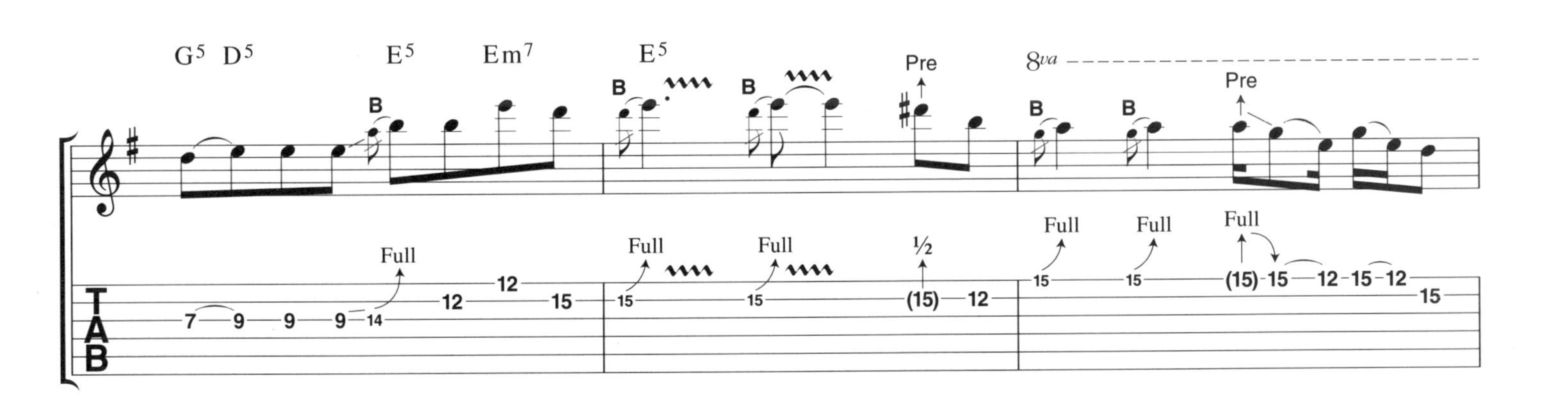
G5 D5 E5 Em7 E5
B
Pre
8va
Full
½
Full
TAB

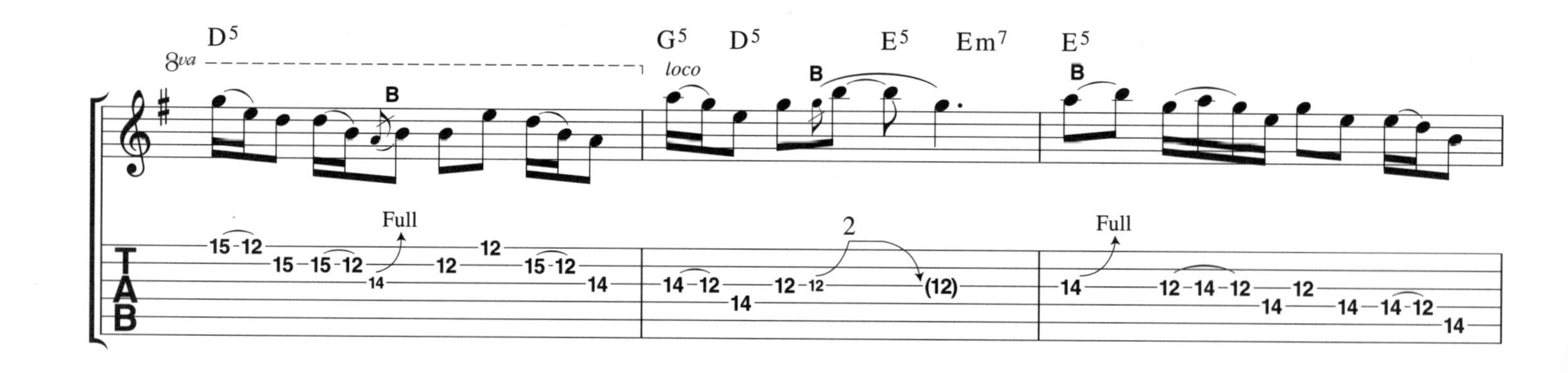
D5
8va
G5 D5
loco
E5 Em7 E5
B
Full
2
TAB

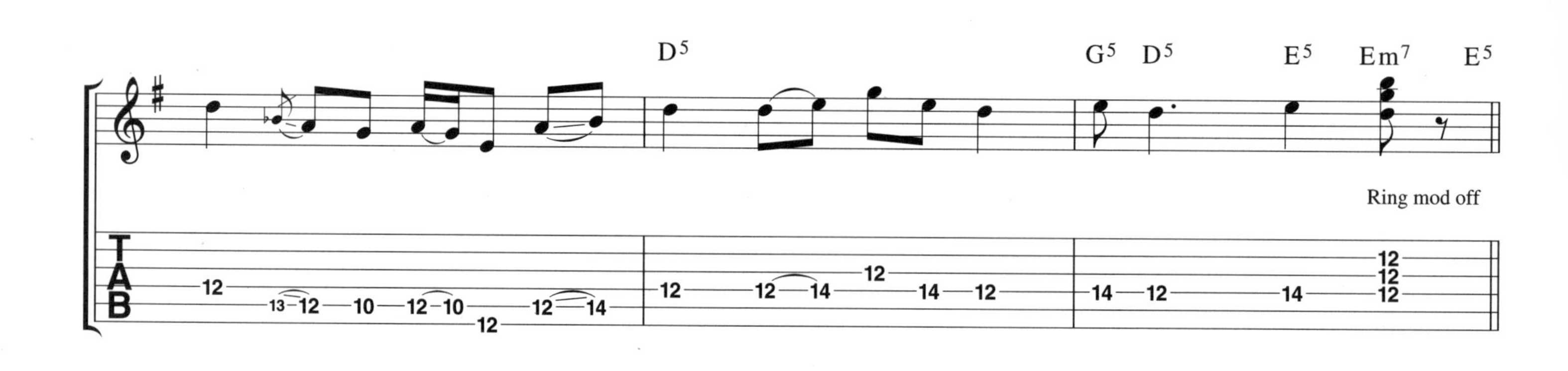
D5
G5 D5
E5 Em7 E5
Ring mod off
TAB

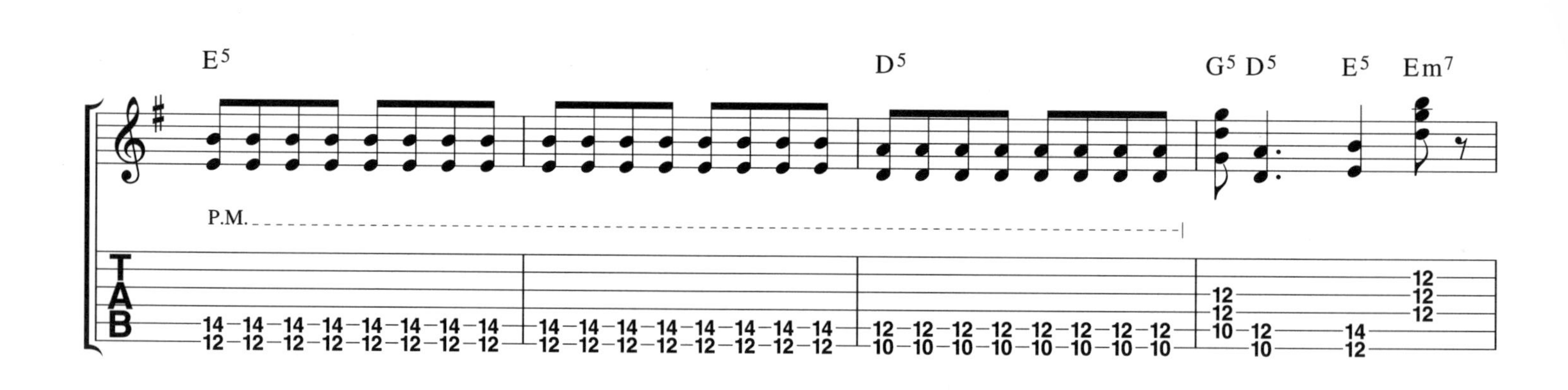
E5
D5
G5 D5
E5 Em7
P.M.
TAB

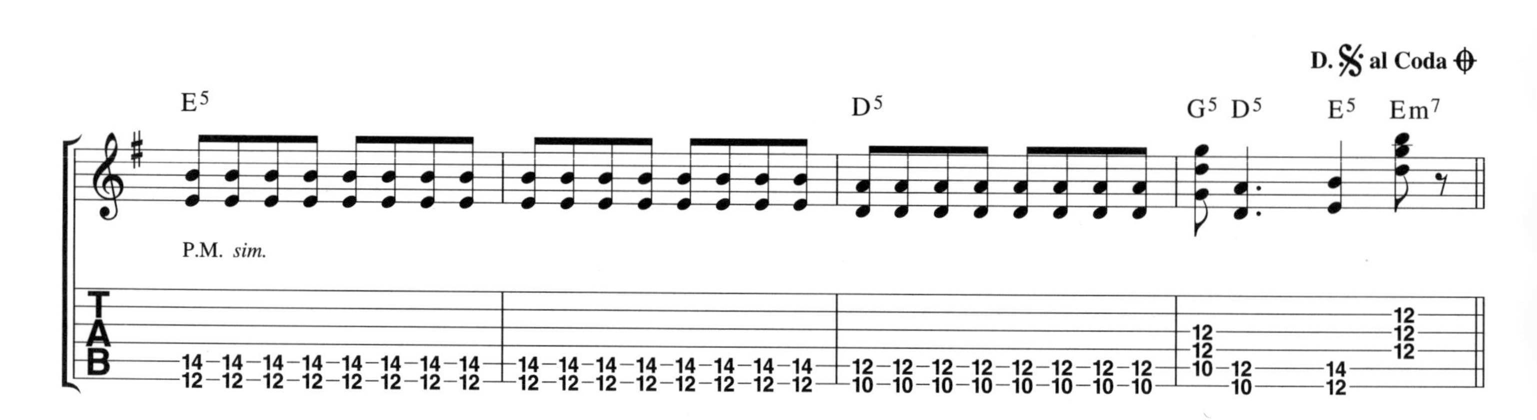
D.S. al Coda
E5
D5
G5 D5
E5 Em7
P.M. sim.
TAB

Coda
E5
D5
And so as you hear these words, tell - ing you now of
G5 D5
E5
Em7
my state.
I tell you to en - joy life I
wish I could but it's too late.
1.
2.
B
½

party hard

Words & Music by Andrew W.K.

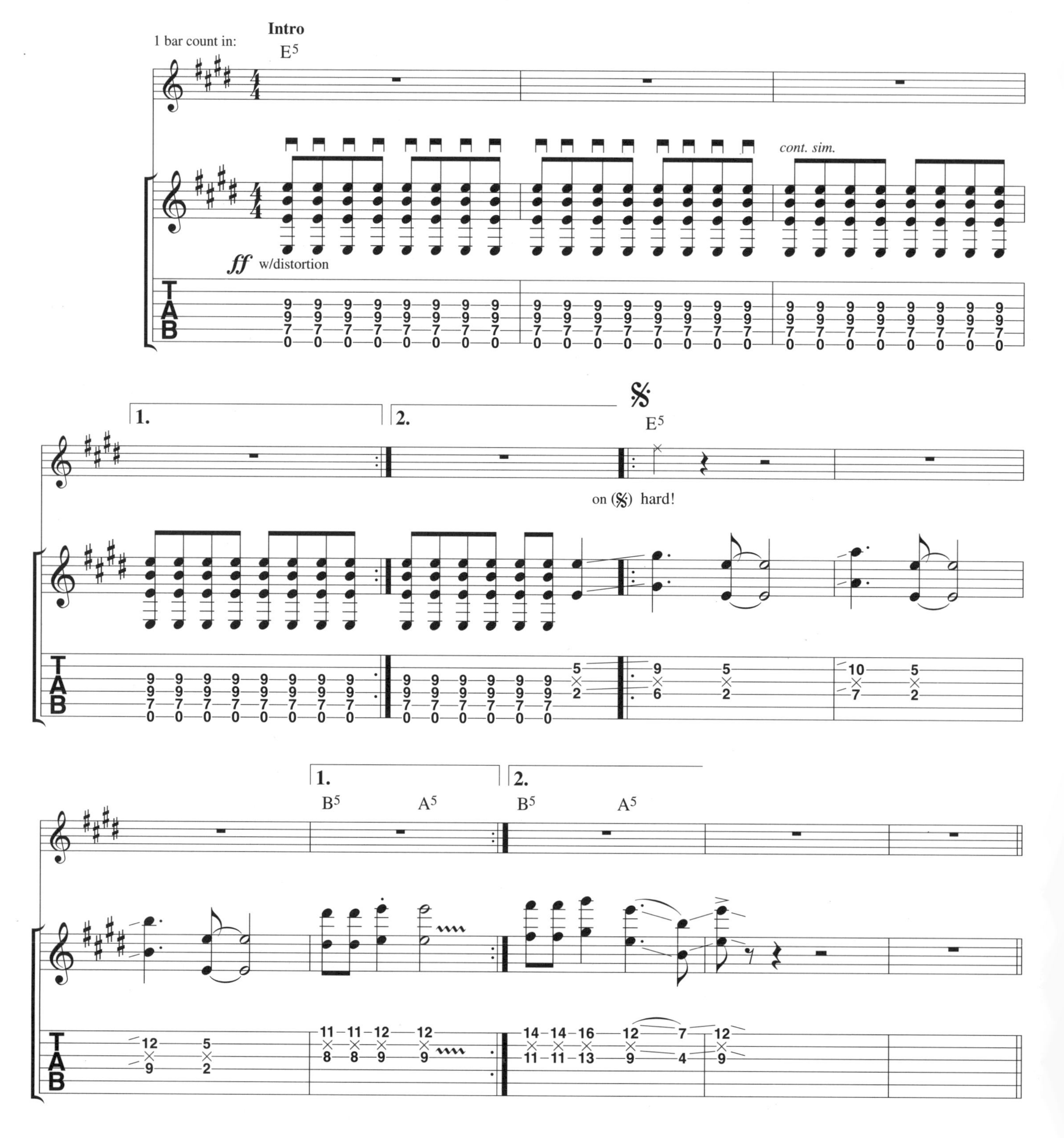

E B5 A5 E/G♯ F♯5 C♯5
1.
B5
2.
B5 E5
Verse
E5 B5
on (𝄋) Al - right!
1. You, you
2. You, you
A5 E/G♯ F♯5 C♯5 B5
work all night and when you're work - in' you feel al - right.
fight that fight (That's right!) and when you fight you feel al - right.
And
E5 B5 A5 E/G♯ F♯5 C♯5
when, when things start feel - in' al - right (Al - right) and ev - 'ry -
T
A
B

B5
N.C. (E5)
- thing is al - right. 'Cause we will nev - er list - en to your rules. No!
We will nev - er do___ what oth - ers do. No! Know what we want___ if we get___
___ it from you. Do what we like and we like what we do. So
(1° only)
Chorus
E
A5
E
let's get a part - y go - in'. (Let's get a part - y go - in'!) Now it's time to part - y if we

A5 D5 A5 E A5
party hard. (Party hard!) Let's get a party goin'. (Let's get a party goin'!)
E F♯5 B5 E5
When it's time to party, we will always party hard.
Party
E A5 E A5 E A5
hard! Party hard! Party hard! Party hard! Party hard! Party hard! Party
B5 E5 D♯5 E5 E A5 E A5
hard! Party hard! Party hard! Party hard! Party hard! Party hard! Party

E A5 F♯5 B5 E5 D♯5 E5
D. 𝄋 al Fine
hard! Part - y hard! Part - y part - y part - y hard! Part - y
(1° only)
E A5 E A5 E A5
hard! Part - y hard! Part - y hard! Part - y hard! Part - y hard! Part - y hard! Part - y
B5 E5 D♯5 E5 E A5 E A5
hard! Part - y hard! Part - y hard! Part - y hard! Part - y hard! Part - y hard! Part - y
E A5 F♯5 B5 E5 D♯5 E5
hard! Part - y hard! Part - y part - y part - y hard! Part - y hard.
TAB

the rock show

Words & Music by Mark Hoppus, Thomas Delonge & Travis Barker

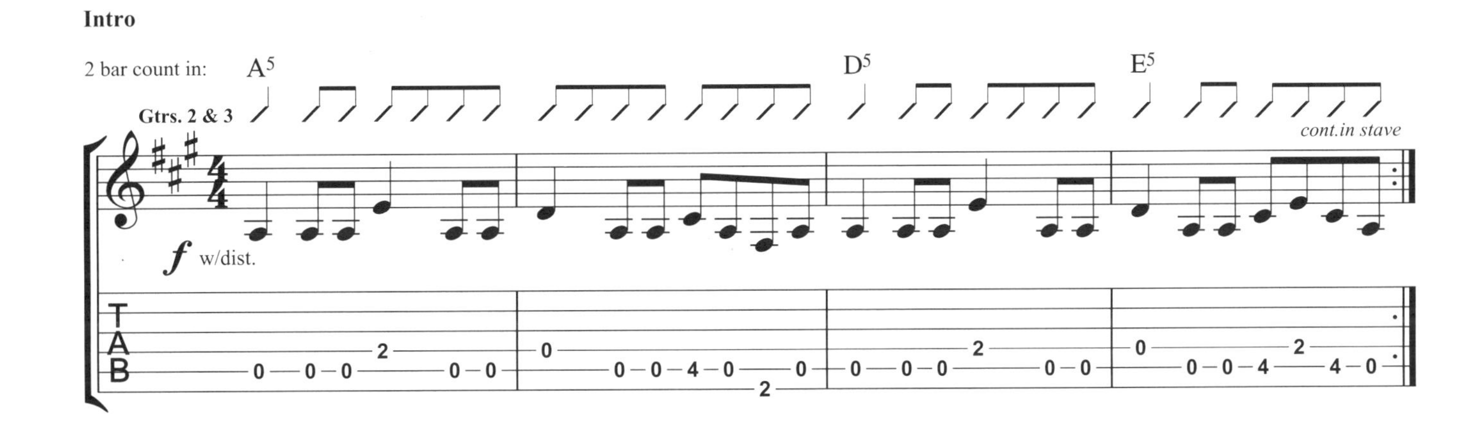

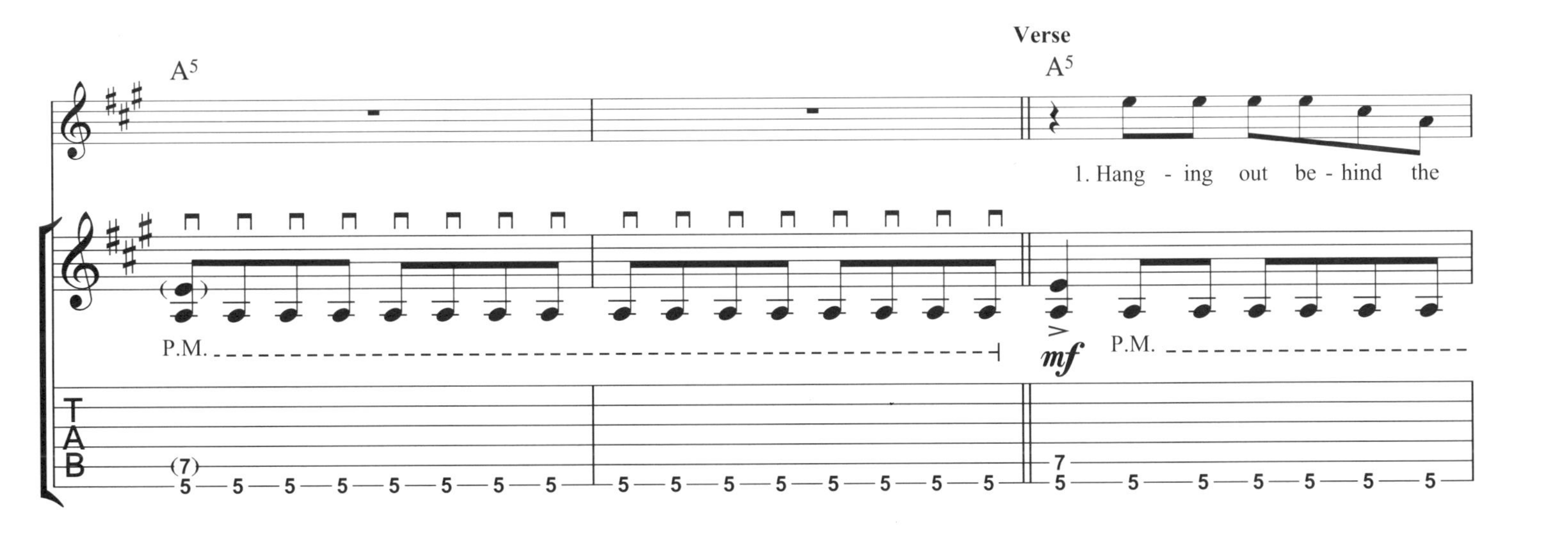

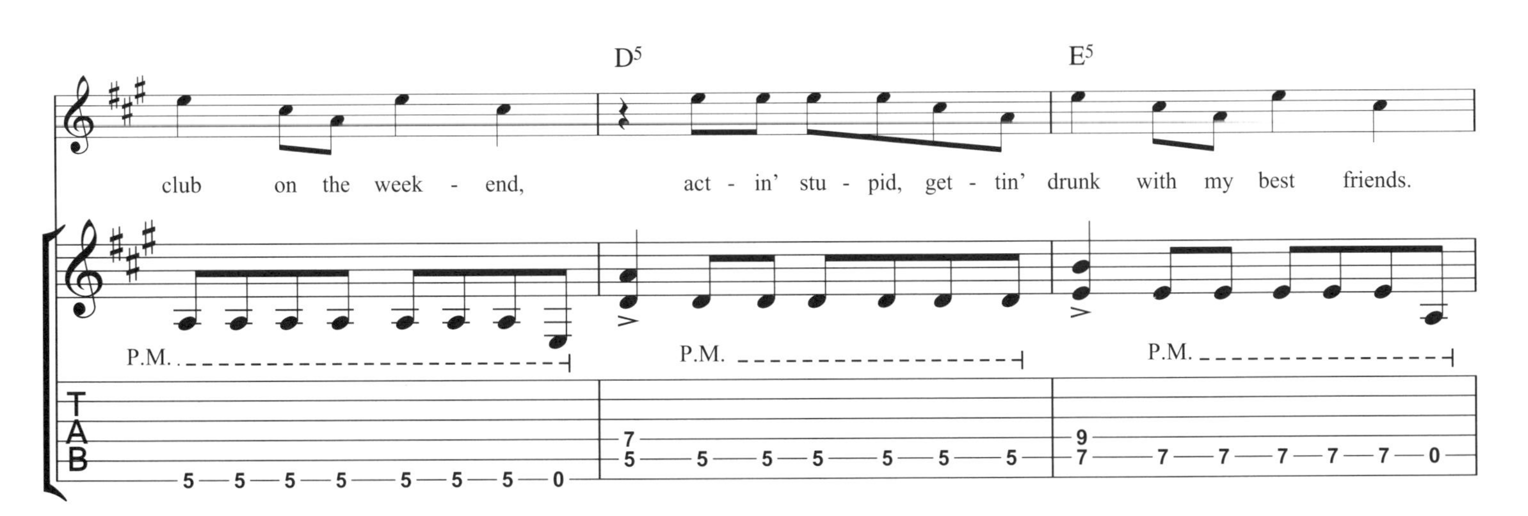

A5
D5
I could-n't wait for the sum-mer and the Warped Tour.
I re-mem-ber it's the
P.M.
E5
A5
D5
first time that I saw her there.
(1° only)
f
E5
A5
D5
E5
Verse
A5
2. She's get-tin' kicked out of school 'cause she's fail-ing.
3. When we said we were gon-na move to Veg-as
mf
1° let ring

D5
E5
A5
I'm kind - a ner - vous 'cause I think all her friends hate me, She's the one, she'll al -
I re - mem - ber the look her moth - er gave us. Sev - en - teen with - out a
2°
P.M.
1° tacet
- ways be there. She took my hand and that made it I swear, be - cause I
pur - pose or di - rec - tion we don't owe an - y - one a fuck - in' ex - plan - a - tion.
Chorus
F♯5
D5*
1. & 𝄋 fell
2. Fell
in love with the girl at the rock show. She said "What?" And I
told her that I did - n't know. She's so cool, I'm gon - na sneak in through her win - dow.
T
A
B

37
E5
D5
E5
Ev - 'ry - thing's bet - ter when she's a - round. I can't wait 'til her par - ents go
P.M.
T
A
B
To Coda
40
D5
E5
D5
D5/C
out of town. I fell in love with the girl at the rock show.
P.M.
Bridge
43
F#m
Dmaj7
Black and white pic - ture of her on my wall. I wait - ed
mf
w/clean tone & slight chorus
let ring . . .
47
A
A/Ebass
for her call. She al - ways kept me wait - ing.

F♯m
Gtr. 2
Dmaj7
cont. sim.
And if I ev - er get an - oth - er chance, I'd still ask
T
A
B

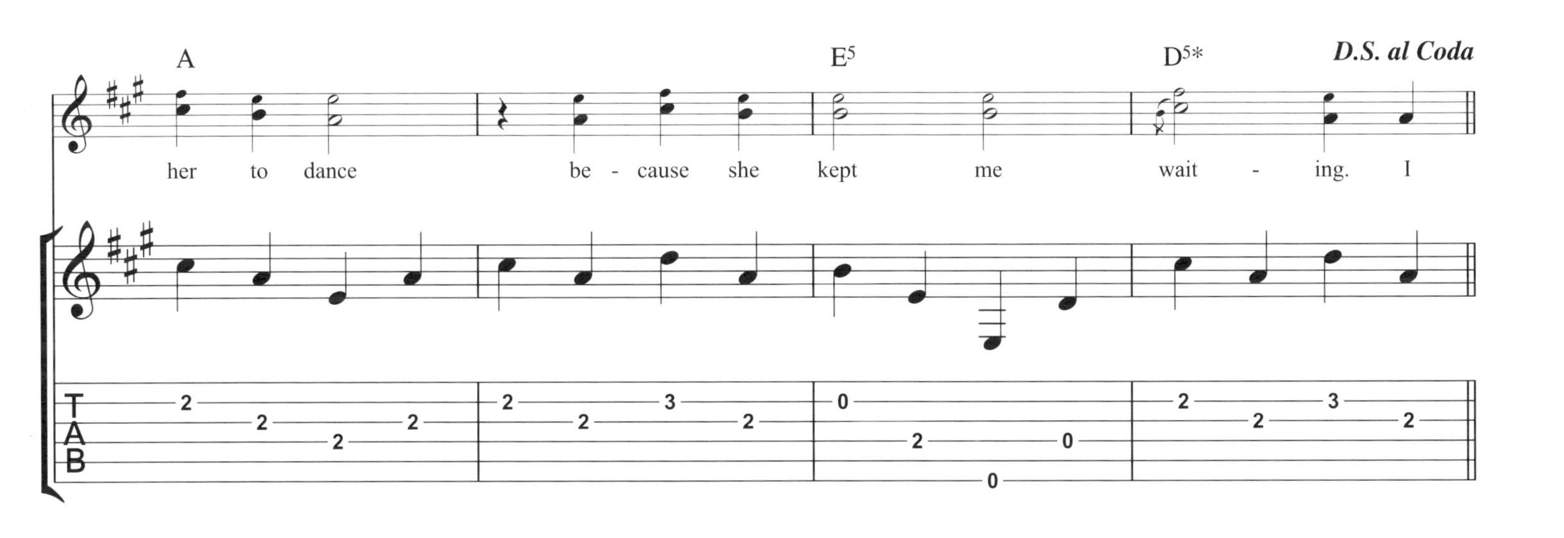
A
E5
D5*
D.S. al Coda
her to dance be - cause she kept me wait - ing. I
T
A
B

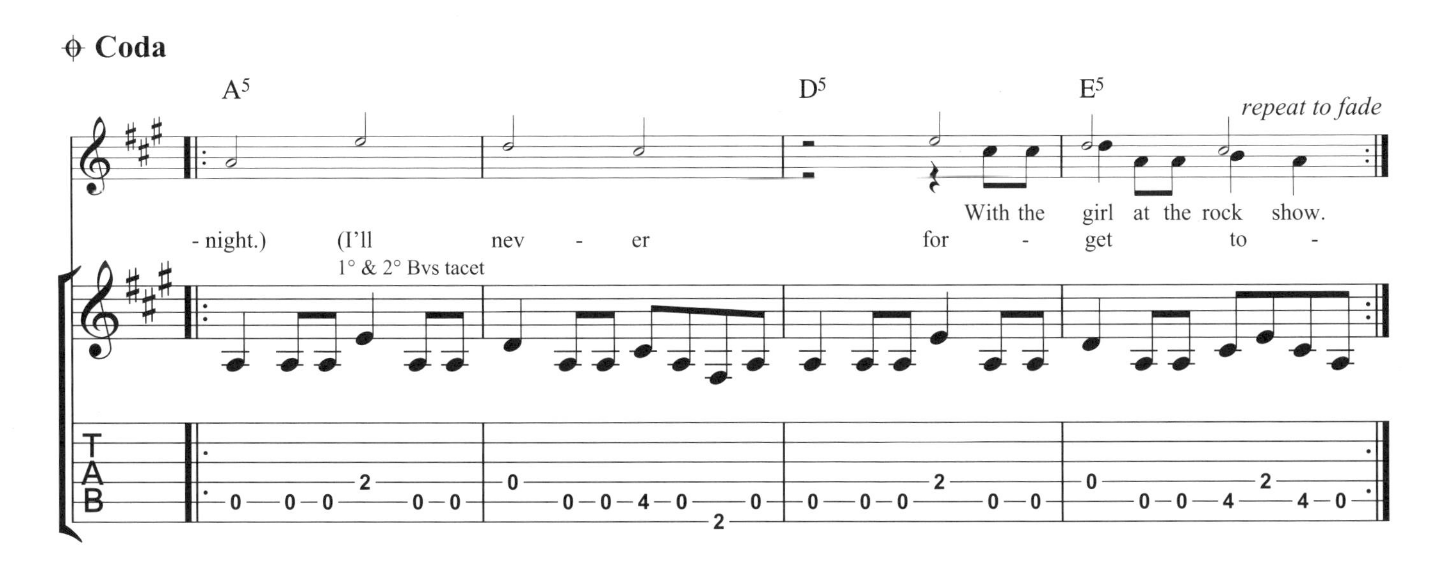
Coda
A5
D5
E5
repeat to fade
With the girl at the rock show.
- night.) (I'll nev - er for - get to -
1° & 2° Bvs tacet
T
A
B

take a look around

Music by Lalo Schifrin
Words by Fred Durst

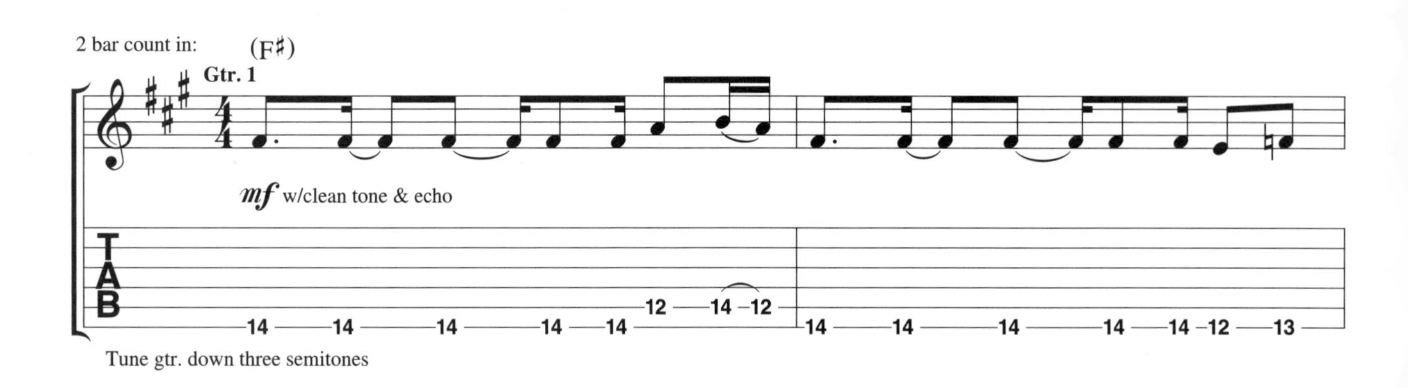

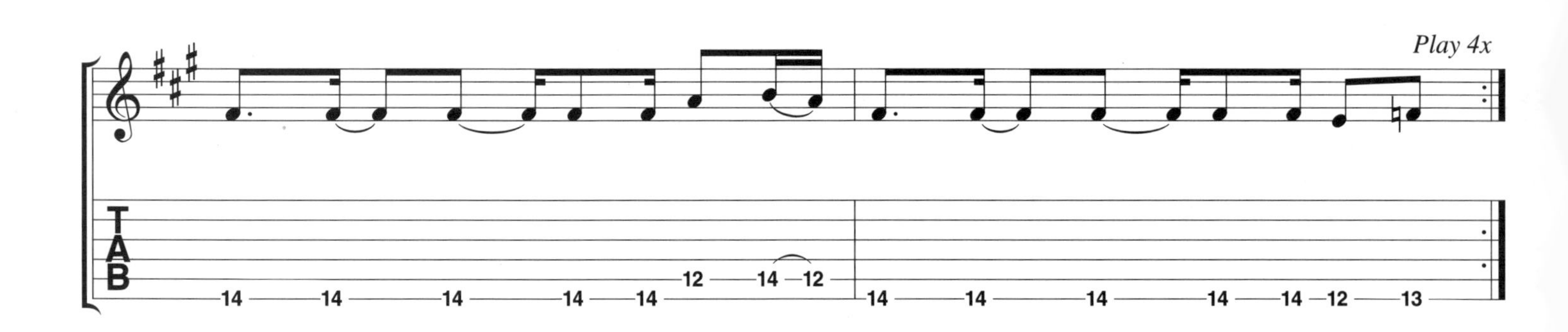

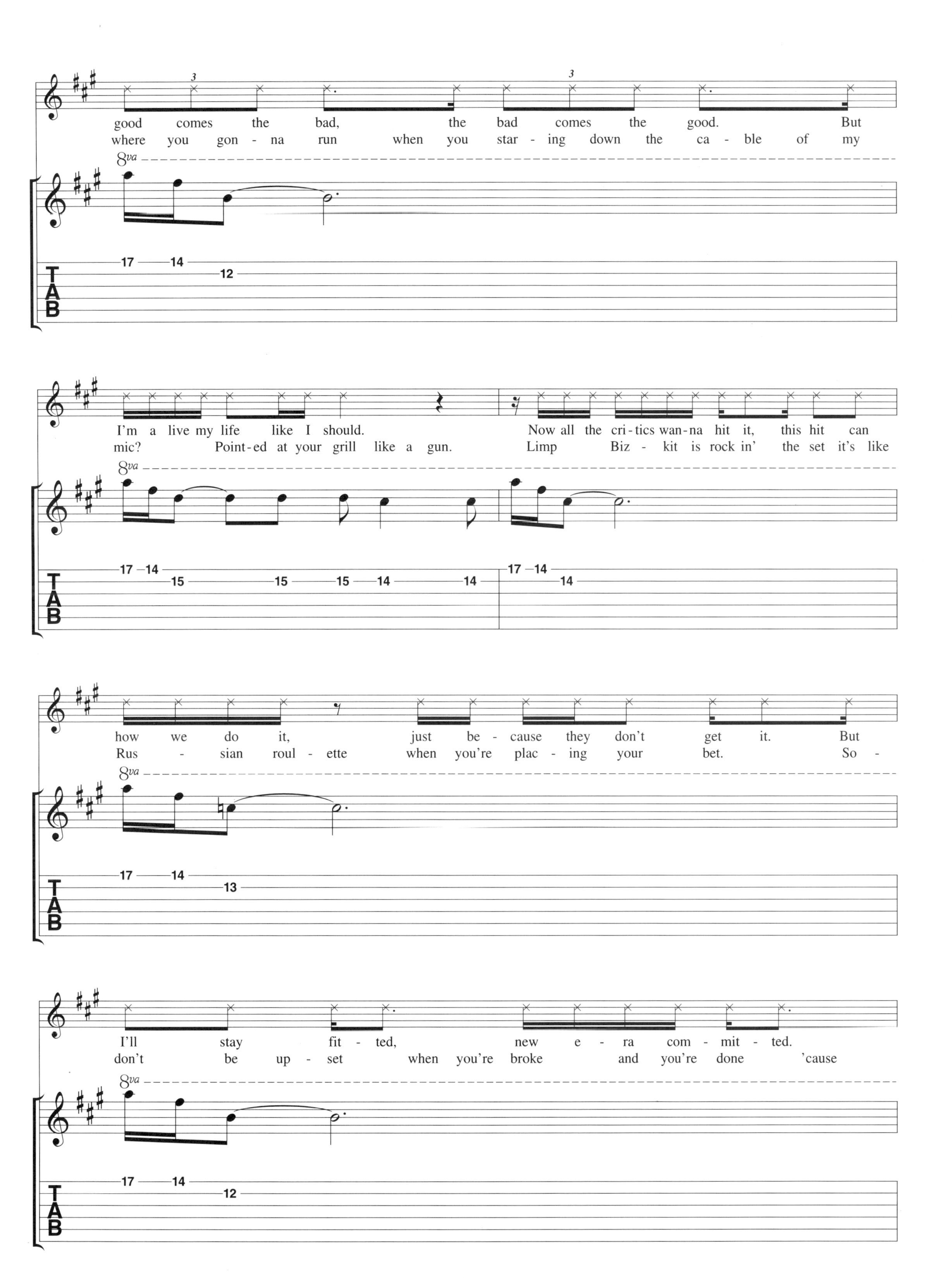
good comes the bad, the bad comes the good. But
where you gon - na run when you star - ing down the ca - ble of my
8va
17 14 12
I'm a live my life like I should. Now all the cri - tics wan - na hit it, this hit can
mic? Point - ed at your grill like a gun. Limp Biz - kit is rock in' the set it's like
8va
17 14 15 15 15 14 14 17 14 14
how we do it, just be - cause they don't get it. But
Rus - sian roul - ette when you're plac - ing your bet. So -
8va
17 14 13
I'll stay fit - ted, new e - ra com - mit - ted.
don't be up - set when you're broke and you're done 'cause
8va
17 14 12

1.
Pre-chorus
Now this red cap gets a rap from his cri-tics.
I'm a be the one till I jet.
Do we al-ways got-ta cry, do we
8va
1. cont.
al-ways got-ta live in-side a lie?
Life's just a blast 'cause it's mov-in' real-ly fast,
1. cont.
2.
Chorus
bet-ter stay on top or life 'll kick you in the ass.
I know why you wan-na hate me.
Gtr. 2
ff w/dist.
I know why you wan-na hate me.
I know why you wan-na hate me, 'cause
T
A
B

hate is all the world has ev - en seen late - ly.
I know why you wan - na hate me,
I know why you wan - na hate me.
Now I know why you wan - na hate me 'cause
hate is all the world's ev - en seen late - ly.
F♯5
A5 B5
F♯5
F5
F♯5
And now you wan - na hate me, 'cause
A5 B5
T
A
B

F♯5
F5
F♯5
A5
B5
hate is all the world's ev - en seen late - ly.
P.M.
T
A
B
C/E
And now you wan - na hate me, 'cause
To Coda
(F♯)
Gtr. 1

Verse
3. Does an - y - bo - dy real - ly know the se - cret, of the
8va
com - bi - na - tion for this life and where they keep it. It's kind - a sad when you don't know the mean - ing but
ev - 'ry - thing hap - pens for a rea - son. I don't ev - en know what I should say, 'cause I'm an
i - di - ot, a los - er, a mi - cro - phone a - bu - ser. I an - a - lyze ev - 'ry se - cond I ex - ist,
T
A
B

beat - ing up my mind ev - 'ry se - cond with my fist.
8va
17 14 15 15 15 14 14
And ev - 'ry - bo - dy wan - na run, ev - 'ry - bo - dy wan - na hide from the gun.
8va
17 14 14 17 14 13
You can take a ride through this life if you want but you can't take the edge off the knife no sir!
8va
17 14 12 17 14 15 15 15 14 14
And now you want your mon - ey back, but you're de - nied but your brain's fried from the sack.
8va
17 14 14 17 14 13

D. 𝄋 al Coda 𝄌
And there ain't no-thing I can do 'cause life is a les - son, you learn it when you're through.
8va
𝄌 Coda
F♯5
D5/A B5 F♯5
F5
(F♯)
P.M.
mf w/clean tone
(P.M.)
Now I know why.

Now I know why.
Now I know why.
f w/dist.
Now I know. why.
B
Full
F♯5 A5 B5 F♯5 F5
Now I know why you wan-na hate me, now I know why you wan-na hate me.

F♯5 A5 B5 F♯5 F5
Now I know why you wan - na hate me 'cause hate is all the world has ev - en seen late - ly.
F♯5 A5 B5 F♯5 C/E F5
'Cause hate is all the world has ev - en seen late - ly.
P.M. P.M. P.M. P.M.
F♯5 A5 B5 F♯5 C/E F5
'Cause hate is all the world has ev - en seen late - ly.
P.M. P.M. P.M. P.M.
Outro
(F♯)
Gtr. 1 8va
Repeat to fade

wake up

Words by Zack De La Rocha
Music by Rage Against The Machine

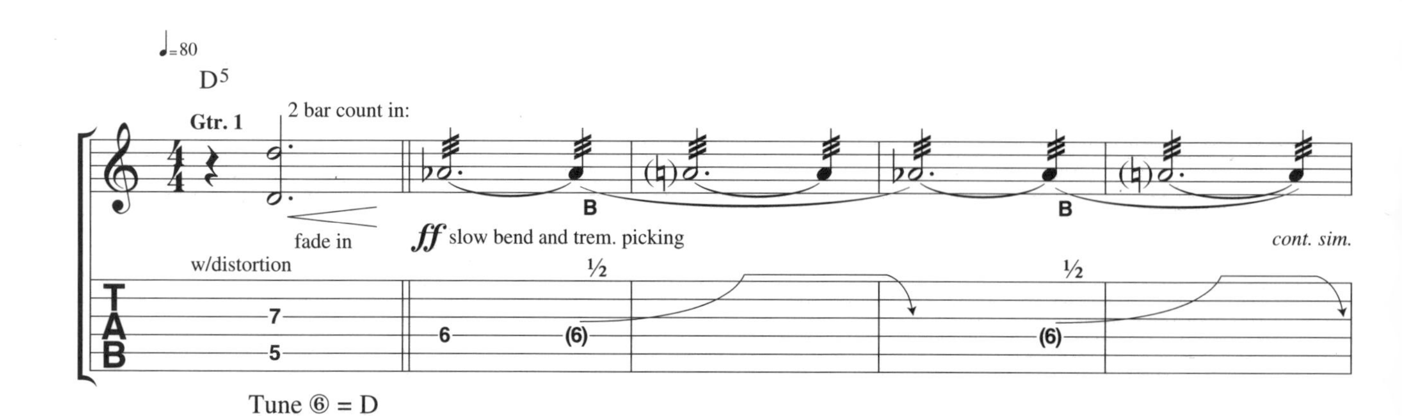

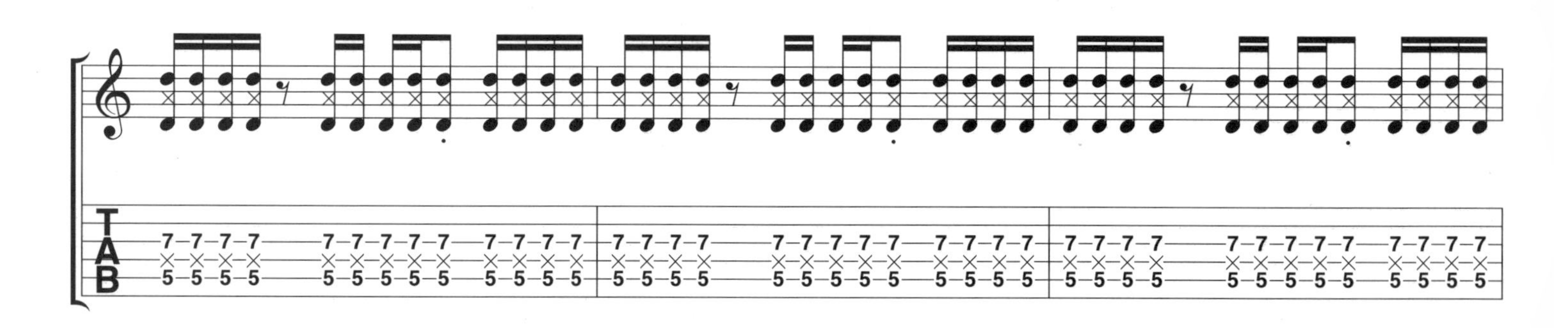

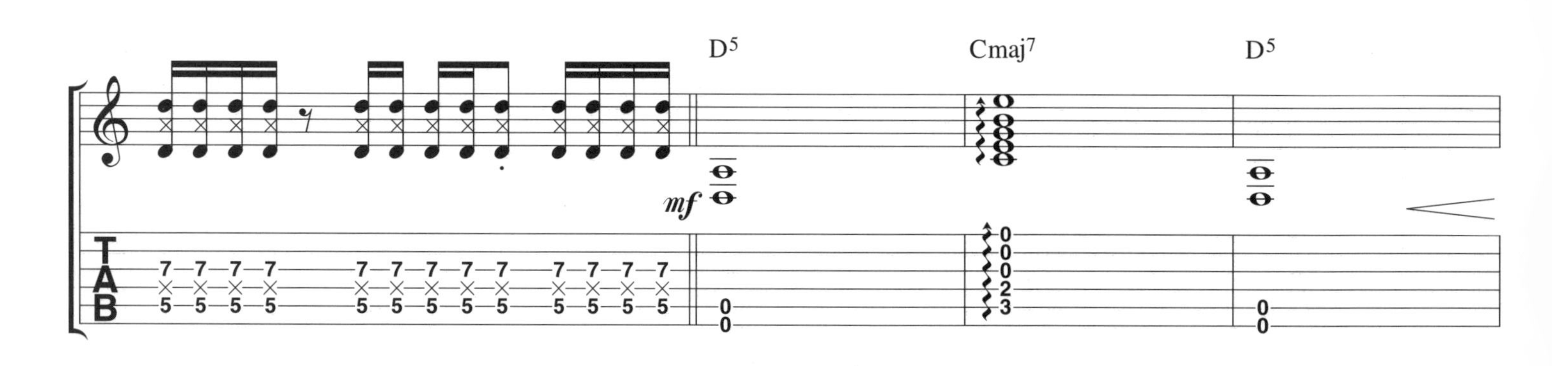

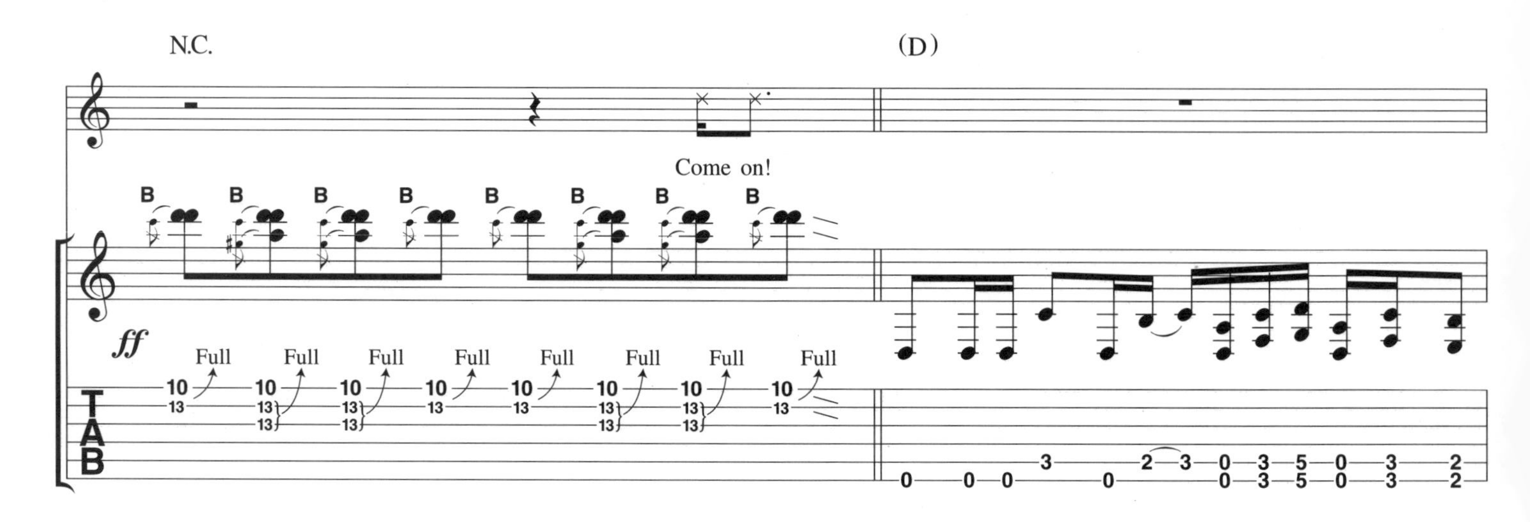

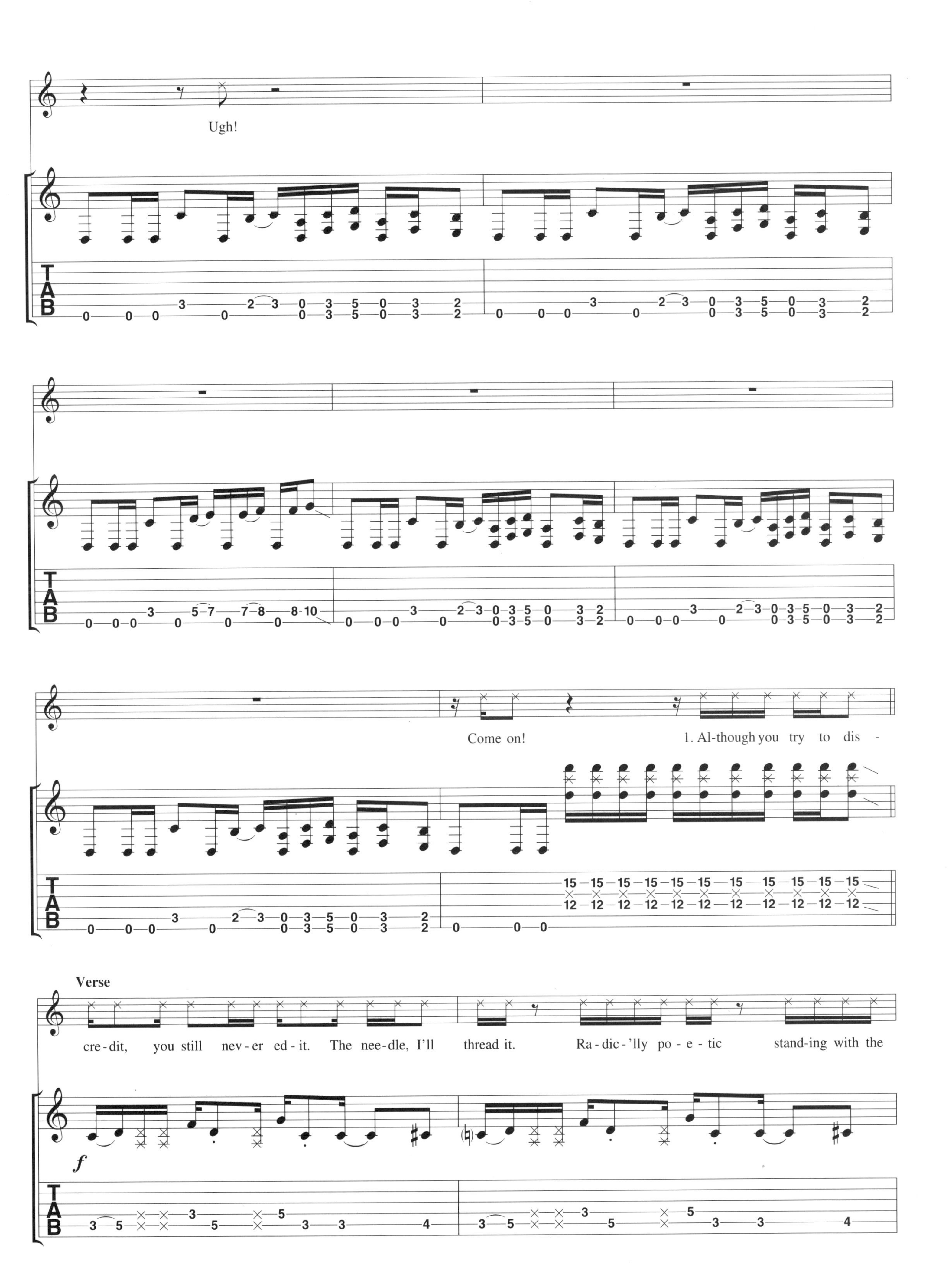
Ugh!
Come on!
1. Al-though you try to dis -
Verse
cre-dit, you still nev-er ed-it. The nee-dle, I'll thread it. Ra-dic-'lly po-e-tic stand-ing with the

fu - ry that they had in six - ty six and like E - dou - ble I'm mad__ still knee-deep in the sys - tem's shit.
T
A
B
3 5 3 5 5 3 3 4
3 5 3 5 5 3 3 4
Hoo - ver, he was a bo - dy re - mov - er, I'll give you a dose,__ but it will nev - er come close__ to the rage
3 5 3 5 5 3 3 4
3 5 3 5 5 3 3 4
built up in - side of me, fist in the air in the land of hy - po - cri - sy.
3 5 3 5 5 3 3 4
3 5
2. Move - ments come and move - ments go, lead - ers speak, move - ments cease when their heads are down.__
3 5 3 5 5 3 3 4
3 5 3 5 5 3 3 4

'Cause all these punks got bul-lets in their heads. De - part-ment of po-lice, the jud-ges, the Feds,
net-works at work keep-in' peo-ple calm. You know they went af-ter King when he spoke out on Vi - et-nam,
he turned the po-wer to the have - nots, and then came the shot.

Yeah!
Yeah back in this.
D7♯9
3. With
H.H.
Verse
(D)
po - e - try my mind I flex, flip like Wil - son, vo - cals nev - er lack - ing that fin - esse.
Whad - da I got to, whad - da I got to do to wake ya up? To shake you up to break the struc - ture up. 'Cause

blood still flows in the gut-ter. I'm like tak-in' pho-tos, mad boy kicks o-pen the shut-ter,
set the groove then stick and move like I was Cas-si - us rip the stut-ter step then bomb a left up-on the fasc - ists.
Yeah the se-ve-ral Fe-der-al men who pulled schemes on the dream and put it to an end. Ya
bet-ter be-ware of re-tri-bu-tion with mind war, twen-ty, twen-ty vi-sion and mu-rals with me-ta-phors.
TAB

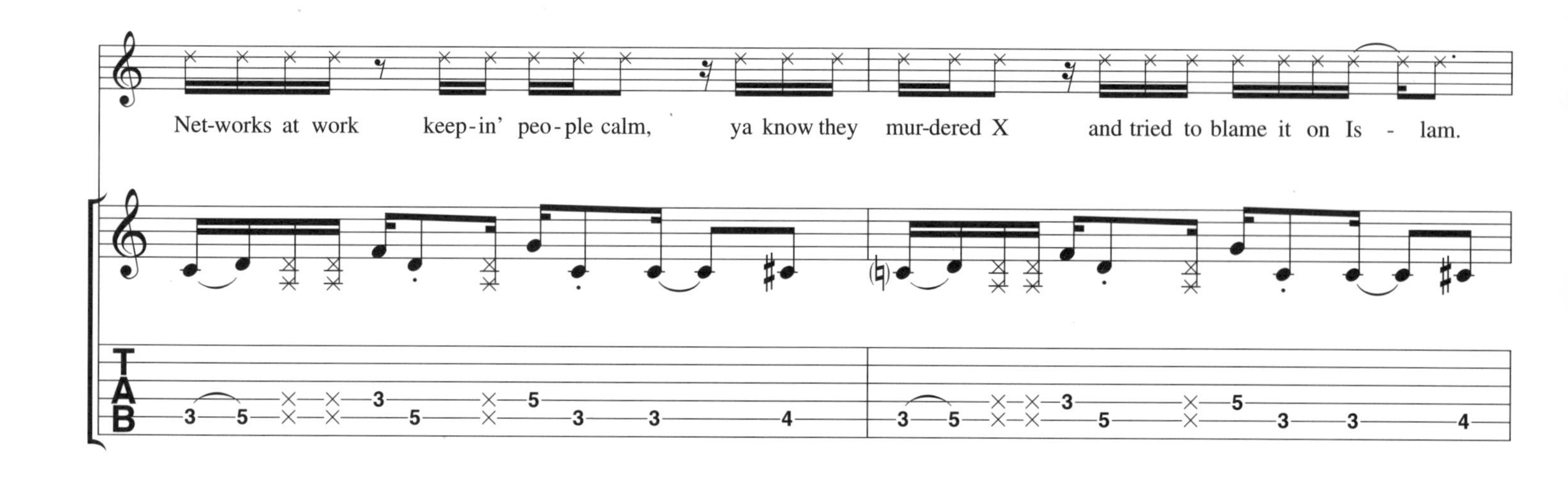
Net-works at work keep-in' peo-ple calm, ya know they mur-dered X and tried to blame it on Is - lam.

He turned the pow-er to the have - nots and then came the shot.
w/talk box

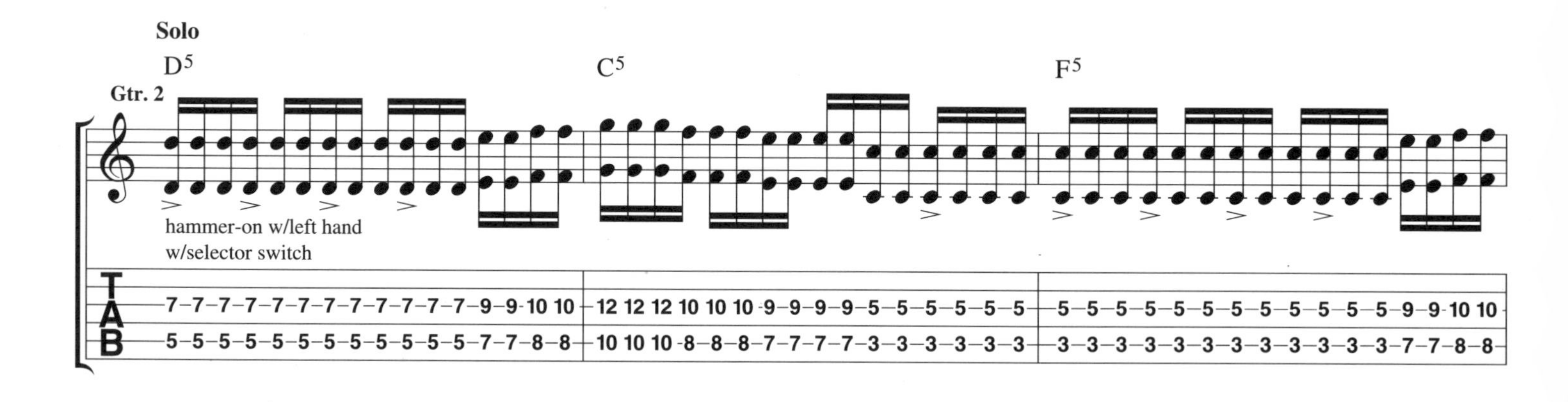
Solo
D5
C5
F5
Gtr. 2
hammer-on w/left hand
w/selector switch

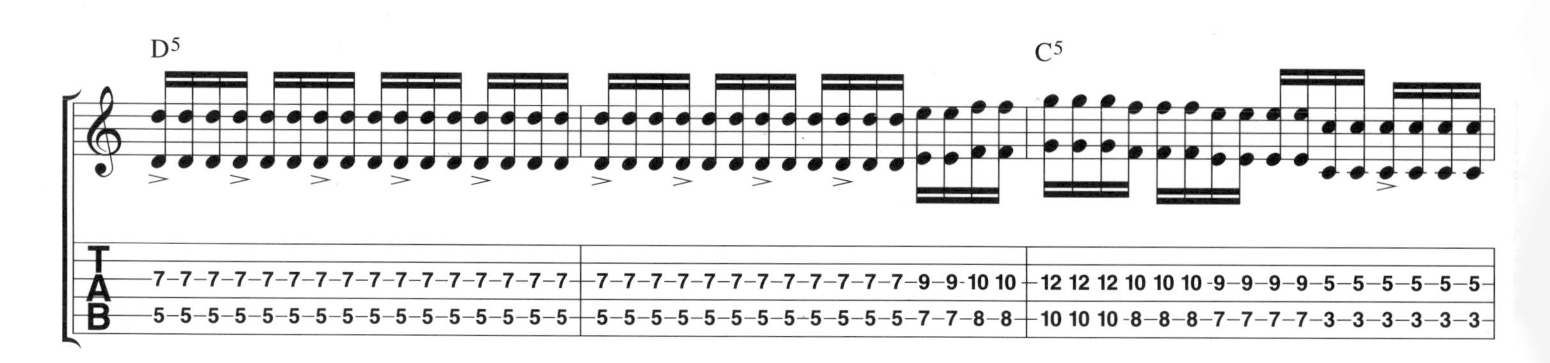
D5
C5

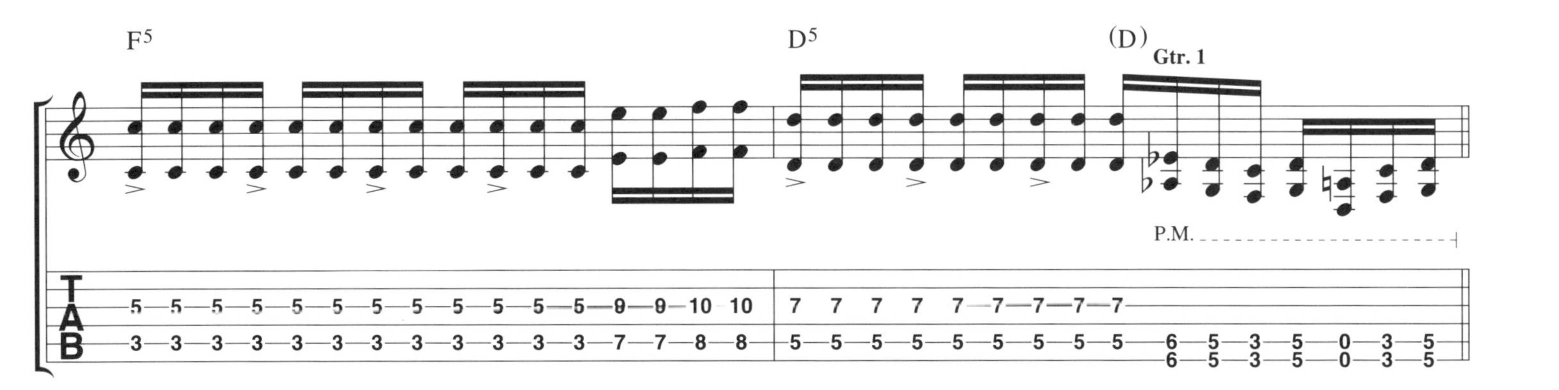
F5
D5
(D)
Gtr. 1
P.M.
TAB
5 5 5 5 5 5 5 5 5 5 5 5 9 9 10 10
3 3 3 3 3 3 3 3 3 3 3 3 7 7 8 8
7 7 7 7 7 7 7 7 7
5 5 5 5 5 5 5 5 5 6 5 3 5 0 3 5
6 5 3 5 0 3 5

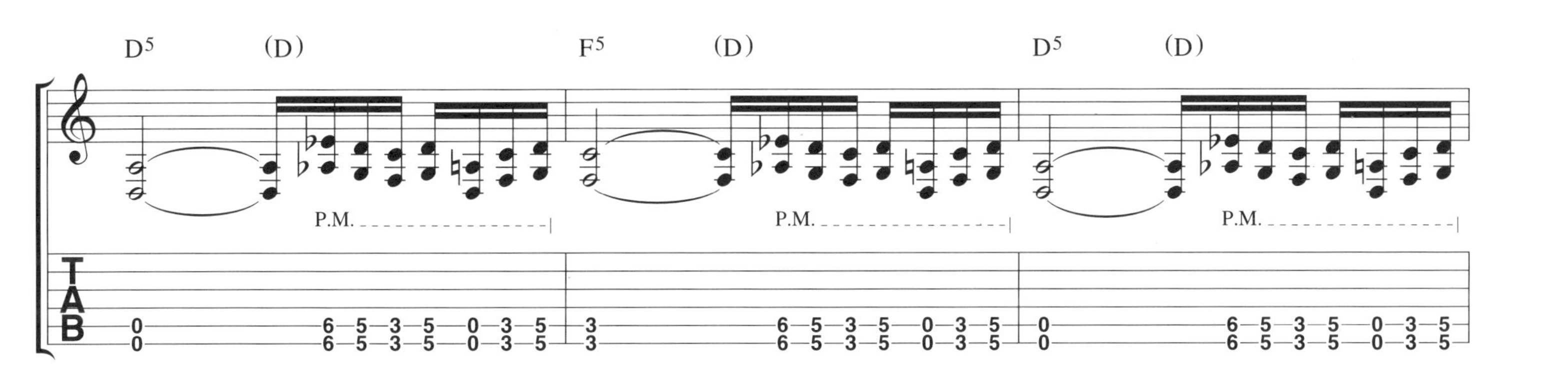
D5
(D)
F5
(D)
D5
(D)
P.M.
P.M.
P.M.
TAB

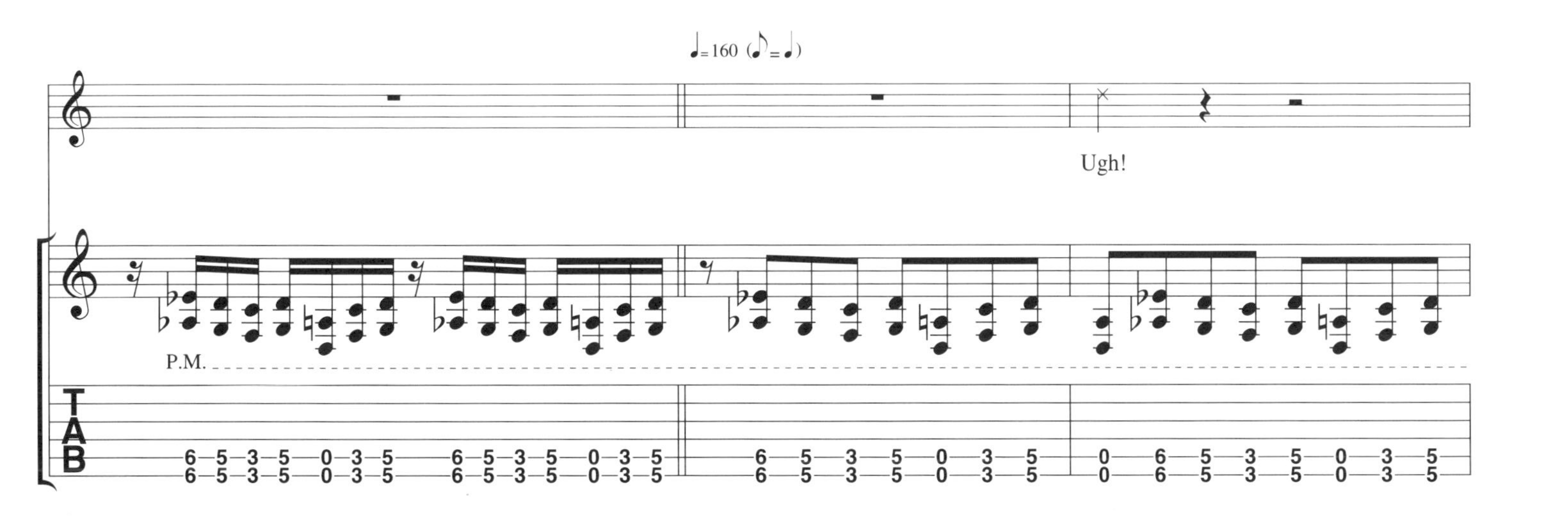
♩= 160 (♪ = ♩)
Ugh!
P.M.
TAB

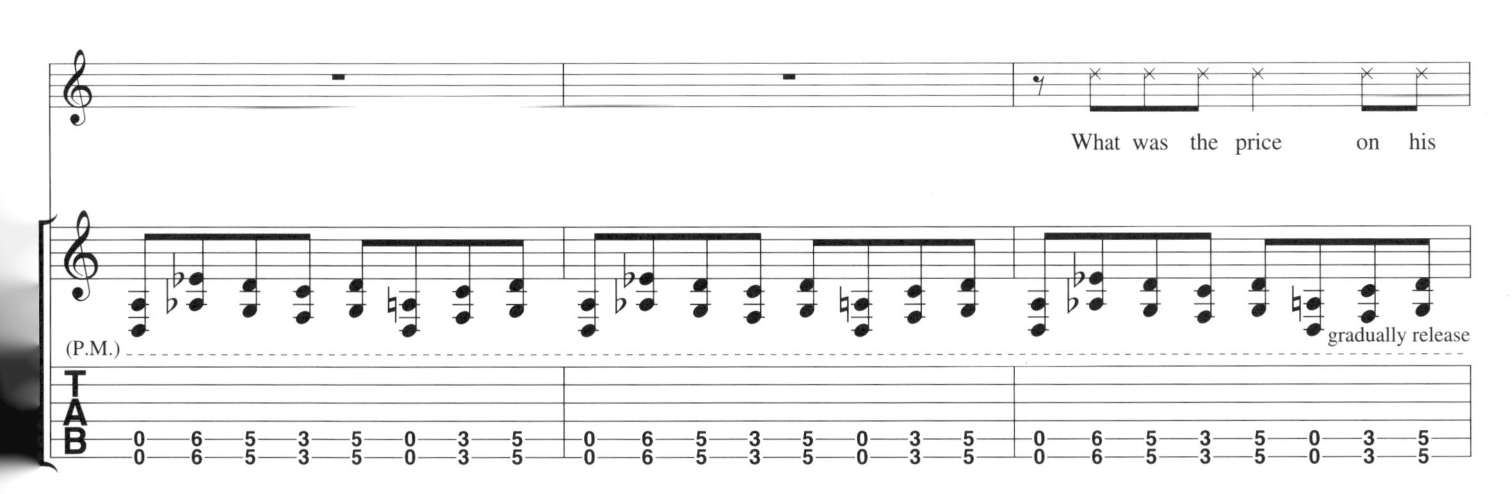
What was the price on his
(P.M.)
gradually release
TAB

head?
ff
(P.M.)
♩=80 (♩=♪)
What was the price on his head?
I think I heard a shot.
mf
P.M.
I think I heard a shot.
(P.M.)
I think I heard a shot.
I think I heard a shot!
(P.M.)

D5
I think I heard a shot.
ff slow bend and trem. picking
cont. sim.
I think I
(D)
heard
I think I heard a shot.
ff
hold
D5
Cmaj7
D5
Cmaj7
mf

D5
N.C.
(D)
ff
B
Full
Wake up.
Wake up.
Wake up.
Wake up.
Wake up.
Wake up.
Wake up.
Wake up.

Outro
Gtr. 3
w/pitch shift set 10 semitones up
loco
Pre
harm.
How long? Not long 'cause what you reap is what you sow.
D5

CD 1

1 **tuning notes**

Full instrumental performances (with guitar)...

2 **alive**
(Curiel/Daniels/Sandoval/Bernardo)
Famous Music Publishing Limited.

3 **chop suey!**
(Tankian/Malakian)
Sony/ATV Music Publishing (UK) Limited.

4 **back in black**
(Young/Young/Johnson) J. Albert & Son (UK) Limited

5 **bring your daughter to the slaughter**
(Dickinson) Zomba Music Publishers Limited.

6 **crawling**
(Bennington/Bourdon/Delson/Hahn/Shinoda)
Zomba Music Publishers Limited.

7 **enter sandman**
(Hetfield/Ulrich/Hammett)
Universal Music Publishing Limited.

8 **fat lip**
(Nori/Whibley/Jocz/Baksh)
Chrysalis Music Limited/EMI Music Publishing Limited.

9 **falling away from me**
(Arvizu/Welch/Shaffer/Silveria/Howsman)
Zomba Music Publishers Limited.

10 **flavor of the weak**
(Jones) BMG Music Publishing Limited.

11 **get free**
(Nicholls) Sony/ATV Music Publishing (UK) Limited.

Backing tracks only (without guitar)...

12 **alive**
13 **chop suey!**
14 **back in black**
15 **bring your daughter to the slaughter**
16 **crawling**
17 **enter sandman**
18 **fat lip**
19 **falling away from me**
20 **flavor of the weak**
21 **get free**

CD

Full instrumental performances (with guitar).

1 **the fight song**
(Warner/Lower)
EMI Music Publishing Limited/Chrysalis Music Limite

2 **last resor**
(Papa Roach) Cherry Lane Music Limite

3 **movies**
(Mitchell/Corso/Zamora/Cosgrov
Cherry River Music Limite

4 **muscle museum**
(Bellamy) Taste Music Limite

5 **no one knows**
(Homme/Oliveri/Lanega
Universal Music Publishing Limited/Copyright Contr

6 **paranoi**
(Osbourne/Iommi/Butler/War
Westminster Music Limite

7 **party har**
(Andrew W.K.) Universal Music Publishing Limite

8 **the rock show**
(Hoppus/Delonge/Barker) EMI Music Publishing Limite

9 **take a look aroun**
(Schifrin/Durst) Famous Music Publishing Limite

10 **wake u**
(De La Rocha) Sony/ATV Music Publishing (UK) Limite

Backing tracks only (without guitar

11 **the fight son**
12 **last reso**
13 **movie**
14 **muscle museu**
15 **no one know**
16 **paranoi**
17 **party har**
18 **the rock sho**
19 **take a look aroun**
20 **wake u**

To remove your CD from the plastic sleeve, lift t
small lip on the right to break the perforated fl
Replace the disc after use for convenient stora